GUIDE TO

Photographic Collections

AT THE SMITHSONIAN INSTITUTION

GUIDE TO
Photographic Collections
AT THE SMITHSONIAN INSTITUTION

National Museum of American History

VOLUME I

Diane Vogt O'Connor

Smithsonian Institution Press

Washington and London

Library of Congress Cataloging-in-Publication Data

O'Connor, Diane Vogt.
    Guide to photographic collections at the Smithsonian
Institution.

    Includes index.
    Contents: vo. 1. National Museum of American History.
    1. National Museum of American History (U.S.)–Photograph
collections.   I. Title.
Q11.S79   1989   026'.779'074753   89-600116
ISBN 0-87474-927-1 (v. 1: alk. paper)

British Library Cataloguing-in-Publication Data available

Manufactured in the United States of America
10 9 8 7 6 5 4 3 2 1
98 97 96 95 94 93 92 91 90 89

⊚ The paper used in this publication meets the minimum requirements of the American National Standard for Permanence
of Paper for Printed Library Materials z39.48-1984.

Contents

Armed Forces History

Physical Sciences

Political History

Public Affairs   301

The Registrar   305

Special Events   309

Foreword

The National Museum of American History

The National Museum of American History (NMAH) collects, preserves and interprets artifacts which illuminate the history and development of the United States from the 17th century to the present. The museum is interested in how objects were made and used, how they express human needs and values, and how they influence society and the lives of individuals. Cultural, political, economic, technological, and scientific growth are all studied in light of the evidence provided by NMAH's artifacts.

The NMAH photographic holdings document the history of photography as a medium; the life works of notable photographers; and images of the people, events, objects, and places that have shaped American history.

In some cases, NMAH photographs are themselves artifacts or art objects with intrinsic value. In others, the images are valuable for the information they contain documenting times, events, and material culture that have vanished. Some are administrative records of artifacts held by the curatorial divisions. The photograph collections reflect the specialized talents and research interests of the men and women who created or assembled them.

The more than one million photographs in the four hundred and seventy-three photographic collections in NMAH form only a portion of the museum's complex research resources. The value of these photograph collections is enhanced by their proximity to unique artifactual, archival, and library resources at NMAH, and to research materials at other Smithsonian Institution museums and research bureaus.

The museum's rich and diverse nonphotographic holdings range from business and family archives to atom smashers, from washing machines to White House memorabilia, from engineering drawings to political banners, and from graphic portrait prints to glass models of architecture.

The museum's earliest collections came from the Smithsonian's ethnological holdings; from the transfer of objects assembled for the 1876 Centennial Exposition in Philadelphia; and from the transfer of patent models and the National Cabinet of Curiosities of the Patent Office in 1908 and 1926.

These artifactual materials were exhibited originally in the Arts and Industries Building and in the Smithsonian Institution Building (the Castle). In 1955 Congress approved the construction of the National Museum of History and Technology, which opened in 1964. The museum's name was changed in 1980 to the National Museum of American History to more accurately reflect the museum's collections and activities.

Roger G. Kennedy, Director
Douglas Evelyn, Deputy Director

Acknowledgments

Many people helped with the production of this volume. First, the administrators, curators, and collections managers of the National Museum of American History offered advice and assistance to the project staff. Their cooperative spirit and informed assistance made this volume possible.

Second, the editors wish to thank the staff and management of the Smithsonian Institution Archives. Without the support and guidance of the Smithsonian Institution Archivist, William W. Moss, this project could not have survived to complete this volume. He fought for the continuation of the project, and offered excellent advice on working within the Institution.

Our liaison with the Smithsonian Institution Press, Editor Amy Pastan, has been a cause for celebration. Without her ongoing support this book would not have been published.

The book indexer, Victoria Agee, deserves applause for both a job well done and grace under pressure. Her extensive cross-referencing has greatly facilitated the use of this volume. Volunteer Lois Edwards used her research skills to confirm the spelling of the names and track down the biographies of the creators and subjects of these photographic collections.

A special thanks to the Smithsonian Institution Libraries Interlibrary Loan Department and the National Portrait Gallery/National Museum of American Art Librarian Cecilia Chin who facilitated the project work through interlibrary loan and database searching services.

Finally, the hard-working project staff of the Photographic Survey Project, including Laura Kreiss, Deborah Kapper, Margaret Stevens, Pamela Whetstone, Donna Longo DiMichele, and B.H. Custer helped survey, write, abstract and edit this volume. They deserve praise for their dedication and skills. Working with them over the years has been a pleasure.

Introduction

The *Guide to Photographic Collections at the Smithsonian Institution: National Museum of American History* is the first volume of a five-part set documenting the Smithsonian Institution's vast holdings of photographs.

This volume provides a comprehensive overview of four hundred and seventy-three collections containing more than one million photographs housed at the National Museum of American History (NMAH). Many of the collections were previously unknown outside their own divisions.

These collections serve many purposes. They document museum artifacts, activities, exhibitions, and staff. They illustrate the lives of the American people including their homes, tools, work spaces, and the communities and events they shaped. The photographs represent the work of both professional and amateur photographers in a wide range of photographic processes and formats.

These diverse photographic collections were surveyed at the archival collection level by the project staff of the Smithsonian Institution Archives. This volume serves as an introduction, not as an inventory, to photographs within fine arts collections and archival research collections, as well as to photographs within the working papers of the curatorial staff.

Researchers come to photographic collections with diverse requirements. Some are interested only in the images' informational content; others in the photographer's relationship to his work; while still others study photographs as physical artifacts. The *Guide* is inclusive in its descriptive strategy, providing access by subject, by collection origins (including photographer), and by process and format in order to serve the broadest audience of researchers.

Scope of the *Guide*

This *Guide* focuses on still photographs, defined here as images captured by the action of radiation (usually light) on a photosensitive surface, often by means of a camera, lens, mirror, or other optical device. This includes photonegatives, photoprints, phototransparencies, and direct positive processes.

Architectural plans, audio recordings, drawings, graphic prints, manuscripts, motion picture footage, photomechanical prints, videotapes, and xerographic copies are mentioned only when they were found in collections which also contained photographs.

Both organic and assembled collections are represented. Organic collections include photographs from a single photographer or studio, or photographs created to further the work of a particular corporate entity.

Assembled collections are photographs gathered from disparate sources around a central purpose or theme.

Preparation of the *Guide*

To develop the collection descriptions in this volume, the project staff visited each NMAH division and office. With the assistance of the division staff, they identified, located, and examined all collections which contain photographs.

Using a collection-level survey form based on the MARC-VM (Machine Readable Cataloging-Visual Materials) format, the project staff gathered data on access policies, copyright, location, origins, ownership, physical characteristics, subject contents, and other pertinent data for each collection.

Descriptive terms are taken directly from collection captions and finding aids. Photographers' and other creators' names were checked in a variety of name authority files listed in the introduction to the Creators Index. During the preparation of this guide, a hierarchical authority file of photographic process and format terminology was created to facilitate consistent image identification and description. This authority file forms the basis for the Forms and Processes index found at the end of the guide.

From the completed survey forms, a survey report was drafted for each collection. Following review by the division curators and custodians, these reports were abstracted for use in this volume. The original survey reports may be found in the respective curatorial divisions or in a master file at the Smithsonian Institution Archives.

Organization and Use of the *Guide*

An introduction to the National Museum of American History, and its collecting interests and history, may be found in the Foreword to this *Guide*. The *Guide* itself is organized alphabetically by division or office name. An introduction to each curatorial division or support office describes its research objectives and collecting policies within the overall museum framework. This introduction also provides information on policies for reference use of the collections, including restrictions; access procedures including the address, telephone number, contact person's name or title, and hours of operation; number of collections; total number of images; major subjects documented in the holdings; photographic processes represented; and other kinds of materials included, such as, manuscripts and objects.

The heart of this *Guide* is a description of each collection found within the curatorial divisions or support offices. A description of the organization and contents of a typical entry is found below.

Each collection is identified by a collection title and by an alphanumeric code assigned by the writers of the *Guide*. The code consists of a two-letter abbreviation for the curatorial division or office in which the collection may be found, for example, PH stands for Photographic History. The number following the two-letter code indicates the sequence of that collection within the division's or office's section of the *Guide*. The table of contents outlines the arrangement of the collections for each division or office. It lists the collections' titles and refers readers to them by this alphanumeric code.

The *Guide* is extensively indexed, providing precise access to specific photographic collections. There are three separate indexes: a Creators Index; a Forms and Processes Index; and a Subject Index. The indexer used the Library of Congress Prints and Photographs Division's *Topical Terms for Subject Access* as the authority file for the subject terms; the Photo Survey Project's "Draft Photographic Thesaurus" for the form and process terms; and the International Museum of Photography's *Photographers Name Authority File,* and other publications (for more information see the Creators Index) for creator names.

The alphabetical index terms are keyed to the unique alphanumeric collection codes. Further information on index search strategies may be found at the beginning of each index.

Collection Level Descriptions

The collection descriptions vary in length, reflecting the size, coherence, and complexity of the collections described. More diverse and eclectic collections demand longer descriptions to provide equivalent descriptive detail. Each collection-level description is itself a complex arrangement of information. A description of its organization follows.

Collection Code.   The unique alphanumeric code assigned to this collection. For more information on this, see "Abbreviations."

Collection Name.   The full title by which the collection is known in the museum. The abbreviation "*A.K.A.*" ("also known as") following a collection name indicates an alternate title or name by which staff may refer to the collection.

Dates of Photographs.   The dates used are inclusive, describing the period during which the images in the collection were produced. These dates do not describe the period during which the nonphotographic materials were produced, nor do they describe the dates of other generations of images which may exist in other repositories, for example, original photonegatives in other museums. Researchers wishing to determine the dates of original negatives which were used to create copy images in NMAH collections should look at the dates listed in the subject description.

Collection Origins.   This section gives the name, dates, and a capsule biography of the collection creator or assembler. It explains by whom, why, when, and for what purpose the collection was created. If a single photographer, studio, or other corporate entity produced these materials as an organic collection, he (or it) will be described in this section.

If the collection is assembled or artificial, the collection origins field will describe who assembled it and list names of specific photographers, studios, or other creators (such as, correspondents or authors) whose work is included in the collection. When the field states "Unknown," no information exists on the collection origins, either within the division's records, or as clear internal evidence within the collection itself.

Physical Description.   The total number of photographs in the collection is given first. This number may change over time as collections continue to grow. Next, all photographic processes and formats are listed. Unusual sizes and support materials are noted, as are albums, scrapbooks, and notebooks. Other materials found with the photographs, such as archival document types, are also listed.

Subjects.   This field opens with a broad, summary statement of the range of subject dates, geographic areas, and major subject emphases in the collection. This summary paragraph may be followed by more specific descriptions of individuals; corporations; cultural groups; occupations; genres (such as, landscapes and portraits); specific geographic locales; and topical information (such as, activities, animals, events, objects, and themes) represented in the collection. Related subject information is listed together alphabetically, for example, "Animals include cats, dogs, and hogs."

Arrangement.   This section identifies the major series into which a collection may be arranged. If the series are few, they will be listed by name. If the series are many, their number and organizing principle will be identified, for example, "Into 25 series by year of creation." A subseries may be noted if it aids in locating photographs, for example, "Series 2, photographic portraits, arranged chronologically by subjects' dates of birth." When a collection consists mainly of other types of materials (nonphotographic), all series containing photographs will be indicated.

Captions.   All information accompanying photographs will be described in this field, including cutlines and album labels. When similar descriptive categories are used in most captions, the categories used will be noted, for example, "With location; date; and bridge name."

Finding Aids.   This includes descriptions of the registers, indexes, and other guides used by the division staff to search the collection. When a finding aid has a title, a full citation is given. When a finding aid uses standard categories of data to describe photographs, those data elements and any cross-referencing will be noted, for example, "A card catalog which lists subject, negative number, and on occasion, the source of the image."

When they are consistent, the filing rules for card catalogs are noted, for example, "The cards are filed by 1) last name of subject; 2) negative number; and 3) object name." If several finding aids exist to a collection, they are described in sequence, for example, "1) card catalog; 2) index." Where another form of document (such as, an object inventory sheet) may serve as a finding aid, it will be described here.

Some major forms of finding aids and their definitions as used in this *Guide* include the following:

Authority file: A list of approved names and terms to be used in describing a collection.

Card catalog: An item-level index on cards which may include cross-references and broader and narrower terms.

Container list: A box-by-box or drawer-by-drawer list of materials to be found in each container, often further divided into folder-by-folder listings.

Guide entry: A brief summary description of a collection as it would appear in a published guide to a repository's holdings or a database.

Index: An alphabetical list of terms used to identify and locate all items relating to that term. An index is often in card form, with one term used per card.

Inventory: A list by document types (forms of material), or occasionally by subject or creator.

List: An item-level enumeration in sequential order.

Log book: An item-level list of photographs created by a photographer as he or she works, sometimes called a "shot log." It can include an image number; date; technical information, such as, light conditions, filters used, camera settings, and film used; a brief summary of the subject in the photographer's own terms; and the purpose of the shot.

Register: An inventory of all collection document types, usually in a book or ledger format.

Restrictions. The last section of the collection-level entry explains any special restrictions that limit access to or use of the collections. The actual effect of the restrictions on the user will be noted in the restrictions field, for example, "For reference only. No copying allowed."

Restrictions may be due to copyright status, donor wishes, preservation issues, privacy legislation concerns, patent or trademark status of the subject matter, or security concerns, for example, insurance photographs of high value items.

Restrictions information may also appear in the "Collection Origins" field, if the creator, in the process of creating the images caused the restrictions, for example, "This copyrighted collection was created for a planned publication."

Abbreviations

The *Guide* is divided into sections by curatorial division and administrative support office. The curatorial divisions appear first in alphabetical order, followed by the support offices, also in alphabetical order. Each division or office is assigned an abbreviation and each photograph collection is assigned a number. For example, the Division of Community Life is CL; the Division of Community Life Photograph Collection is CL2. These alphanumeric codes are used throughout the book indexes. A full list of division abbreviations is available in the table of contents.

Other abbreviations used throughout the book are as follows:

A.K.A.	Also Known As. This phrase is used to indicate alternate titles of collections or pseudonyms of photographers.
ANON.	Anonymous. The creator of the images or the collection is unknown.
DOP	Developing-Out Paper photoprints.
ND	No Date. The dates of these images are unknown.
NMAH	National Museum of American History.
NMNH	National Museum of Natural History.
OPPS	Office of Printing and Photographic Services, the central Smithsonian photographic duplication laboratory.
POP	Printing-Out Paper photoprints.
SEM	Scanning Electron Microscope images.
SI	Smithsonian Institution.
TEM	Transmitting Electron Microscope images.

Public Access

Appointments are required for any collection not on public exhibition. The accuracy of the information in the *Guide* will change over time, as collections grow and divisions reorganize. Calling ahead will save researchers time and trouble searching for collections and staff which have moved. With the exception of the NMAH Archives Center, no division or office has a full-time reference staff. Researchers should allow ample time for scheduling appointments, locating collections, and creating copy images.

Recommended times for research appointments are stated in the division introductions, as are appropriate addresses and phone numbers. Written requests for appointments should explain the purpose and scope of the research project, and any publication or exhibition plans. The

NMAH research facilities are generally open to the public from 10 a.m. to 5:30 p.m., Monday through Friday, (except national holidays).

Handling Photographs

Researchers must respect the requests of staff members in handling and security requirements which have been established to ensure the preservation of Smithsonian photographic collections. Photographs are fragile. Do not bend or touch photographic emulsions. Gloves may be required while working with these collections. Use only pencil while taking notes near photographs. Do not eat, drink, or smoke while working near photographs. Return photographs to their original position in the collection. Future availability of these collections depends upon the care with which they are treated today.

Photoduplication Service

Unless restricted, xerographic or photographic copies of images in Smithsonian collections are available to researchers after written permission has been obtained from the appropriate division. Restricted materials may require additional clearance. If the copyright is held outside the Smithsonian, the researcher is responsible for obtaining necessary permissions.

Researchers requesting photographs for publications, exhibitions, or other commercial use, must complete a permission request form (form SI-2940). The completed form must be approved by the Institution before copying can take place. These photographs shall not be used to show or imply Smithsonian endorsement of any commercial product or enterprise, or to indicate that the Smithsonian concurs with opinions expressed in, or confirms the accuracy of, any text used with these photographs.

Photo order forms (SI-318), photographic policies and charges explanation sheets (SI-318a), and permission request forms (SI-2940) are available from the Customer Services Branch of the Smithsonian Institution Office of Printing and Photographic Services (OPPS), Washington, D.C. 20560; or call (202) 357-1933.

Photo order forms must be completely filled out. The forms require that researchers have the negative numbers for images to be copied. There is no master index to the negative numbers of the more than ten million images at the Smithsonian. Negative numbers must be obtained from the images' custodial divisions.

Obtaining the negative number may require that the researcher coordinate research with the division curatorial staff, or hire an outside researcher to visit the Smithsonian to do the negative number search. Use the division introductions to locate the name and address of the contact person who can provide further instructions on how to proceed.

The photo order form must be submitted with a check or money order. Reproduction costs are determined by the Smithsonian. In general, allow four weeks from the time the completed order and advance payment arrive at OPPS for routine processing. All orders are shipped via U.S. mail.

Researchers must follow the specific policies of each division regarding captions, publication, credit lines, and exhibitions. This information is listed in division introductions.

Other Related Publications

This volume follows two nonphotographic guides:

Lynda Corey Claassen. *Finders' Guide to Prints and Drawings in the Smithsonian Institution*. Washington, D.C.: Smithsonian Institution Press, 1981.

Christine Minter-Dowd. *Finders' Guide to Decorative Arts in the Smithsonian Institution*. Washington, D.C.: Smithsonian Institution Press, 1985.

Both are available from the Smithsonian Press at Department 900, Blue Ridge Summit, Pennsylvania 17214.

Subsequent volumes in the series will cover photographic collections in other Smithsonian museums, research bureaus, public service bureaus, and administrative offices. The next volume will be the *Guide to Photographic Collections at the Smithsonian Institution: The National Museum of Natural History, the National Zoological Park, the Smithsonian Astrophysical Observatory, and the Smithsonian Tropical Research Institute.* These 151 collections contain almost two million photographs, primarily in the biological sciences.

AG

Division of Agriculture and Natural Resources

Division of Agriculture and Natural Resources
National Museum of American History
Smithsonian Institution
Washington, D.C. 20560
Pete Daniel or Terry Sharrer, Curators
(202) 357-2323 or 357-2813
Hours: Monday–Friday, 10 a.m.–5 p.m.

Scope of the Collections

There are four photographic collections with approximately 15,700 images in the Division of Agriculture and Natural Resources.

Focus of the Collections

The photographs in this division are used primarily as research material to document the history and technology of American agriculture. Included are photographs of agrarian artifactual accessions, agricultural history, food technology, and industries related to agriculture.

Photographic Processes and Formats Represented

Division collections contain standard 20th century slide, photoprint, and photonegative processes, such as, color dye coupler slides and silver gelatin photoprints and photonegatives.

Other Materials Represented

This division also collects blueprints; buttons; candy and ice cream molds; catalogs; combs; corporate minutes; drawings of machinery; engravings; interview transcripts; leases for the mining of coal; letterpress books of correspondence; lists; manuscripts of corporate histories; microfilm copies of newspapers; notes; patents; prints and specifications for patents; record books of foreign patents; reports; scrapbooks; sketches; tooled leather saddles; walking sticks; and objects related to the study of agriculture including fisheries, food, forestry, mining, and whale processing.

Access and Usage Policies

These photograph collections are to be used for research purposes only. While researchers may make xerographic copies of images and captions for information purposes, no photographic reproductions will be allowed without special written permission of the curator. There are partial finding aids to several collections in this division.

Publication Policies

In addition to obtaining permission from the Smithsonian Institution to reproduce a photograph, researchers may have to obtain permission from the copyright holder. The Smithsonian Institution is not necessarily the copyright holder. Division staff will assist researchers in determining the source of the original prints. The preferred credit line is: "Courtesy of the Division of Agriculture and Natural Resources, National Museum of American History, Smithsonian Institution."

AG·1

Consolidated Photograph Collection

Dates of Photographs: 20th Century

Collection Origins

This collection was assembled by division staff member Margorie Berry from photograph collections previously called the Agrarian Accession Files; the Agrarian Photograph Collection; the Food Technology Photograph Collection; and the Southern Life and Labor Collection.

Many of these photographs were taken by OPPS. Other photographs were acquired or purchased, and some were copied from early books and magazines. Note: Photographs of accessioned objects form part of the official accession records of the division.

Physical Description

There are 5,000 drymounted silver gelatin photoprints (with typed captions on the boards).

Subjects

The photographs document world agricultural history in the 18th, 19th, and 20th centuries through photographs of advertisements, people, processes, specimens, and techniques. A large part of the collection is agricultural implements and machines.

There are photographs of animal husbandry; barbed wire; barns; bee culture; canning and preserving; cigar making; cotton; crop production; the dairy industry; exhibits; fairs; farm scenes; fishing; food production; forestry; inventors; patent models; rural life; tobacco; wind erosion; and windmills.

Arranged: By subject headings.

Captioned: With a typed descriptive caption which includes location, date, and a negative number.

Finding Aid: An indexed catalog is being prepared which will be published as a finding aid for the photographs in the Division of Agriculture and Natural Resources.

Restrictions: For reference only. No duplication allowed.

AG·2

John Hoffman Mineral Industries Collection

Dates of Photographs: 1870s–1974

Collection Origins

This collection was assembled by division staff from a number of archival collections originally collected by (now deceased) former Curator John Hoffman.

The original order of these materials was lost, as were most of the acquisitions records and provenance information.

The collection includes the following: 1) Mineral Industries Collection, circa 1820; 2) Alabama Mining Institute Collection; 3) American Mining Congress Photographs, circa 1960 to 1974; 4) Coxe Brothers and Company Records, 1886 to 1935; 5) Jeffrey Manufacturing Company Collection, 1877, 1960; and 6) Philadelphia and Reading Coal and Iron Company Records, 1866 to 1927.

Physical Description

There are 4,500 photographs, including color dye coupler slides; silver gelatin dry plate lantern slides and photonegatives; and silver gelatin photonegatives, photoprints (five are matted), and radiographs. Other materials include blueprints; correspondence; drawings of machinery; leases; manuscripts; microfilm copies of newspapers; prints and specifications for patents; reports; and sketches.

Subjects

The photographs document international mining industries between the 1820s and 1974. Images are of anthracite and bituminous coal mining; gold mining; iron mining; lead mining; platinum mining; silver mining; sulphur mining; titanium mining; and uranium mining.

There are also photographs of the mining operations and miners' housing and town facilities of the following firms: Alabama Fuel and Iron Company; Burnwell Coal Mining Company; Central Iron and Coal Company; DeBardeleben Coal Company; Gulf States Steel Company; Nelson Coal Company; New Castle Coal and Coke Company; Railway Fuel Company; Republic Iron and Steel Company; Roden Coal Company; Southern Coal and Coke Company; and Woodward Iron Company.

Other firms represented include Bucyrus Mining Machine Company; Ford Foundry Model Plant; Goodyear Rubber Company; Mellon Institute of Industrial Research; National Mine Company; Pittsburgh Consolidated Coal Company; U.S. Integrated Steel; U.S. Vanadium Company; and Vulcan Iron Works.

Images illustrate aluminum end uses; leather processing; logging; mining; platinum processing; rubber gathering, marketing, and processing; steel manufacturing; and South African uranium mining (including concentrating, deep mining, end uses, milling, open pit mining, and prospecting). There are photographs of petroleum drilling (including the catamaran drilling platform rigs, the drilling floor, drilling personnel, and oil drilling ships).

There are several small groups of mining disaster photographs, both authentic and staged. Some medical photographs, such as, radiographs of miners' lungs are also included.

Arrangement: Some by creator, then by type of material or chronologically.

Captioned: With subject information.

Finding Aid: No.

Restrictions: Due to the dispersed nature of this collection, some of the materials may be unavailable. Special restrictions apply to certain materials within the collection which make it impossible to allow the production of photographic or xerographic copies of photographs.

AG·3

1927 Mississippi Flood Photograph Collection

Dates of Photographs: April–October, 1927

Collection Origins

This collection was assembled by division curator Pete Daniel as source material for his book *Deep'n As It Come: The 1927 Mississippi River Flood.* New York: Oxford University Press, 1977.

The collection was assembled from photographs collected in various archives around the country, such as, the Army Signal Corps, the Library of Congress, the Mississippi State Archives, and the Red Cross, as well as from original photographs donated by eyewitnesses to the flood.

Physical Description

There are 200 photographs, including silver gelatin photonegatives and photoprints.

Subjects

These photographs document the 1927 Mississippi River flood. There are photographs of damage in towns and cities along the river, as well as the flood in progress. There are some rescue scenes, as well as images of doctors, firemen, national guardsmen, and policemen.

Arranged: No.

Captioned: No.

Finding Aid: No.

Restrictions: The collection is available for reference purposes only. Researchers may make xerographic copies of the images for information purposes. No photographic reproductions will be allowed. Individuals interested in obtaining photographic reproductions and permission to publish should contact the original photographer or source of the images.

AG·4

John and Roma Rouse Photograph Collection Of World Cattle

Dates of Photographs: 1950s–1970s

Collection Origins

This collection was assembled by John E. and Roma Rouse for John Rouse's book *World Cattle*. Norman: University of Oklahoma Press, 1970.

Physical Description

There are 6,000 photographs, including color dye coupler photonegatives and photoprints.

Subjects

The photographs document cattle from all over the world, including such breeds as French Canadians and Holsteins. The cattle are shown individually and in groups.

Arrangement: Chronologically and by country.

Captioned: No.

Finding Aid: No.

Restrictions: For reference only. No duplication allowed.

AC

Archives Center

Archives Center
National Museum of American History
Smithsonian Institution
Washington, D.C. 20560
David Haberstich, Head, Photographic Collections
Robert Harding, Head, Manuscript Collections
(202) 357-3270
Hours: Monday–Friday, 10 a.m.–5 p.m.

Scope of the Collections

There are 66 photographic collections with approximately 240,000 images in the Archives Center.

Focus of the Collections

These photographs are archival research materials for use by scholars. There are three major collection divisions: 1) The Collection of Advertising History; 2) Major photographic collections, such as, the Underwood and Underwood Collection and the Donald H. Sultner-Welles Collection; and 3) Manuscript collections which may include some photographs. The focus of all three types of collections is American history and the history of science and technology between the 18th century and the present.

Photographic Processes and Formats Represented

In addition to standard 20th century slide, photoprint, and photonegative processes there are a few examples of early photographic processes, such as, albumen stereographs; collodion wet plate lantern slides; cyanotypes; platinum photoprints; radiographs; salted paper photoprints; silver gelatin dry plate photonegatives; tinted silver gelatin photoprints (POP); and tintypes.

Other Materials Represented

The Archives Center's collections also include annual reports; audiotapes; bank books; batch books; biographical information; blueprints; brochures; building plans; business cards; business ephemera; business plans; business records; catalogs; certificates; certificates of membership; charts; clippings; commercial art work for advertisements; contracts; convention minutes; corporate histories; correspondence; and court testimony records.

Other collection materials include diagrams; diaries; dissertation typescripts; employee handbooks; engineering drawings; financial records; folios; formula books; halftone reproductions; hospital bulletins; invitations; invoices; journals; lectures; ledgers; legal documents; manuals; manuscripts; memorabilia; newsletters; order books; pamphlets; patents; personal papers; photostats; plays; postage stamps; posters; price lists; professional records; programs; promotional literature; record books; reprints; research notes; salesman's kits; schematics; scrapbooks; scripts; sketches; stereoscopes; stock certificate books; technical papers; tests; test records; timebooks; and videotapes.

Access and Usage Policies

The Archives Center is open to the public for research. Finding aids exist for many collections within the Center. Each collection is documented in the Archives Center control file which may include preliminary accession documents, inventories and other listings of material.

Xerographic copies will be made at no charge for the first ten pages, and for 20 cents per page thereafter. There is a charge for the creation of photoprints which is dependent on the prevailing rates at OPPS. There may be restrictions on making copy prints of photographs in this division. Please contact the Archives Center for further information.

Publication Policies

In addition to obtaining permission from the Smithsonian Institution to reproduce a photograph, researchers may have to obtain permission from the copyright holder. The Smithsonian Institution is not necessarily the copyright holder. The preferred credit line is: "[Collection Name], Archives Center, National Museum of American History, Smithsonian Institution, SI Negative Number."

AC·1

Albany Billiard Ball Company Records

Dates of Photographs: 1869–1973

Collection Origins

The Albany Billiard Ball Company was established in 1868 in Albany, New York. John Wesley Hyatt, inventor of celluloid, was one of the founders of the company. He registered the word "Celluloid" as a trademark in 1873. Celluloid replaced ivory as the material from which billiard balls were made. This company, one of the earliest plastics firms, is still in business today. OPPS created the copy photographs in this collection.

Physical Description

There are 21 photographs, including six original and 15 copy silver gelatin photoprints. Other materials include bank books, contracts, correspondence, financial records, invoices, journals, ledgers, legal documents, patents, and timebooks.

Subjects

These photographs document the factory and workers of the Albany Billiard Ball Company of Albany, New York, circa 1869 to 1973.

Arranged: By type of material.

Captioned: No.

Finding Aid: A preliminary inventory for this collection which describes the types of material and gives a brief historical sketch of the company.

Restrictions: No.

AC·2

American Car and Foundry Photographs

Dates of Photographs: 1875–1927

Collection Origins

The American Car and Foundry Company of Wilmington, Delaware, manufactured street and railroad cars. These photographs were taken by employees of company to document the manufacturing process. They functioned as builder's photographs of products produced by the company. The first four photograph albums were produced by the Jackson and Sharp Company which was a predecessor to the American Car and Foundry Company.

Physical Description

There are 1,000 silver gelatin photoprints housed in 21 albums.

Subjects

The photographs are shop construction views of railroad cars and streetcars.

Arranged: By subject, and then chronologically into 21 albums. Albums 1 through 4 are labeled "Electric-Jackson & Sharp, Co." The next 17 albums are labeled "American Car and Foundry Company."

Captioned: With the name of the railroad; whether it is private or public; the date of construction; the railroad builder's name; and the original negative number as assigned by the American Car and Foundry Company.

Finding Aid: An index sheet in each album lists the photographs by geographical area and original negative number. It also includes narrative subject description and caption information.

Restrictions: No.

AC·3

Famous Amos Collection

Dates of Photographs: Circa 1980

Collection Origins

Wally "Famous" Amos established a chocolate chip cookie production company in Los Angeles during the late 1970s. This collection was acquired as a gift from Wally "Famous" Amos in 1981.

   Note: The hat and shirt in this collection were worn by Amos for the photograph which is on the front of his cookie packages.

Physical Description

There are six photographs, including one color dye coupler photoprint and five silver gelatin photoprints (one is autographed). Other materials include cookie bags, correspondence, a Panama hat, posters, a shirt, and a videotape.

Subjects

Most of the photographs are portraits of Wally "Famous" Amos, alone or with unidentified people. There is also a picture of a chocolate chip cookie.

Arranged: No.

Captioned: No.

Finding Aid: A preliminary inventory.

Restrictions: No.

AC·4

Waldman A. Ayres Collection

Dates of Photographs: 1961–1966

Collection Origins

Waldman A. Ayres received his A.B. from Antioch College. He was a technical consultant for IBM from 1932 to 1942. This collection was created to document the invention and testing of Ayres's artificial gill, an apparatus designed to enable a human to breathe underwater. Ayres received a patent for this invention in 1966.

Physical Descriptions

There are 30 silver gelatin photoprints. Other materials include clippings, correspondence, legal papers, notes, and patents.

Subjects

These photographs document the creation and testing of an artificial gill for breathing underwater. The images are largely of unidentified equipment used in testing the gill device.

Arranged: No.

Captioned: No.

Finding Aid: A register.

Restrictions: No.

AC·5

Leo H. Baekeland Papers

Dates of Photographs: 1881–1968

Collection Origins

Leo H. Baekeland (1863–1968) was a Belgian chemist and inventor. In 1893 he founded the Nepera Chemical Corporation in New York, for whom he invented "Velox" photographic paper. Eastman Kodak bought the company in 1899.

Baekeland was also responsible for the invention of the first commercial synthetic resin, "Bakelite." In 1910 Baekeland established the General Bakelite Company in New York, later the Bakelite Corporation, to produce and distribute the raw materials for making phenolic parts.

Some of the photographs in this collection were reproduced in Baekeland's book *A Family Motor Tour Through Europe*. New York: The Horseless Age, 1907.

Physical Description

There are 1,600 photographs, including platinum photoprints; silver gelatin dry plate photonegatives; and silver gelatin photonegatives and photoprints (some tinted). Other materials include Baekeland's batch books; blueprints; diaries; formula books; journals; order books; patents; personal and professional records; record books; student notebooks; and technical papers.

Subjects

These photographs document Baekeland's family and their motor and bicycle travels worldwide. The photographs are of cityscapes and landscapes of the Adirondacks in New York; Anchorage, Alaska (including photographs of the effects of the September 30, 1929 tornado); Canada; Colombia; Costa Rica; Florida; Hong Kong; Indochina; Morocco; and Switzerland.

Arranged: By type of material, by size, and then by subject into ten collection divisions and eight series.

Captioned: With subject and date information.

Finding Aid: 1) A preliminary inventory describes the types of material in the collection and gives dates and a brief biographical statement. 2) A container list describing Collection Divisions I–X and Series 1–8.

Restrictions: No.

AC·6

Billings-Merriam Family Vaudeville Scrapbooks

Dates of Photographs: 1890–1913

Collection Origins

The Billings family, consisting of Gay and Esa Billings, and Billy and Eva Merriam Billings, performed as vaudeville entertainers throughout the southeastern United States from 1890 to 1913.

Professional names by which the family were known included: the "Billings Trio," "Clark's Dog and Pony Circus," the "Flying Merriams," "Gay's Electric Company," "Gay's One Horse Circus," the "Merriam Merry Makers," "The Merriams: Billy-Eva-Zoe Novelty Aerial Artists," and the "Vanity Fair Company."

Note: One advertisement described the family in the following way: "The Three B's—Esa Billings—Serpentine dance and poses plastic; Gay Billings—Picture operator and song illustrator; and Eva Billings—Song and dance artist and soubrette."

Physical Description

There are 30 silver gelatin photoprints. Other materials include advertisements; business cards; fliers of specialty acts; magazine illustrations; and programs of plays and comedies. There are also two audiotapes with comments on the scrapbooks by Norma Christiani and Billie Plunkett, who is a daughter of Billy and Eva Merriam.

Subjects

The photographs are formal and informal portraits of the Billings-Merriam Family of vaudeville performers, including Gay and Esa Billings, Billy and Eva Merriam Billings, Billie Plunkett, and Ethel Billings. Family members are shown performing as acrobats; comedians; contortionists; dancers; escape artists; jugglers; novelty actors; singers; and trapeze artists. They also performed in blackface routines.

Arranged: In four labeled scrapbooks. 1) Circa 1904. 2) Circa 1910–1911. 3) "1897, the Merriam Trio: Billy-Eva-Zoe Novelty Aerial Artists." 4) Circa 1905–1909.

Captioned: No. Two audiotapes contain commentary on the images.

Finding Aid: A preliminary inventory which lists dates and types of materials in the collection, and includes brief biographical information.

Restrictions: No.

AC·7

Brad J. Bogart Collection

Dates of Photographs: 1914–1927

Collection Origins

This collection was assembled by Brad J. Bogart. It consists of a desk diary by Frank E. Lark containing 60 photographs taken on a trip on the Mississippi, Ohio, and Tennessee rivers in June 1914. Also included are three pages of court record proceedings recorded in 1927 from the Justice's Court of Swansea, Yuma County, in the territory of Arizona. One page concerns an inquest over the remains of W.C. Gilbert, found dead on the Colorado River Indian Reservation, 15 miles from Parker, Arizona.

These items were donated to the Archives Center by Brad J. Bogart in 1984.

Physical Description

There are 60 silver gelatin photoprints pasted in a desk diary. Other collection material includes three pages of court record proceedings.

Subjects

The photographs document a boat trip down the Mississippi, Ohio, and Tennessee rivers in June 1914, including images of Illinois (the penitentiary

at Chester) and Tennessee (Clifton and the Shiloh Battlefield). About half the photographs are individual or group portraits.

Arranged: Chronologically.

Captioned: With subject information on the notebook pages.

Finding Aid: A register.

Restrictions: No.

AC·8

William W. Brown Collection

Dates of Photographs: 1920–1950

Collection Origins

William W. Brown was an electrical engineer who worked for the General Electric Company (GE) in New York. These materials document Brown's career while he was working for GE on low frequency antennae and transmitter systems. The General Electric Company created many of the photographs in this collection.

Physical Description

There are 20 photographs, including cyanotypes and silver gelatin photoprints housed in albums. Other materials include blueprints, charts in binders, correspondence, engineering drawings, and reports.

Subjects

The photographs document products of the General Electric Company of New York including alternators, antennae, insulators, and transmitters.

Arranged: By subject, such as, type of General Electric product.

Captioned: No.

Finding Aid: 1) A preliminary inventory that includes an index of subjects. 2) A container list.

Restrictions: No.

AC·9

Henri Gaston Busignies Papers

Dates of Photographs: 1905–1981

Collection Origins

Henri Gaston Busignies was an electronic communications engineer with the International Telephone and Telegraph Corporation (ITT) in Paris (1928–1941) and in Nutley, New Jersey (1941–1946).

These papers document Busignies's role in the development of electronic communications equipment during World War II. They are his business and personal papers.

Physical Description

There are 25 silver gelatin photoprints. Other materials include articles, business papers, correspondence, and personal papers.

Subjects

The photographs document electronic communications equipment, such as, instrument landing devices, radar devices, and radio direction finders developed by Henri Gaston Busignies.

Arranged: No.

Captioned: No.

Finding Aid: A guide entry description.

Restrictions: No.

AC·10

Caterpillar Tractor Company Photographic Collection

Dates of Photographs: 1948–1949

Collection Origins

The collection was originally part of the Warshaw Collection of Business Americana. It was removed from the Warshaw Collection to function as a separate collection documenting the Caterpillar Tractor Company and its products.

Photographers represented include Broden, Don Chandler, and W.J. Holling.

Physical Description

There are 11 silver gelatin photoprints.

Subjects

The photographs document Caterpillar brand tractors at work building roads and constructing cemeteries. There are also views (including two aerial views) of the Caterpillar Tractor Company plant in Peoria, Illinois.

Arranged: No.

Captioned: With narrative subject information and negative number.

Finding Aid: A guide entry description.

Restrictions: No.

AC·11

Celluloid Corporation Records

Dates of Photographs: 1892–1935

Collection Origins

The Celluloid Corporation of Newark, New Jersey, was founded in 1872 as the Celluloid Manufacturing Company. The word "Celluloid" was registered as a trademark in 1873 by its inventor, John Wesley Hyatt. The first product of the Celluloid Corporation was plates for artificial teeth. In 1882, the corporation began to use amyl acetate as a nitrocellulose solvent, which led to the development of the lacquer industry. In 1910, nonflammable safety film was made from cellulose acetate. In 1912, the corporation invented Lumarith, a true thermoplastic. This collection consists of the corporate records of the company.

Photographic studios represented include Rohm and Haas of Philadelphia.

Physical Description

There are 25 silver gelatin photoprints, including bound photographic facsimiles of original company catalogs. Other materials include notebooks, patents, price lists, promotional literature, and a salesman's kit containing celluloid samples.

Subjects

These photographs document the catalogs and products of the Celluloid Corporation of Newark, New Jersey. The products include airplanes, celluloid dentures, phonographic discs, radios, and toothbrushes. Also included are images of factories in Newark, New Jersey, and unidentified Celluloid Corporation staff members.

Arranged: No.

Captioned: Some with subject and date information.

Finding Aid: A preliminary inventory.

Restrictions: No.

AC·12

George H. Clark Radioana Collection

Dates of Photographs: 1880–1950

Collection Origins

This collection was assembled by George H. Clark (1881–1956), a radio engineer and executive of the Radio Corporation of America (RCA) of New York. Clark collected materials relating to the history of radio from diverse sources throughout his life.

Thomas Coke Knight, an RCA photographer, is the primary photographer represented in this collection. Other photographers and studios represented include American Telephone and Telegraph; Philip Farnsworth; Fessenden Companies; the de Forest Companies; Dr. Alfred Goldsmith; Marconi Wireless Company; Julius Martin; RCA; Stone Telegraph and Telephone Company; Telefunken; the U.S. Army; the U.S. Navy; and Roy A. Weagent.

Physical Description

There are 10,000 photographs, including cyanotypes, and silver gelatin photonegatives and photoprints. Other materials include articles; blueprints of diagrams and drawings; clippings; correspondence; patent specifications; technical literature; and trade literature.

Subjects

The photographs document the history of radio, with the greatest emphasis from 1900 to 1935. There are photographs of aircraft receivers; antennae; batteries; broadcasting and TV stations; centralized radio systems; distance records and tests; laboratory testing methods and systems; log books; low frequency indicating devices; mobile radio systems; name plates of apparatus; patents; radio companies; radio frequency switches; radio frequency measuring instruments; radio use in education; radio personalities; radio stations; receivers; and vacuum tubes.

Arranged: The collection was arranged by Clark according to the 1915 Navy Classification System which he devised. The system consists of dividing a collection into subjects (series), each of which is assigned a number or letter. Each item is then numbered sequentially as it is processed. The collection thus reflects the order in which materials were received. There are a total of 246 series in this collection, 233 numbered series, and 13 (A–M) lettered series. Of these, four series consist entirely of photographs.

Captioned: No.

Finding Aid: Robert S. Harding. *Register of the George H. Clark Radioana Collection, c. 1880–1950.* Washington, D.C.: Archives Center, National Museum of American History, 1985.

Restrictions: No.

AC·13

Mille Gade Corson Collection

Dates of Photographs: 1920–1930

Collection Origins

Mille Gade Corson (1899–   ), born in Denmark, emigrated to New York City in 1919. In 1921 Corson became the first woman to swim around Manhattan Island. In 1923 she made her first unsuccessful attempt to swim the English Channel. In August of 1926, Corson beat all male records with her successful completion of the English Channel swim with a time of 15¾ hours. She was the second woman and the first mother to swim the channel. This collection documents several of her long-distance swims and the events which honored her accomplishments.

Photographers and studios represented include Chidnoff of New York and White Studio of New York. The collection was donated to the Smithsonian by a private donor from Suffern, New York.

Physical Description

There are 100 silver gelatin photoprints. Other materials include albums and scrapbooks containing clippings (some are in Danish), and promotional material.

Subjects

Most of these photographs are portraits of Mille Gade Corson, a long distance swimmer. There are also photographs of civic celebrations (such as her New York City welcome); Corson in training; her English Channel swim; her family; and publicity photographs.

Arranged: No.

Captioned: No.

Finding Aid: A register.

Restrictions: No.

AC·14

Harmon Deal Collection

Dates of Photographs: 1920–1930

Collection Origins

Harmon Deal attended the Massachusetts Institute of Technology before serving as electrical engineer; first for the Atwater Kent Company of Philadelphia, Pennsylvania; and later for RCA of New Jersey. Deal researched improvements in television transmission, including the development of a circuit arrangement to incorporate an automatic synchronizer for television.

Photographic studios represented include the Atwater Kent Company and RCA.

Physical Description

There are 40 silver gelatin photoprints. Other materials include blueprints, diagrams, notes, reports, technical reprints, and textbooks.

Subjects

These photographs document projects which Harmon Deal worked on at Atwater Kent Company and RCA. They are primarily images of installed television apparatus, such as receivers and transmitters.

Arranged: No.

Captioned: No.

Finding Aid: Preliminary inventory with description of material, dates, and a brief biographical sketch.

Restrictions: No.

AC·15

Draper Family Collection

Dates of Photographs: 1880s–1970s

Collection Origins

Draper family members were actively involved in astronomy, chemistry, medicine, meteorology, and photography during the 19th and early 20th centuries in New York. John William Draper, primarily a chemist, did pioneer work in photography and on the chemical effects of radiant energy. He took early photographs of the moon and the first photograph of the diffraction spectrum.

Draper's three sons also did notable work. John Christopher Draper was a physician and chemist. Henry Draper was an early astronomical photographer who also did work on stellar spectra and spectrum analysis. Daniel Draper was a meteorologist. He established the New York Meteorological Observatory in Central Park in 1868.

Other photographers and studios represented include Hyn Ksander, Prague, Bohemia; Mora, 707 Broadway; and the New York Meteorological Observatory.

Physical Description

There are 55 photographs, including albumen photoprints and silver gelatin photoprints. Formats include cartes-de-visite, imperial cards, and stereographs. There are 25 rolls (unknown film type) of experimental prints. (Note: These are too tightly rolled for viewing.) Other materials include correspondence, publications, and reprints.

Subjects

The photographs are images of astronomical objects and meteorological instruments; and portraits of the Draper family and friends. Portrait images include: Daniel Draper, Henry Draper, John C. Draper, John W. Draper, and Professor J. Purkyne.

The collection also contains experimental images of the stellar spectra and clouds. There is one stereographic cityscape of Washington, D.C., and vicinity.

Arranged: By series. 1) Draper Family, 1829–1936. 2) John W. Draper, 1811–1882. 3) Henry Draper, 1837–1882. 4) Daniel Draper, 1841–1931. 5) John Christopher Draper, 1835–1885. Each series is further broken down by type of material.

Captioned: With subject information (such as, personal names).

Finding Aid: A register.

Restrictions: No access to rolled film (due to condition).

AC·16

J. Harry DuBois Collection in the History of Plastics

Dates of Photographs: 1890–1975

Collection Origins

This collection was assembled by J. Harry DuBois who worked for General Electric and chemical engineering and plastics firms (such as Tech Art Plastics). DuBois compiled these materials while writing *Plastics History U.S.A.* Boston, 1972.

Photographic studios represented include Schill Photo of Newark, New Jersey.

Physical Description

There are 65 silver gelatin photoprints (DOP). Other materials include catalogs, correspondence, historical material relating to the history of plastics, and research reports.

Subjects

The photographs document Bakelite products; Charles Burroughs Company products; other early plastics products; the production of Rayon; and rubber products.

Arranged: No.

Captioned: With subject information, such as, product or tool name.

Finding Aid: Preliminary inventory which describes the types of material.

Restrictions: No.

AC·17

Allen Balcom Dumont Collection

Dates of Photographs: 1929–1962

Collection Origins

The DuMont Laboratories, Inc., was an early television manufacturing company established in 1931 on Long Island, New York. The founder, Allen Balcom DuMont (1901–1965), was an electrical engineer who graduated from Rensselaer Polytechnic Institute in 1924. He worked for Westinghouse Lamp Company until 1928, when he became chief engineer for the DeForest Radio Company.

In 1931 DuMont established DuMont Laboratories, which began producing reliable cathode ray tubes for industrial and educational use. In 1937 the company produced the first television receivers for sale in America. DuMont directed the company until 1960 when the laboratory was acquired by Fairchild Instrument and Camera Company.

The collection of business records was donated in 1966 by the DuMont estate.

Physical Description

There are 2,500 silver gelatin photoprints (DOP). Other materials include clippings, financial records, photomechanicals (halftone), plant operations records, and technical publications.

Subjects

These photographs document the activities, facilities, products, and staff of the DuMont Laboratories, Inc., an early television manufacturing company on Long Island, New York.

There are also photographs of studio installations; television screens; and work diagrams and drawings. Locations shown include California (Los Angeles), New Jersey (Clifton and East Paterson), and New York City. Among the executives portrayed are Lawrence Beville, Allen B. DuMont, and Ernest Marx.

Arranged: Into 10 series by subject or type of record. 1) Personal files. 2) Legal proceedings. 3) Radio Technical Planning Board. 4) Sales and trade literature. 5) DuMont Technical Publications. 6) Fiscal records. 7) Plant operations. 8) Photographs. 9) Clippings notebooks. 10) Extra and miscellaneous clippings.

Captioned: With subject information such as event or location.

Finding Aid: 1) A preliminary inventory. 2) A container list.

Restrictions: No.

AC·18

DuPont Nylon Collection

Dates of Photographs: Circa 1947

Collection Origins

The DuPont Corporation was founded as E.I. DuPont de Nemours and Company in 1802 on Brandywine Creek near Wilmington, Delaware. The company's chemical research and production facilities are located in Wilmington, Delaware; Chattanooga, Tennessee; Martinsville, Virginia; and Washington, D.C.

This collection was created to document the invention and production of nylon.

Studios represented include the Sanborn Studio of Wilmington, Delaware. The collection was donated to the Smithsonian in 1977.

Physical Description

There are 35 silver gelatin photoprints. Other materials include clippings, catalogs, an employee handbook, pamphlets, and promotional booklets.

Subjects

These photographs document the development of the synthetic fiber, nylon, by the DuPont Corporation. They illustrate the construction and equipment of the DuPont Corporation's nylon production facilities at Petersburg, Virginia; Washington, D.C.; and Wilmington, Delaware.

Arranged: Into three series. 1) Nylon production. 2) Promotional materials. 3) "Delrin" acetal resin.

Captioned: Some are captioned with a subject description and dates.

Finding Aid: A preliminary inventory gives a description of contents in the collection and brief historical information.

Restrictions: No.

AC·19

Saul Dushman Papers

Dates of Photographs: 1924–1954 and Undated

Collection Origins

Russian born Saul Dushman (1883–1954) immigrated to the United States in 1891. Dushman worked for the Research Laboratory of General Electric Company from 1912 to 1948, with one interruption from 1922 to 1925, when he served as director of the Research Division of the Edison Lamp Works.

Physical Description

There are 270 photographs, including silver gelatin photonegatives and photoprints. Other materials include blueprints, correspondence, lectures, photostats, and technical papers.

Subjects

The photographs document Saul Dushman's equipment and his experiments in atomic structure, electromotive force, electron emission, high vacuum work, quantum mechanics, and unimolecular force.

There are photographs of equipment including a bulb containing a molybdenum cup for determination of gas in metals; a pure nickel filament lamp; and a packaged pumping unit.

Arranged: Into series by type of materials. 1) Lectures, 1926–1952, and undated. 2) Correspondence, 1936–1954. 3) Books, articles, and reviews, 1939–1952. 4) Technical reprints, 1930–1954. 5) Research notes and technical data, 1924–1952.

Captioned: With narrative subject information.

Finding Aid: A register.

Restrictions: No.

AC·20

Lloyd Espenschied Papers

Dates of Photographs: 1907–1969

Collection Origins

This collection was assembled by Lloyd Espenschied (1889–1986), of St. Louis, Missouri. Espenschied graduated from Pratt Institute in electrical engineering in 1909. He was an electrical engineer for Telefunken Wireless Telegraph Company (1909–1910); American Telephone and Telegraph in New York (1910–1934); and Bell Telephone Laboratories of New York (1934–1937).

Espenschied's chief interests were carrier waves and wide-band (wave) systems for communications. This collection documents the history of electricity, motion pictures with a recorded sound track, sound recordings, and telephonic and wireless communication.

Photographic studios represented include the Bell Telephone Laboratories of New York and the U.S. Navy.

Physical Description

There are 50 silver gelatin photoprints. Other materials include correspondence, lecture materials, papers by Espenschied, and patents.

Subjects

The photographs document Espenschied's colleagues, his family, and his research facilities (including a radio facility in Arlington, Virginia). Among the individuals portrayed are Captain Bullard; Mrs. Lloyd Espenschied; Captain Hooper; F.B. Jewett; and John Mills.

Arranged: Into four series by type of material. 1) Subjects file (1907–1964). 2) Papers and talks (1923–1969). 3) Patents (1928–1953). 4) Correspondence (1940–1965).

Captioned: With a description of subject and often the date.

Finding Aid: A preliminary inventory.

Restrictions: No.

AC·21

C. Willard Geer Collection

Dates of Photographs: 1944–1962

Collection Origins

This collection was assembled by C. Willard Geer (1902–1975), Assistant Professor of Physics at the University of Southern California, Los Angeles, from 1943 to 1968. The albums document Geer's role in color television research and development. Geer was the inventor of the first practical color television receiving tube. He was granted a patent for this tube in 1944.

Physical Description

There are four silver gelatin photoprints. Other materials include biographical information, clippings, correspondence, drawings, and legal papers.

Subjects

The photographs show C. Willard Geer in his laboratory (unidentified location), and Geer with a model of the first practical color television receiving tube.

Arranged: No.

Captioned: No.

Finding Aid: A guide entry description.

Restrictions: No.

AC·22

Elisha Gray Collection

Dates of Photographs: 1871–1938

Collection Origins

This collection was assembled by Lloyd W. Taylor of Oberlin College for an unpublished book on Elisha Gray.

Elisha Gray (1835–1901) was born in Ohio and studied the physical sciences and electrical mechanisms at Oberlin College in Ohio. Gray was an inventor and co-founder of the Western Electric Company of Chicago. Among his inventions were an automatic self-adjusting telegraphic relay, a private telegraph line printer, a telegraphic repeater, and a telegraph switch and annunciator for hotels.

In 1876, Gray filed a patent application for a speaking telephone device on the same day Alexander Graham Bell applied for a similar, but less sophisticated, device. Over the next five years a battle ensued concerning the priority over the invention of the telephone (Gray vs. Bell). This collection consists of documents relating to this legal controversy.

Physical Description

There are 50 photographs, including a platinum photoprint and silver gelatin photoprints. Other materials include original and reproductions of clippings, correspondence, and legal papers.

Subjects

The photographs document telephone apparatus designed by Elisha Gray, including receivers, transmitters, and unidentified apparatus.

Arranged: No.

Captioned: No.

Finding Aid: A preliminary inventory.

Restrictions: No.

AC·23

Gerald Connop Gross Collection

Dates of Photographs: 1900–1946

Collection Origins

This collection was assembled by Gerald Connop Gross, a radio engineer from Brooklyn, New York, to document his career. Gross served with the Federal Communications Commission, the Federal Radio Commission, and the International Telecommunications Union. This collection of professional records was acquired by the Smithsonian in 1980.

Physical Description

There are seven silver gelatin photoprints. Other materials include clippings, correspondence, legal documents, publications, and reports.

Subjects

The photographs document radio and television apparatus used in the development of international communications.

Arranged: No.

Captioned: With subject and location information.

Finding Aid: A guide entry description.

Restrictions: No.

AC·24

Halacsy and Von Fuchs Documentation for Transformer History

Dates of Photographs: 1884–1899

Collection Origins

This collection was assembled by Dr. Andrew Halacsy and Dr. George Von Fuchs to document the history of the transformer. Dr. Halacsy and Dr. Von Fuchs were electrical engineers, who wrote jointly on the creation of the transformer. The collection was assembled in 1960 when both were members of the American Institute of Electrical Engineers.

Physical Description

There are nine photographs, including a diazo photoprint, and silver gelatin photoprints. Other materials include articles, correspondence, patents, and research notes.

Subjects

These photographs document the history of the transformer. There are photographs of an exhibition of Ganz and Co. products in Europe in the 1890s; an open iron core; patents; a power station in Innsbruck, Austria, in 1889; and transformers (1884 and 1885).

Arranged: By subject into two series. 1) Transformer history. 2) Product engineering.

Captioned: With inventors' names, transformers produced, locations, and dates.

Finding Aid: A preliminary inventory gives dates, brief historical information, and lists the types of materials in the collection.

Restrictions: No.

AC·25

William Joseph Hammer Collection

Dates of Photographs: 1879–1935

Collection Origins

This collection was assembled by William Joseph Hammer (1858–1934), an inventor and consulting electrical engineer. Hammer was an early associate of Thomas Edison at his Menlo Park, New Jersey, laboratory. As a member of Edison's staff, he worked on projects such as the telephone and the incandescent light.

In 1881 Hammer represented the Edison laboratories in England where he installed an exhibition of 12 dynamos at the Crystal Palace. He invented the first sign made entirely of electric lights which he exhibited in England in 1884. Hammer was dedicated to the collection and preservation of Edison's work, and gathered the material in this collection throughout his career.

Photographers represented include Barr, San Antonio, Texas; Fredericks, New York City; Gubelman, New Jersey; George P. Hall & Son, New York City; Hastings, Boston, Massachusetts; Percy L. Lancaster; Alva Pearsall, New York City; E. Rabending, Frankfurt, Germany; M.P. Rice, Washington, D.C.; and N.L. Stebbins, Boston, Massachusetts.

Physical Description

There are 700 photographs, including albumen photoprints; platinum photoprints; collodion gelatin photoprints (POP); silver gelatin dry plate photonegatives; silver gelatin photoprints; and tintypes. Other materials include articles, blueprints, clippings, diagrams, photomechanical reproductions, and scientific notes and notebooks.

Subjects

Many photographs in this collection illustrate electrical apparatus; electrical research laboratories; electrical signs; electrical trains; light bulbs; lighting apparatus; phonographs; and portraits of Edison's colleagues.

Portraits include Patrick Alexander; William A. Anthony; W.F. Ayerton; George F. Barker; Charles

Bachelor; Alexander Graham Bell; Louis Bell; Henry Bequerrel; James Dewar; Louis Duncan; Thomas Edison; Elisha Gray; William Joseph Hammer; J. Allen Heany; Benedict Herzog; D.C. Jackson; A.A. Knudson; Sir Oliver Lodge; Alexander Mungle; H.C. Orstead; Nelson W. Perry; Ernst Ruhmer; George Tanzelmann; George Westinghouse; Joseph Wetzler; Wilbur Wright; and E.L. Zalinski.

Arranged: Into four series. 1) Biographical. 2) Edisoniana. 3) Reference materials. 4) Photographs. Then by subject or format.

Captioned: With subject information and dates.

Finding Aid: Robert S. Harding. *Register to the J. Hammer Collection, c. 1874–1935, 1955–1957.* Washington, D.C.: Archives Center, National Museum of American History, 1986.

Restrictions: No.

AC·26

Charles Cohill Harris Collection

Dates of Photographs: 1904–1960

Collection Origins

This collection was assembled by Charles Cohill Harris to document the history of the Tropical Radio Telegraph Company of the United Fruit Company. Harris was a radio engineer who worked for the United Fruit Company in Central America, Florida, and South America from 1904 to 1960.

In 1904 the United Fruit Company established the earliest wireless telegraph system from Costa Rica to Panama. The images in this collection were taken by unknown photographers in Central America, South America, and the United States from 1904 to 1960.

Physical Description

There are 175 silver gelatin photoprints within three bound volumes of manuscripts. Other materials include blueprints, manuals, reports, schematics, and a scrapbook.

Subjects

These photographs document the history of the communications systems of the Tropical Radio Telegraph Company of the United Fruit Company.

The photographs are of equipment, radio station machine shops, radio telephone terminals, radio transmitters, and transmitting stations in Florida (Miami), Guatemala (Puerto Barrios), Louisiana (New Orleans), Massachusetts (Hingham), and Panama (Panama City).

Arranged: Into two series by subject. 1) "The History of the Communications System of the Tropical Radio Telegraph Company" (one volume). 2) "Pictorial Wireless History of the United Fruit and Tropical Radio Telegraph Companies" (two volumes).

Captioned: With date, location, and/or type of equipment.

Finding Aid: A guide entry description.

Restrictions: No.

AC·27

Herder's Cutlery Collection

Dates of Photographs: 1847–1980

Collection Origins

Clarenbach and Herder, a cutlery company, was founded by Herman Herder of Solingen, Germany, and Charles Clarenbach in Philadelphia, Pennsylvania, in 1847. Retail sales and repair of cutlery were the company's primary business concerns. This collection consists of business records of this company.

Some of the photographs in this collection were created by OPPS, where the negatives remain on file. Studios represented include F. Gutenkunst of Philadelphia and Woodcrest Photography.

Physical Description

There are 15 photographs, including albumen photoprints (mounted together as one image), a tinted salted paper photoprint, and silver gelatin photoprints. Other materials include clippings, corporate records, correspondence, financial records, personal papers, and sales records.

Subjects

These photographs document a cutlery sales and repair business. There are photographs of two company storefronts and a cutlery display (arranged in the shape of an American eagle). There are also portraits of an unidentified woman and several unidentified cutlery workers.

Arranged: By type of material into seven series. 1) Clippings. 2) Correspondence. 3) Herder family documents. 4) Financial records. 5) Sales records. 6) Corporate records. 7) Photographs.

Captioned: With subjects and dates.

Finding Aid: 1) A preliminary inventory. 2) A container list.

Restrictions: No.

AC·28

Ira Hill Collection

Dates of Photographs: 1910–1953

Collection Origins

The Ira Hill Studio operated from 1910 to the 1950s in New York City. It specialized in studio portraits of prominent New Yorkers and theatre personalities.

Photographers represented include Ray Martin, Hill's successor, and several unidentified studio assistants.

This collection, consisting of a portion of the studio's output, was given to the Division of Photographic History in 1966 and 1967 and transferred to the Archives Center in 1983.

Several photographs from the collection were published in *Vanity Fair* magazine in the 1930s.

Physical Description

There are 86,000 photographs, including silver gelatin dry plate photonegatives and silver gelatin photonegatives.

Subjects

Most of the images in the Ira Hill Collection are formal studio portraits of New Yorkers, theatrical personalities, and other well-known people (such as, Eleanor Roosevelt) taken from 1910 to the 1950s.

Arranged: By studio negative number.

Captioned: No.

Finding Aid: A card file of sitting records, arranged by date, includes the subject's name, the sitting date, prices, and order number.

Restrictions: No.

AC·29

Howe Scale Company Records

Dates of Photographs: 1868–1963

Collection Origins

The Howe Scale Company of Brandon, Vermont, was founded in 1868 as the Brandon Manufacturing Company by John Howe, Jr. Its name was changed to the Howe Scale Company in 1878. Howe purchased the patents for a simplified ball bearing protection design from Frank Strong and Thomas Ross. The company went out of business in the early 1980s. The collection was donated to the Smithsonian by an antique store in 1983.

Physical Description

There are 10,000 photographs, including albumen photoprints and silver gelatin photoprints. Other materials include cash books, catalogs, certificate books, charters, clippings, financial records, inventories, journals, ledgers, legal documents, minutes, reports, specifications, and stock price lists.

Subjects

The photographs document the product line of the Howe Scale Company, including hand trucks, scales, and scale parts.

Arranged: Into five series by type of material, and then chronologically. 1) Corporate records. 2) Financial records. 3) Inventories. 4) Reports and newsclippings. 5) Photographic scrapbooks.

Captioned: No.

Finding Aid: 1) A preliminary inventory gives historical information about the Howe Scale Company and the types of materials produced by the company. 2) A container list describes the collection at the box and folder level.

Restrictions: No.

AC·30

Imperial Glass Company Collection

Dates of Photographs: 1909–1912

Collection Origins

The Imperial Glass Company of Bellaire, Ohio, was in business from 1901 to 1984. The company first manufactured glass items, such as, berry bowls, butter dishes, jelly glasses, and pressed tumblers for mass-marketing in stores, such as, the S.S. Kresge Company and McCrory Stores. It then went on to produce iridescent glassware and art glass.

Physical Description

There are 30 tinted silver gelatin photoprints (mounted on linen and bound into company product catalogs).

Subjects

The photographs document glass items manufactured by the Imperial Glass Company, such as, drinking glasses; goblets; lighting globes; and pitchers. Many of the items shown are hand-engraved, hand-painted, or sandblasted glassware.

Arranged: Into two series. 1) Catalogs. 2) Photographs.

Captioned: With handwritten instructions for ordering the glass shown in the photograph.

Finding Aid: A register.

Restrictions: No.

AC·31

Chevalier Jackson Papers

Dates of Photographs: 1932

Collection Origins

Chevalier Jackson (1865–1958) and his son, Chevalier Lawrence Jackson (1900–1961), were eminent surgeons, specializing in esophago-bronchoscopy. Both Jacksons were associated with the Temple University Medical School, where son followed father as professor of bronchoscopy.

The elder Jackson was a pioneer in the field and wrote numerous articles and books on the subject. As a result of his clinical experience treating children for the ingestion of lye, Jackson worked to obtain federal standards regulating the sale and labeling of lye and similar household caustics.

Physical Description

There are 40 photographs, including silver gelatin photonegatives (nitrate and safety) and photoprints. Other materials include books, clippings, envelopes, notes, radiographs, reprints, and stationary.

Subjects

The photographs document the interests and work of both Chevalier Jackson and his son Chevalier Lawrence Jackson. There are photographs of tree leaves, and of unidentified individuals (1932); and radiographs of esophagi and lungs.

Arranged: No.

Captioned: With some narrative subject information.

Finding Aid: A register.

Restrictions: No.

AC·32

Jean King Glass Negative Collection

Dates of Photographs: Circa 1890–1894

Collection Origins

This collection was assembled by Jean King. It was originally given to the Division of Ceramics and Glass by King. It was transferred to the Archives Center in January 1985.

Physical Description

There are 12 photographs, including silver gelatin dry plate photonegatives; and silver gelatin photonegatives and photoprints.

Subjects

The images in this collection depict the production and display of ceramic items, such as, household dishes and tableware in the late 19th century.

Arranged: No.

Captioned: No.

Finding Aid: A guide entry description.

Restrictions: No.

AC·33

Edmund A. LaPorte Collection

Dates of Photographs: 1920–1950

Collection Origins

This collection was assembled by Edmund A. La-Porte (1902–   ), of Nashua, New Hampshire, from 1920 to 1950. LaPorte served for several years as Director of Broadcast Engineering for the Radio Corporation of America (RCA) in New Jersey. La-Porte was responsible for innovative contributions to the fields of international communications and antenna engineering.

The collection was acquired in 1974 from LaPorte.

Physical Description

There are 300 photographs, including cyanotypes and silver gelatin photoprints. Other materials include xerographic reproductions of the negative envelopes.

Subjects

The photographs document broadcast installations; microwave relay equipment; radio antenaae; radio telegraph receivers and transmitters; and testing and measuring equipment.

Arranged: By subject.

Captioned: Detailed subject descriptions including type of apparatus, date, and location are on the envelopes.

Finding Aid: 1) The guide entry description. 2) Sixty-three xerographic copies of the descriptions on the outside of the photonegative envelopes.

Restrictions: No.

AC·34

Ladislaus Laszlo Marton Collection

Dates of Photographs: 1940s–1960s

Collection Origins

Ladislaus Laszlo Marton (1901–1979), a Hungarian physicist, taught in American universities until 1946 when he joined the National Bureau of Standards in Washington, D.C. This collection consists of Marton's documentation of his pioneering work with the electron microscope, radar, and the telephone.

Photographic studios represented include Bell Photo Labs; General Dynamics; Hughes Air Craft; Raytheon Photo; Science Service Inc.; United States Air Force; United States Army Signal Corps; United States Department of Defense; and Westinghouse.

Physical Description

There are 1,080 photographs, including silver gelatin dry plate lantern slides (20) and silver gelatin photoprints. Other materials include blueprints, correspondence, drawings, notebooks, and two reels of 16mm color motion picture film footage.

Subjects

The photographs in this collection consist primarily of scanning electron photomicrographs (SEM) of bacteria and viruses, such as, TMU. (Note: One reel of motion picture footage is labeled "Standard Electron Microscope.") Other photographs depict installations, radar antennae, telephones, and weather balloons.

The lantern slides are portraits of scientists, such as, Descartes, Benjamin Franklin, Galileo, Michael Faraday, Gustav Hertz, and Isaac Newton, as well as more modern figures. Most images are photographic reproductions of graphic portraits.

Arranged: Into three series. 1) Notebooks. 2) Photographs. 3) Printed materials.

Captioned: With subject information.

Finding Aid: A register describes materials in the collection by box down to the folder label.

Restrictions: No.

AC·35

Medical and Chirurgical Faculty of the State of Maryland Collection

Dates of Photographs: Circa 1880–1920

Collection Origins

This collection was assembled by the Medical and Chirurgical Faculty of the State of Maryland from 18th, 19th, and 20th century materials deposited by various donors. The materials are chiefly related to the practice of medicine in Maryland.

Physical Description

There are 14 photographs, including an albumen photoprint and silver gelatin photoprints. Other materials include certificates of membership, correspondence, and newspaper clippings.

Subjects

All the photographs are portraits of members of the Medical and Chirurgical Faculty of the State of Maryland taken in the early 1900s. Portraits include John Buckler, William Osler, and Charles Wellmore.

Arranged: No.

Captioned: No.

Finding Aid: A register.

Restrictions: No.

AC·36

Mexican Border Veterans Inc. and Auxiliary Scrapbooks

Dates of Photographs: 1916–1981

Collection Origins

The Mexican Border Veterans Inc. (MBV) is a civilian association founded by Clairice A.G. Closson of Independence, Missouri, in 1929. The association consists of men who patrolled the Mexican-American border between May 9, 1916, and April 1917. They were called to duty by President Woodrow Wilson to guard the border, which had been repeatedly invaded by Francisco (Pancho) Villa. The MBV was formed so the men could seek and receive recognition and benefits as veterans of a foreign war.

Physical Description

There are four silver gelatin photoprints. Other materials include annual reports, convention minutes, maps (including a War Department map of the United States), newsletters, and newspaper clippings (including the front page of *The Chicago Tribune* June 19, 1916).

Subjects

The photographs are portraits of Pancho Villa.

Arranged: No.

Captioned: No.

Finding Aid: A register.

Restrictions: No.

AC·37

Dewey Michaels Collection

Dates of Photographs: Circa late 1920s–1967

Collection Origins

This collection was assembled by Dewey Michaels (circa 1898–1982), owner, director, and producer of the Palace Burlesk Theater in Buffalo, New York. Michaels operated this theater from the late 1920s until 1977 when he was 79 years old.

Photographers represented include Aleo, Boston; Bruno, Hollywood; Goldie Cohan, Freddy, and Garbo, Chicago; and John E. Reed, Hollywood.

Physical Description

There are 250 silver gelatin photoprints. Other materials include brochures, clippings, and scripts.

Subjects

These photographs document performers and events at the Palace Burlesk Theater in Buffalo, New York, from the early 1920s to 1967. There are photographs of comedians, novelty acts, and striptease acts. The photographs feature Dewey Michaels, as well as performers, including Abbott and Costello; Red Buttons; Sammy Davis, Jr.; Jerry Lewis; and Phil Silvers. Other performers documented include Aurora; Johnny Barker; Virginia Ding Ding Bell; Johnny Morris and Delilah; the Sparkling Seminole; Stinky Fields; and Tinker Bell.

Arranged: Alphabetically by last name of performer.

Captioned: Some with the name of the performer.

Finding Aid: A register.

Restrictions: No.

AC·38

Faris and Yamna Naff Arab-American Collection

Dates of Photographs: 1890–1930

Collection Origins

This collection was assembled by Dr. Alixa Naff, for her book on the experiences of Arab-Americans from 1880 to 1940. On December 21, 1983, this collection was given to the Archives Center by Dr. Naff. Related artifacts were given to the Division of Community Life.

Materials from this collection were placed on display at the National Museum of American History from July to September 1984.

Physical Description

There are 165 silver gelatin photoprints. Six images are oversize panoramas taken with a cirkut camera. Other materials include articles, cassettes, folios, magazines, notes, pamphlets, and transcripts.

Subjects

The photographs document Arab-American culture, immigration, and life from 1890 to 1930. Most of the images are portraits of members of the Naff family and group portraits of Arab-American clubs and organizations. There are also images of battle scenes from an unidentified war.

Arranged: By series according to type of material. 1) Articles about Arab-Americans. 2) Bibliographies. 3) Arab-American press. 4) Oral history interview data. 5) Articles. 6) Statistical data. 7) Books, bound journals, and dissertations. 8) Material from informants and others. 9) History of project. 10) Photographs.

Captioned: Most with subject information and identification of individuals.

Finding Aid: A published brochure.

Restrictions: No.

AC·39

A.J. Noerager Collection

Dates of Photographs: 1914–1940

Collection Origins

This collection was assembled by A.J. Noerager while working as a mining engineer at power stations in Chile, South America, from 1914 to 1940.

Physical Description

There are 2,000 silver gelatin photoprints within nine albums. Other materials include two bound volumes and some blueprints.

Subjects

The photographs document construction, equipment, operations, and workers at Chilean power stations and mining sites from 1914 to 1940.

Arranged: No.

Captioned: With brief subject descriptions, an original negative number, and subject dates.

Finding Aid: A preliminary inventory.

Restrictions: No.

AC·40

Osteopathy Collection

Dates of Photographs: 1880s–1897

Collection Origins

This collection was assembled by Andrew Taylor Stillman (1828–1917), the founder of osteopathy. Osteopathy is a medical therapy that emphasizes manipulative techniques for correcting physical abnormalities that cause disease and inhibit recovery.

Stillman developed the doctrine and practice of osteopathy in the late 1860s. In 1892 he incorpo-

rated the American School of Osteopathy in Kirksville, Missouri. He established the *Journal of Osteopathy* in 1894. Stillman spent the rest of his life teaching and writing on osteopathy, and treating patients.

Photographers represented include: Bushnell, Portland and Seattle; Gilbert and Baron, Philadelphia; Henry Moore, Kansas City, Missouri; and Solem, Kirksville, Missouri.

Physical Description

There are 125 photographs, including albumen photoprints, platinum photoprints, and silver gelatin photoprints. Other materials include catalogs, journals, newspaper clippings, and pamphlets.

Subjects

Most of the photographs are portraits of osteopaths, such as, John Baum, Etta Elizabeth Curry, John Johnson, Janet Kerr, J.J. Moriarty, Theodore Paul, Mabel Lake Phelps, and Margaret Thompson.

There are also exterior views of the Atlantic School of Osteopathy; the Kansas City College of Osteopathy and Surgery; and unidentified buildings. There is a circa 1900 photograph of a human dissection class.

Arranged: No.

Captioned: No.

Finding Aid: A register.

Restrictions: No.

AC·41

Pittsburgh Locomotive and Car Works Records

Dates of Photographs: Circa 1882–1902

Collection Origins

These records are the official files of the Pittsburgh Locomotive and Car Works Company from 1882 to 1902.

Physical Description

There are 10 silver gelatin photoprints. Other materials include 25 blueprints of locomotive boilers (1893 to 1894); cylinder and smoke box details (circa 1900); erecting cards for locomotives (circa 1882 to 1902); laboratory reports and test results; lists of valve settings; price lists (1893 and 1895); specification sheets for boilers; and statements of labor costs.

Subjects

The photographs document the physical plant and products of the Pittsburgh Locomotive and Car Works between 1882 and 1902. There are photographs of car design; cylinder and smoke box details; locomotive boiler designs; locomotive boilers; locomotive design; and other railroad equipment details.

Arranged: By type of material.

Captioned: No.

Finding Aid: Container list.

Restrictions: No.

AC·42

James W. Queen and Company Collection

Dates of Photographs: 1850–1952

Collection Origins

The James W. Queen and Company of Philadelphia, Pennsylvania, manufactured scientific instruments for laboratory and industrial use between 1850 and 1952. This collection consists of the company's business records.

Physical Description

There are 150 silver gelatin photoprints. Other materials include business records, company catalogs, and photomechanical (halftone) reproductions.

Subjects

The photographs document James W. Queen and Company products, including ascent and descent indicators; barometers; chronoscopes; compasses for airplanes; mica condensers; pyrometers; recording thermometers; and tachometers.

Arranged: By type of material and then by subject.

Captioned: No.

Finding Aid: A register which lists by box the types of materials in the collection.

Restrictions: No.

AC·43

Harold R.D. Roess Papers

Dates of Photographs: Circa 1920–1964

Collection Origins

Harold R.D. Roess was a radio engineer for Westinghouse Electric and Manufacturing Company in Hastings, Nebraska, and for the Naval Research Laboratory in Washington, D.C. He worked on projects concerning radio transmitting and receiving apparatus. This collection consists of Roess' professional papers.

Photographers represented include NBC Photos and Bentz & Gentsch of Hastings, Nebraska.

Physical Description

There are 200 photographs, including silver gelatin dry plate lantern slides and silver gelatin photoprints (some of which are wire photographs transmitted by shortwave). Other materials include blueprints, correspondence, literature, manuals, notes, reprints of articles, schematics, and technical literature.

Subjects

The photographs document radio engineer Harold R.D. Roess's work with antennae; equipment installations (including the Naval Research Laboratory); radio receivers; radios; and radio transmitters.

There are photographs of NBC radio performers including Arline Blackburn, Dorothy Branthoover, Jean Rogers, and Virginia Torrell. There are also surveillance photographs.

Arranged: By type of material into six series. 1) Reports. 2) Blueprints. 3) Correspondence. 4) Publications. 5) Radio instruction manuals. 6) Photographs (organized by subject heading).

Captioned: With subject and location information.

Finding Aid: A register that lists by box the type of materials in the collection.

Restrictions: No.

AC·44

Scientists and Inventors Portrait File

Dates of Photographs: 1960s–Present

Collection Origins

This collection was assembled by the Division of Physical Sciences to serve as a visual finding aid to original images found elsewhere. It consists primarily of OPPS prints copied from original paintings, photographs, and prints in other Smithsonian collections. Some photonegatives were made from illustrations and photomechanical reproductions in books, magazines, and newspapers. It was transferred to the Archives Center in 1983.

Photographers represented include Anstalt von August Brasch of Leipzig, Austria; Giacomo Brogi, Firenze, Italy; Heinrich Memment, Erlangen, Germany; Reichard and Lindner, Berlin, Germany; C.H. Reutlinger, Paris, France; J. Russell and Sons, London, England; H.C. Stimpson, Westfield, Massachusetts; and Wm. Curtis Taylor, Philadelphia.

Physical Description

There are 1,440 photographs, including albumen cartes-de-visite and imperial card photoprints and silver gelatin photoprints. Most of the images (95%) are modern copy or duplicate photoprints.

Subjects

All the photographs in this collection are formal portraits of male scientists and inventors who worked in the biological and physical sciences, including astronomy; mathematics; physics; and those who made scientific instruments such as compasses, scales, and telescopes. Many images are photographic reproductions of graphics.

Among the individuals portrayed are Louis Agassiz, Jacob Bigelow, Curvier, Jean Bernard Foucault, Sir A. Geike, H. von Helmholtz, Joseph Henry, Amasa Holcomb, Lord Kelvin, Fireau Kolbe, Isaac Newton, John Roach, John Phillips, and James Smithson.

Arranged: Alphabetically by the last name of the scientist or inventor into two groups. 1) Mounted prints. 2) Envelopes containing unmounted prints.

Captioned: With the subject's name and date. Negative numbers are noted on the storage envelopes.

Finding Aid: A card catalog (that also includes images not found in this collection) lists the subject's name, nationality, immediate source of the image, image size, and artist or publisher.

Restrictions: No.

AC·45

J.B. Simpson, Inc., Records

Dates of Photographs: Circa 1888–1955

Collection Origins

This collection was assembled by Lewis and Thomas Saltz of Washington, D.C. They were employees of J.B. Simpson, Inc., and later gave the collection to the Smithsonian Institution. Note: Inscriptions on the photographs indicate that the Saltz's gave discounts on clothing to entertainers.

Photographers represented include Roralaugh and Millsap of Wichita, Kansas.

Physical Description

There are 90 photographs, including a color dye coupler photoprint and silver gelatin photoprints.

About 40 photoprints are in an album. Many are autographed and others are inscribed. Other materials include a business survey, correspondence, fiscal records, measuring and cutting books and instructions, newsletters, notes, profit sharing plan records, recollections, and salesmen's instructions.

Subjects

The photographs show some of the 22 branch offices of J.B. Simpson, Inc. (an American ready-to-wear clothing manufacturer); the company's sales managers, and the "20 Year" salesmen.

There are also publicity photographs of various entertainers, such as, Bartos, the Bondini Brothers, Nick Copeland, Jess Libonate, Paul Nervous, the O'Neil Twins, the Rigoletto Brothers, Edie Riley, Sam Vello, Bert Wheeler, and Joe Whiteliad.

Arranged: By type of material.

Captioned: Many with autographs. Fifty photographs are inscribed to "Mr. Hill of Hill Clothing."

Finding Aid: No.

Restrictions: No.

AC·46

George W. Sims Papers

Dates of Photographs: 1919–1976

Collection Origins

George W. Sims (circa 1896–1986) was a tax lawyer, certified public accountant, world traveler, and collector of pre-Columbian artifacts. He was employed in the Panama Canal Zone by the Panama Railroad Company, Commissary Branch, from 1915 to 1916. Between 1918 and 1919 he served in the aviation section of the Signal Corps and was stationed at the Vichy Hospital Center.

In 1919 Sims and some friends traveled west on one of the earliest automobile trips across the United States. After 1946 he traveled extensively. Sims collected artifacts and art objects and kept notebooks throughout his life.

Other photographers represented include H.G.

Downs, Warren, Ohio; Sherman S. Skeete; and Topix by Laval.

Physical Description

There are 4,000 photographs including color dye coupler photoprints (Kodacolor), and color dye coupler slides (Kodachrome). Note: About 75 percent are slides.

Subjects

Most images in this collection illustrate automobile travel and tourism in the United States and Europe from 1919 to 1976. Travel images include cityscapes, landscapes, and nature studies.

Some images document George Sims's collection of art objects and native handicrafts from Africa, Europe, South America, and the United States, as well as his adobe Boronda home (1946–1959) in Carmel, California.

Sims also documented a French military hospital at Vichy and wounded soldiers during World War I.

Arranged: By type of material.

Captioned: With narrative subject information and dates.

Finding Aid: Robert S. Harding. *The Register of the George W. Sims Collection, 1896–1981.* Washington, D.C.: Archives Center, National Museum of American History, 1986.

Restrictions: No.

AC·47

Kenneth Sparnon Collection

Dates of Photographs: 1912–1961

Collection Origins

Kenneth Sparnon (1895–1972) was born in Chatham, New Jersey. He was the musical director of radio stations WSYR in Syracuse and WHEC in Rochester, New York. Sparnon was part of a piano duo called "Twin Keyboards" with Matt Pierce, and led musical groups, such as, "Ken Sparnon's R-K-Olians" and "Ken Sparnon's String Orchestra."

This collection of four scrapbooks documents his career as an orchestra leader and entertainer. It was donated by his family in 1983.

Physical Description

This collection contains 30 silver gelatin photoprints. Other materials include business documents, clippings, correspondence, and programs.

Subjects

The photographs document the professional activities, colleagues, and performance facilities of musical director, orchestra leader, and entertainer Kenneth Sparnon.

Colleagues portrayed include J. Gordon Baldwin, Vance Beach, Justin Conlon, Maurice Cox, Carl Hedquist, Peter Laurini, Thomas Marraco, Louis Savarino, and Arabella Sparnon (his wife). Bands shown include the "Downtown Cowboys," "Silver and Gold," and the "Streamliners."

Facilities shown include Keith's RKO Vaudeville Theater in Syracuse; WHEC radio station in Rochester; and WSYR radio station in Syracuse, New York.

Arranged: Into four albums, chronologically, and then by medium. 1) 1912–1931 (clippings). 2) 1930–1943 (clippings and photographs). 3) 1929–1940 (clippings and photographs). 4) 1938–1946 (clippings).

Captioned: No.

Finding Aid: A register.

Restrictions: No.

AC·48

Clyde W. Stauffer Family Photograph Album

Dates of Photographs: 1935–1940

Collection Origins

This collection was assembled by Mr. and Mrs. Clyde W. Stauffer to document several vacation motor trips from 1935 to 1940. The collection was donated to the Smithsonian in 1985.

Physical Description

There are 135 silver gelatin photoprints in a 109-page photograph album. Other materials include photomechanical reproductions, postcards, and a World's Fair ticket stub (1939) housed in the album.

Subjects

The collection documents several Veterans of Foreign War business trips and vacation motor trips taken in the U.S. by the Clyde W. Stauffer family from 1935 to 1940. Most of the images (80%) are scenic shots of Bryce Canyon; Denver; Fort Worth; New Orleans; and Pike's Peak. The other images depict the Stauffers and their friends.

Arranged: Chronologically.

Captioned: With subjects and dates.

Finding Aid: Guide entry descriptions.

Restrictions: No.

AC·49

Richard Steele Papers

Dates of Photographs: 1948–1980

Collection Origins

Richard Steele (1916–1980) was a ceramic engineer. While working at the Research Foundation at Ohio State University in 1948, he invented the Ram process with A.R. Blackbirn. The Ram process is an automated machine process whereby reinforced gypsum cement dies are pressurized on a hydraulic press to produce a ceramic piece. This work led to the formation of the Ram Company of Columbus, Ohio. The collection was donated to the Smithsonian by Steele's family in 1983.

Physical Description

There are 165 photographs, including color dye coupler photoprints and phototransparencies; and silver gelatin photonegatives, photoprints, and phototransparencies. Other materials include business records, correspondence, journals, manuals, records, sketches, and tests.

Subjects

These photographs document the development, operations, and production of Ram Company presses between 1948 and 1980. Objects shown include the ceramic products (such as, ashtrays and plates) made with the Ram process; miscellaneous Ram presses; Ram press installations (such as, the "Canuck Press No. 35"); and reinforcing and coil holder units.

Activities shown include the step-by-step production of a nose cone for a missile using the Ram process. There are images of unidentified workers in some views.

Arranged: By series. 1) Sketches, drawings, journals, tests. 2) Financial and business-related material. 3) Photographs (arranged by subject and format).

Captioned: No.

Finding Aid: A preliminary folder-level inventory.

Restrictions: No.

AC·50

C.L. Stong Papers

Dates of Photographs: 1952–1976

Collection Origins

C.L. Stong (1902–1975) was an electrical engineer with Western Electric Company from 1926 to 1962. He was editor of the "Amateur Scientist" feature of the *Scientific American* from 1952 until his death.

This collection consists of Stong's files of approximately 250 manuscripts by over 200 authors published by the magazine after his death.

Physical Description

There are 50 silver gelatin photoprints. Other materials include manuscripts of articles published in *Scientific American.*

Subjects

The photographs are illustrations for science-related magazine articles compiled from 1952 to 1976. Topics depicted include aerodynamics, analog devices, anti-bubbles, archeology, birds, clocks, color, crystals, electronics, fish, glass, gravitation, lasers, liquids, machines, mathematics, meteorology, microscopy, molecular biology, optics, paleontology, particle physics, photography, plants, rockets and satellites, seismology, sports, telescopy, and zoology.

Arranged: Chronologically by date of publication.

Captioned: No.

Finding Aid: A guide entry description which incorporates an alphabetical subject index listing titles of articles along with the date of publication.

Restrictions: No.

AC·51

W. Oscar Sullivan Papers

Dates of Photographs: 1906–1955

Collection Origins

W. Oscar Sullivan (1891–   ) of Savannah, Georgia, was a vaudeville and medicine tent show entertainer. He worked with his wife, Aline Moore, and two daughters, Laverne and Virginia, in small towns throughout the southeastern United States. Their act included acrobatics, comedy (including blackface), dancing, monologues, and singing.

Photographers and studios represented include Haggard Studio of Ashland, Kentucky; Perry and Loveridge's of Savannah, Georgia; Silver and Friedman of Chicago, Illinois; and J.N. Wilson of Savannah. The collection was acquired in 1980.

Physical Description

There are 990 photographs, including albumen cartes-de-visite; cyanotypes; a silver gelatin photonegative (nitrate) and photoprints (including photobooth photoprints); and tinted tintypes. Other materials include correspondence, diaries, personal records, publicity papers, and work papers (performance routines, scripts, and songs).

Subjects

Most of the photographs illustrate the W. Oscar Sullivan family of entertainers (W. Oscar; his wife, Aline Moore; and their daughters, Laverne and Virginia).

Also depicted are acrobats; business associates; a family show dog; group photographs (unidentified); marquees; and unidentified show people. Locations shown include Kentucky (Hickman), Mississippi (Tupelo), Missouri (St. Charles), North Carolina (Plymouth and Scotland Neck), and Tennessee (Henderson).

Arranged: By type of material, and then by date. 1) Correspondence, diaries, appointment books, and financial information. 2) Miscellaneous, personal, photographs, and publicity. 3) Publicity, work papers, scripts, songs, and routines.

Captioned: Some with names and dates.

Finding Aid: A register.

Restrictions: No.

AC·52

Donald Sultner-Welles Collection

Dates of Photographs: Circa 1940s–1981

Collection Origins

Donald Sultner-Welles (1914–1981) was born in York, Pennsylvania, where he spent most of his life. He took up photography in college. After a brief musical career, Sultner-Welles became a professional photographer in the 1950s. Sultner-Welles also gave slide-illustrated lectures to garden clubs, museums, as well as aboard pleasure cruise ships.

Among Donald Sultner-Welles's audiences were the Academy of Arts and Sciences (St. Louis, Missouri); the Cincinnati Art Museum (Ohio); the Corcoran Gallery of Art (Washington, D.C.); the International Museum of Photography at George Eastman House (Rochester, New York); the Smithsonian Institution; and the Walker Art Center (Minneapolis, Minnesota).

This collection, representing Sultner-Welles's professional work, was donated to the Smithsonian in 1982. Note: Approximately 50,000 of the photographs are reproduced on an Archives Center videodisc.

Physical Description

There are over 73,000 photographs, including color dye coupler photonegatives, photoprints, and slides; and silver gelatin photonegatives and photoprints. (Note: About 72,000 are color dye coupler slides.) Other materials include business and personal records, clippings, correspondence, flyers, lecture notes, literature pertaining to lecture subjects, and scrapbooks.

Subjects

This collection consists primarily of pictorialist cityscapes, landscapes, portraits, and seascapes. Locations documented include Bermuda, Burma,

Cambodia, European countries, Hong Kong, India, Iran, Korea, Laos, Monaco, Morocco, Norway, the Philippines, Scotland, Taiwan, Thailand, Tunisia, Turkey, the United States, and Vietnam.

Major topics depicted include architecture, children, color, covered bridges, fountains, gardens, holidays, light, pollution, portraits, sculpture, seasons, ships, sports, stained glass, and sunsets. There are also portraits of Donald Sultner-Welles and his family.

Arranged: By type of material, location, general subject, and theme.

Captioned: No.

Finding Aid: 1) Laurie A. Baty. *Register of the Donald Sultner-Welles Collection, 1913–1981.* Archives Center, National Museum of American History, Smithsonian Institution. 2) A videodisc of selected images.

Restrictions: No.

AC·53

Kenneth M. Swezey Papers

Dates of Photographs: 1921–1942

Collection Origins

This collection was assembled by Kenneth M. Swezey (1905–1972) to document the life of Nikola Tesla, a Yugoslavian designer of dynamos and inventor of the first polyphase synchronous motor. Swezey was a writer for the *New York Sun* during his late teens and early twenties.

Photographers and studios represented include the Franklin Institute; OPPS; Leo Rosenthal, New York; Ross Photos, New York; and Skelton Studios, San Francisco. Margaret Cheney's *Tesla: Man Out of Time.* New Jersey: Prentice-Hall, 1981, includes photographs from this collection.

Physical Description

There are 375 silver gelatin photoprints. Other collection materials include articles, brochures, correspondence, manuscripts, newsletters, pamphlets, copies of patents, and postage stamps.

Subjects

These photographs document the life of Yugoslavian inventor Nikola Tesla, and include images of Tesla, his colleagues, family, and friends; Tesla's laboratories; and the Tesla museum in Yugoslavia.

There are also images of places associated with or of interest to Tesla, including Colorado Springs, the Library of Congress, the National Academy of Science, Niagara Falls, and the planet Mars.

Arranged: By series. 1) Correspondence and subject file (with some photographs). 2) Photographs in albums. 3) Bibliographies, biographies, articles, and some miscellaneous photographs.

Captioned: No.

Finding Aid: A preliminary inventory includes biographical information on Kenneth Swezey and Nikola Tesla, and describes the types of material in the collection.

Restrictions: No.

AC·54

Charles Sumner Tainter Papers

Dates of Photographs: 1890–1919

Collection Origins

Charles Sumner Tainter (1854–1940) was a manufacturer of electrical apparatus and an inventor. Tainter worked with Alexander Graham Bell on the photophone, the first wireless telephone. Tainter also invented the graphophone, which was the first commercially practical dictating machine.

Photographic studios represented include the Hartsbok Studio, San Diego, California.

Physical Description

There are three photographs, including an albumen photoprint and silver gelatin photoprints. Other materials include drawings, manuscripts, notebooks, notes, patents, and records of court testimonies.

Subjects

The photographs are all individual or group portraits of Emile Berliner, Charles S. Tainter, George Sumner Tainter, and Mrs. George Tainter.

Arranged: Into three series by type of material. 1) Papers (photographs in chronological order). 2) Laboratory notes. 3) Artifacts.

Captioned: With personal name and date.

Finding Aid: A register.

Restrictions: No.

AC·55

William Dandrige Terrell Papers

Dates of Photographs: 1911–1965

Collection Origins

This collection was assembled by William Dandrige Terrell (1871–   ), a government wireless radio communications specialist, to document his career.

Terrell's career began on Atlantic-based United States Naval ships in 1911. In 1915, Terrell was appointed Chief of the Radio Division for the Commerce Department in Washington, D.C. From 1934 he served as Chief of Field Operations for the Federal Radio Commission (later the Federal Communications Commission) until he retired in 1943.

Physical Description

There are four photographs, including color dye coupler photoprints and silver gelatin photoprints. Other materials include correspondence and a program from an American Wireless Operators convention (held in Terrell's honor).

Subjects

The photographs include portraits of Terrell and unidentified family members and friends.

Arranged: No.

Captioned: No.

Finding Aid: A preliminary inventory gives dates and a brief biographical sketch.

Restrictions: No.

AC·56

Elihu Thomson Collection

Dates of Photographs: 1900–1932

Collection Origins

Elihu Thomson (1853–1937) was an Englishman and a teacher of chemistry and physics at Central High School in Philadelphia. He invented the first electric welding process in 1887. Thomson also collaborated with Edwin Houston to make improvements in the field of arc-lighting and developments in centrifugal force. The two men formed the Thomson-Houston Company which later merged with Edison-Electric to form the General Electric Company. Concurrently, Thomson formed another company, the Thomson Electric Welding Company of Lynn, Massachusetts.

Physical Description

There are 150 silver gelatin photoprints. Some are mounted on fabric and bound for use as sales catalogs, and some are mounted on board. Other materials include clippings, promotional materials, a record book, and Thomson Electric Welding news bulletins.

Subjects

This collection documents the products of the Thomson Electric Welding Company of Lynn, Massachusetts, including automatic butt welders, seam welders, and spout welders.

Arranged: No.

Captioned: With the product name.

Finding Aid: A preliminary inventory gives dates, a brief biographical sketch, and lists types of materials.

Restrictions: No.

AC·57

Trade School Photographs

Dates of Photographs: Circa 1890

Collection Origins

This collection was given to the Division of Ceramics and Glass. It was transferred to the Archives Center in 1984. No other information is available.

Physical Description

There are ten silver gelatin photoprints.

Subjects

The photographs are of female and male trade school students in unidentified classrooms and machine shops, and an unnamed school building (circa 1890).

Arranged: No.

Captioned: With negative numbers.

Finding Aid: A guide entry description.

Restrictions: No.

AC·58

Underwood and Underwood Glass Stereograph Collection

Dates of Photographs: 1895–1920

Collection Origins

The Underwood and Underwood Company started in 1882 in Kansas as a stereograph sales office. The firm was started by Bert Elias Underwood (1862–1943) and Elmer Underwood (1860–1947), two brothers who were news photographers and businessmen from Oxford, Illinois. Later, their nephew, C. Thomas Underwood, headed their New York illustrations office.

By 1884 the firm was selling stereographic views on the Pacific coast. They had a large door-to-door sales force, which led to huge volume sales. They also pioneered the sale of boxed sets of images on a particular theme, such as, Egypt or the Grand Canyon.

By 1886 they had opened offices in Baltimore, New York, Chicago, and Toronto. In 1896 the firm began providing news photographs to the *Illustrated London News* and *Harper's Weekly*. Bert Underwood covered the Greco-Turkish War and the coronation of King Edward VII and Queen Alexandra (of England).

The collection includes material originally in the files of the H.C. White Company and several other publishers later acquired by Underwood and Underwood. The collection was donated to the Smithsonian Institution in 1966 by an heir of a partner. (Note: See PH·54.)

Physical Description

There are 28,200 photographs, including silver gelatin dry plate photonegatives and lantern slides (some stereographs); and silver gelatin photonegatives. Other materials include cards, catalogs, and stereoscopes.

Subjects

This documentary collection consists of images of animals; news events; outstanding political, sports, and theatrical figures; and travel pictures dating between 1895 and 1920. Places such as Cairo, Egypt, and Zululand are documented. There are images of the Spanish-American War and Prince Henry's visit to America.

Arranged: By catalog numbers assigned by Underwood and Underwood.

Captioned: With subject information, such as, location. The photographs are interleaved with cards stating when the plates were reprinted.

Finding Aid: 1) A guide entry description. 2) Underwood and Underwood Company catalogs which describe the travel photographs in catalog number order.

Restrictions: No.

AC·59

University of Pennsylvania Dental Collection

Dates of Photographs: 1917, 1923, 1924

Collection Origins

This collection was assembled by the staff of the University of Pennsylvania to document the history of dentistry at the University of Pennsylvania between 1917 and 1924.

This collection was transferred from the Division of Medical Sciences to the Archives Center on May 2, 1983.

Physical Description

There are 75 photographs, including silver gelatin photoprints and radiographs (nitrate). Other materials include correspondence, invitations, notebooks, papers, and reprints.

Subjects

The photographs document the staff and teaching of dentistry at the University of Pennsylvania. There are portraits of Dr. Jesse Cope Green and Dr. Edwin Tyler Darby.

There are also photographs of bacteria under a microscope, dental tools, patients' mouths, and teeth.

Arranged: No.

Captioned: Some with plate numbers and subject's name.

Finding Aid: A guide entry description.

Restrictions: No.

AC·60

Warshaw Collection of Business Americana

Dates of Photographs: 19th and 20th Centuries

Collection Origins

This collection was assembled by Isadore "Sonny" Warshaw (1900–1969), a dealer in rare books. He collected ephemera and advertising materials from nearly every major business firm in the United States. These materials document the history of American advertising and marketing from the early 19th century through the 1940s.

There are 33 known photographers and studios represented in the collection including J.H. Abbott, Saratoga Springs, New York; Anderson, New York City; E. and H.T. Anthony, New York City; Charles K. Bill, New York City; Bradley and Rulofson; Mathew Brady, New York City; George W. Butler, Rhode Island; Caldwell, Brocton, New York; E.H. Camp, Camp Meade, Maryland; G.W. Carter, Stereoscopic Gems of Utah Scenery; and Dana Portraits, New York City.

Other photographers and studios represented include: W. and D. Downey Photo, New Castle and London, England; Charles Eisenmann, New York; Elite, San Francisco, California; S.M. Fassett, Chicago, Illinois; C.D. Fredericks and Co., New York City; J. Gurney and Son, Albany, New York; Haines and Wickes, Albany, New York; F. Jay Haynes, Fargo, North Dakota; Paul Hoffmann and Co., Berlin-Schoneberg; J.S. Johnston, View and Marine Photo, New York City; and J.E. McClees, Philadelphia, Pennsylvania.

Also included are photographs by Mora, New

York City; Mundy and Williams, Utica, New York; Pach Bros., New York City; Sarony and Co., New York City; C.R. Savage, Salt Lake City, Utah; Sawyer Photographer, Philadelphia, Pennsylvania; Thomas Gallery, Albany, New York; William Troxell, Brooklyn, New York City; H. Ulke, Washington, D.C.; Carleton E. Watkins, San Francisco, California; Julius M. Wendt, Albany, New York; Windeatt, Chicago, Illinois; and Wood and Brothers, Albany, New York.

Note: As of the date of this publication, some materials in this collection are being transferred to the Division of Photographic History.

Physical Description

There are 11,300 photographs including albumen photoprints; color dye coupler phototransparencies and slides; cyanotypes; platinum photoprints; silver gelatin dry plate photonegatives; as well as silver gelatin photonegatives (some Eastman) and photoprints. (Note: About 10,000 items are nonvintage duplicate photographs.)

Special formats include: cartes-de-visite, lantern slides, a soldier's portrait inset into a Civil War commemorative medal, and stereographs.

The Warshaw Collection consists of over 2 million items. Other materials include advertising art, bills, business correspondence, invoices, labels, magazines, pamphlets, posters, price lists, receipts, trade cards, trade catalogs, and other business ephemera.

Subjects

The photographs document American citizens and visitors; American corporate advertisements, displays, and products; events, including wars, expositions, and fairs; and world travel imagery, including architectural studies, cityscapes, and landscapes.

Half of the images are individual or group studio portraits, including such notables as Jefferson Davis; Stonewall Jackson; Fred May as Davy Crockett; Tom Thumb (including his wedding); Andrew Van Buren; and Daniel Webster.

Thirty percent of the photographs are of scenery and events which include Canada (including the House of Parliament in Ottawa and scenes of Quebec); Europe (including England, France, and Germany around 1872, and German World War I battle scenes); Japan (including street scenes); the Middle East (circa 1870); and the United States (including Albany, New York; Hartford, Connecticut; San Francisco, California; and Yellowstone Park).

Ten percent are images of products, such as, boats, cheese, chewing gum, picture frames, soap, and stoves.

Ten percent of the images relate to expositions and fairs, such as, the Philadelphia Centennial Exposition of 1876, and the 225th Anniversary Philadelphia Historical Pageant of October 1902.

Arranged: By 375 subject headings.

Captioned: With subject and date; several portraits are autographed.

Finding Aid: Two finding aides are being developed. 1) A card catalog organized by subject which includes a short description of the item and in some cases a negative number. 2) An annotated 23-page listing of subject headings which includes the number of storage boxes, scope notes, existence of duplicates, and any oversize materials. This list is followed by 34 brief descriptive scope notes covering selected subject headings. These notes describe the item, type of materials, dates, content, organization, quantity, and subject terms used. This listing will be expanded to cover the entire collection.

Restrictions: No.

AC·61

Washburn Wire Company, Inc., Collection

Dates of Photographs: Circa 1953

Collection Origins

The Washburn Wire Company, Inc., of New York City was founded in 1870 to manufacture insulated cable for the new telephone industry. It later operated as a wire drawing fabricator for automotive and electrical appliance industries until the company closed in 1981. The collection was acquired as a gift in 1982.

Physical Description

There are 20 silver gelatin photoprints. Other materials include business plans, illustrations, and sales literature.

Subjects

The photographs show the exterior of the New York City plant of the Washburn Wire Company about 1953.

Arranged: By subject heading.

Captioned: No.

Finding Aid: A preliminary inventory including a history of the company and types of materials in the collection.

Restrictions: No.

AC·62

Paul G. Watson Collection

Dates of Photographs: 1920s–1965

Collection Origins

This collection was assembled by Paul G. Watson (–1966), a retired naval commander, to document the history of radio. Much of the material was written by Watson.

Studios represented include the United States Navy and the Marconi Company Limited, Chelmsford, Essex, England.

Physical Description

There are 300 silver gelatin photoprints. Other materials include articles, clippings in an album, reports, and a text by Watson.

Subjects

These photographs document the history of the electron vacuum tube (1920s–1963) and the Arlington, Virginia, Radio Transmitter between 1963 and 1965.

The photographs are of pages reproduced from related literature; radio apparatus (such as, frequency transforming transformers and oscillating valves); and radio tubes (such as, vacuum receiving tubes and three-element tubes).

There are also portraits of Dr. Lee De Forest (known as the Father of Radio); Henry Wallace McCandless; and Abraham White (President of the American De Forest Wireless Telegraph Company).

Locations shown are Arlington, Virginia; New York; and St. Louis.

Arranged: By subject.

Captioned: No.

Finding Aid: The preliminary inventory describes types of materials and gives a synopsis of the information in the six volumes in the collection.

Restrictions: No.

AC·63

The Carlos de Wendler-Funaro Gypsy Research Collection

Dates of Photographs: 1899–1966

Collection Origins

This collection was assembled by Dr. Carlos de Wendler-Funaro (deceased) to document Gypsy life in Europe and the United States.

The collection was brought to the attention of the Smithsonian by Matt T. Salo and was donated to the Smithsonian by Dr. de Wendler-Funaro's family in May 1985.

Photographers and studios represented include Alexander Alland; Keystone Press; Sovfoto (Soviet Foto Agency); Tvist; Underwood and Underwood; and A. Witko.

Photographs from this collection were used in a 1937 article by Carlos de Wendler-Funaro; in two 1938 articles by Victor Weybright; and in Victor Weybright's lectures on the subject of Gypsy Americana.

Physical Description

There are 2,000 photographs, including silver gelatin photonegatives and photoprints (many are modern copies or duplicates). Other materials include book manuscripts, clippings (magazine and newspaper), correspondence, periodicals, and postcards.

Subjects

The photographs document Gypsy groups and Hungarian musicians in Europe and the United States between 1899 and 1966. Among the groups shown are the Black Dutch, Ludar, Rom, Romnichels, and Sinti.

Images include cooking activities and equipment; costumes; housing (apartments, storefronts, and tents); motion studies; ornaments; transportation (automobiles, trailers, trucks, and wagons); and work-related equipment and activities (coppersmithing, fortune-telling, and manufacturing of rustic furniture). Included are studio and informal portraits of groups and individuals.

Over half of the photographs were taken in New York City. Other locations shown include Austria (Burgenland); Bulgaria; England (Cornwall); France (Paris); Germany (Altona); Hungary; Mexico; Russia; Spain; the United States (New Jersey; Long Island and Sheepshead Bay, New York; Pennsylvania; Virginia; and West Virginia); and Yugoslavia.

Arranged: By origin and type of material into ten series. Photographs are in series nine and ten.

Captioned: With narrative subject information.

Finding Aid: Sheila Salo. *Register of the Carlos de Wendler-Funaro Gypsy Research Collection, c.1920–1975.* Archives Center, National Museum of American History, Smithsonian Institution, 1986.

Restrictions: No.

AC·64

J. Walter Wilkinson Papers

Dates of Photographs: Circa 1940s

Collection Origins

J. Walter Wilkinson (1892–   ), an award-winning commercial artist, is best known for a series of six World War II bond posters he and his son, Walter G. Wilkinson (1917–1971), created for the United States Treasury Department. In addition to his war posters and other government commissions, J. Walter Wilkinson created a number of outdoor

billboard and magazine advertisements and many magazine covers. Wilkinson gave this collection to the Smithsonian Institution in 1984.

Physical Description

There are 40 photographs, including color dye coupler photoprints and silver gelatin photoprints. Other materials include original advertisements; an album of clippings, awards, and other materials documenting the Wilkinsons' careers; materials documenting a mechanical drafting instrument patented by Wilkinson and his son, Walter G. Wilkinson; oral history interviews with Wilkinson; and original sketches.

Subjects

Most of the images are photographic reproductions of J. Walter Wilkinson's and Walter G. Wilkinson's commercial art. Among the items shown are World War II posters; and advertising art for products (such as, Ballantine beer, Ivory soap, and Pabst beer). Five percent of the images are of unidentified people.

Arranged: By type of material.

Captioned: No.

Finding Aid: A register.

Restrictions: No.

AC·65

Winton-Anderson Scrapbook Collection

Dates of Photographs: 1890s–1920s

Collection Origins

This collection was assembled by Blanche Anderson Kitteredge to document the work of her husband, Harold B. Anderson, chief engineer of Winton Motor Carriage Company. Blanche Anderson later married Lewis Harris Kitteredge.

Harold B. Anderson and Alexander Winton, a builder and driver of early racing cars, built the Bullet No. 2. The Bullet No. 2 was the third car Winton produced, and was one of the first automobiles to use an 8-cylinder, in-line engine. These albums document the creation of the automobile for the Fourth Gordon Bennett Road Race held in Ireland in 1903.

Studios represented include Webb and Fergeson of Baltimore, Maryland.

Physical Description

There are 380 photographs, including color dye coupler photoprints; cyanotypes; and silver gelatin photoprints in an album. Other materials include clippings, correspondence, programs, and ribbons.

Subjects

Most (80%) of the photographs document automobile production and racing from the 1890s to the 1920s in the United States and Ireland. There are pictures of the building, development, and testing of race cars, especially the Winton Bullet No. 2 and the Winton touring car.

There are also photographs of employees of the Winton Company in Cleveland, Ohio (and the employees' families); leisure activities in Ireland and Cleveland, Ohio; steam yachts; and Winton's family, friends, homes, and travels.

People shown include Blanche Van Glahn Anderson; Harold Anderson; Kittredge Brown; and Pearl Miller.

Arranged: By subject.

Captioned: With subject information.

Finding Aid: A guide entry description.

Restrictions: No.

AC·66

Henry Wurtz Papers

Dates of Photographs: 1861–1885

Collection Origins

Henry Wurtz (circa 1828–1910) was a consulting chemist who specialized in the development of distillation processes for the production of paraffins and oils. Wurtz studied at the College of New Jersey (later Princeton University) under Joseph Henry and John Torrey. He was state chemist and geologist with the New Jersey Geological Survey from 1854 to 1856.

In 1858 Wurtz was appointed Professor of Chemistry and Pharmacy at the National Medical College of Washington, D.C. (later George Washington University). From 1861 to 1889, he ran a private consulting laboratory in New York which specialized in paraffin hydrocarbons and other chemical products. This collection consists of Wurtz's business records, which were donated by his family.

Physical Description

There are 20 photographs, including albumen photoprints, silver gelatin dry plate photonegatives (housed in cold storage at OPPS), and silver gelatin photoprints. Other materials include books, catalogs, a certificate, clippings, correspondence, and notebooks.

Subjects

The photographs are primarily portraits of Wurtz's family between 1861 and 1885. One photograph is a copy of a certificate received by Wurtz as a member of the Whig Society at the College of New Jersey.

Arranged: By subject and date.

Captioned: No.

Finding Aid: A guide entry description.

Restrictions: No.

AF

Division of Armed Forces History

Division of Armed Forces History
National Museum of American History
Smithsonian Institution
Washington, D.C. 20560
Edward C. Ezell, Curator Supervisor
Harold Ellis, Museum Specialist
(202) 357-1883 or 357-1781
Hours: Monday–Friday, 10 a.m.–4 p.m.

Scope of the Collections

There are 19 photographic collections with approximately 18,000 images in the two sections of the Division of Armed Forces History: 1) Military History and 2) Naval History.

Focus of the Collections

These photographs are used primarily for research relating to the material and social history of the U.S. Army, Navy, Marine Corps and Coast Guard. This division has information on the history of artifacts, such as, ammunition; armor; edged weapons; firearms; flags; military and naval uniforms (including footgear and headgear); ship models; as well as biographical memorabilia. The division also documents fields of concern to the armed forces, such as, civil engineering, exploration, privateering, and the development of commerce and navigation.

Photographic Processes and Formats Represented

In addition to standard 20th century slide, photoprint, and photonegative processes there are also early photographic processes, such as, albumen cartes-de-visite, collodion wet plate photonegatives, and silver gelatin dry plate photonegatives.

Other Materials Represented

This division also collects, to a limited extent, blueprints; booklets; chromolithographs; clippings; correspondence; drawings; engravings; financial documents; invitations; journals; lithographs; logs; manuals; newspapers; official and personal notes; passes; posters; publications; public notices; recruitment information; reports; ship plans; and war bonds. Original art work represented includes paintings and watercolors. Ordnance material represented includes accouterments; associated equipment; edged weapons; firearms; and munitions. Quartermaster holdings represented include armor; artifacts from historic underwater sites; flags; items of military heraldry (such as, badges, decorations, insignia, and medals); models; navigation instruments; powder flasks; and powder horns. The Naval Section holds artifacts from historic underwater sites, navigation instruments, and ship models.

Access and Usage Policies

Division collections are open by appointment to all scholarly researchers. Several collections are partially indexed; see the collection reports for more information. Photographic copies of many images are available from OPPS at the prevailing rate.

Publication Policies

In addition to obtaining permission from the Smithsonian Institution to reproduce a photograph, researchers may have to obtain permission from the copyright holder. The Smithsonian Institution is not necessarily the copyright holder. The preferred credit line for photographs in the collection may vary. In general, it is: "Courtesy of the National Museum of American History, Division of Armed Forces History, Smithsonian Institution."

AF·1

Biographical Information Files

Dates of Photographs: 1920s–Present

Collection Origins

The collection was assembled by the Military History section of the division for staff research and reference purposes. The collection provides information on prominent figures in United States military history and includes material relating to the history of firearms.

Steel engravings cut from a volume of *Notable Americans* are included in the collection.

Physical Description

There are 480 photographs, including albumen cartes-de-visite and silver gelatin photoprints (both original and copy). Other materials include articles, biographical information, chromolithographs, clippings, correspondence, lithographs, notes, service data, and steel engravings.

Subjects

The photographs document individuals in military history, including the history of firearms, from the 1700s to the present. Among them are General Dwight D. Eisenhower, General Ulysses S. Grant, and General John Pershing. Note: Many images are photographic reproductions of portraits in other processes, such as, chromolithographs, lithographs, or steel engravings.

Arranged: By series. 1) General files. 2) Firearms files. 3) Ordnance inspector's files. Within these series materials are arranged alphabetically by the individual's last name.

Captioned: With the OPPS negative number, some with the name of the individual shown, and his dates.

Finding Aid: No.

Restrictions: No.

AF·2

Joseph Cummings Chase Military Portrait Collection

Dates of Photographs: 1917–1984

Collection Origins

Joseph Cummings Chase was a professional portrait artist who painted American military personnel who served abroad between 1917 and 1955.

The painted portraits reproduced in these photographs were created and maintained by Chase prior to their donation to the Smithsonian Institution. The photographs described here were created by OPPS to document these accessioned art objects.

Physical Description

There are 250 silver gelatin photoprints.

Subjects

These are photographic reproductions of painted portraits of U.S. military personnel who served abroad, predominantly in Europe, Korea, and the Pacific during World War I, World War II, or the Korean Conflict.

There are studio portraits of General Dwight D. Eisenhower, General Douglas MacArthur, General George C. Marshall, and Alvin York. Most subjects are posed frontally, from the bust up.

Arranged: Alphabetically by the subject's last name.

Captioned: With the subject's name and a date.

Finding Aid: A card catalog index arranged alphabetically by the last name of the subject.

Restrictions: No.

AF·3

Jacob Peter de Gheyn Manual

Dates of Photographs: 1970s

Collection Origins

This collection was assembled by division staff to document artifacts held by the division for research purposes. OPPS took most of the photographs.

According to the staff, the images are photographic reproductions of tinted illustrations from a 17th century manual by Jacob Peter de Gheyn. The manual gives directions (in Dutch, English, French, and German) for firing a musket. The title of the manual is *Maniement d'Armes, d'Arquebuses, Mousquets, & Picques*. Zutphen: Andre Jansien d'Aelft, 1608.

Physical Description

There are 270 photographs, including color dye coupler photoprints and silver gelatin photoprints.

Subjects

The images are photographic reproductions of tinted drawings (copied from Jacob Peter de Gheyn's 17th century publication) which illustrate the techniques and processes of musket firing. Activities shown include musket ball production, musket cleaning, and musket loading.

Arranged: In the same order as the plates in de Gheyn's book.

Captioned: With OPPS negative numbers.

Finding Aid: An index which gives the plate titles of the illustrations and their page numbers.

Restrictions: No.

AF·4

Dudley Collection

Dates of Photographs: 20th Century

Collection Origins

Thomas C. Dudley was a U.S. Navy purser's assistant aboard the U.S.S. *Powhatan* between 1853 and 1855. He was also an amateur artist who made informal sketches of his travels and pastel portraits of his acquaintances.

The photographs were created to document Dudley's personal effects, including his art work created in Japan.

Physical Description

There are 500 silver gelatin photoprints. Other materials include Japanese artifacts, journals, letters, pastels, playbills, prints, sketch books, and watercolors.

Subjects

The photographs reproduce pastel portraits, pencil sketches, and watercolors made by Thomas Dudley. Dudley's sketches are primarily of Japan, including images of architecture, ceremonial meetings (between Admiral Matthew Galbraith Perry and Japanese officials), landscapes, objects, and U.S. Navy shipboard scenes (including crew).

Arranged: By negative number.

Captioned: Some with name and date.

Finding Aid: No.

Restrictions: No.

AF·5

Benjamin P. Lamberton Collection

Dates of Photographs: 1834–1917

Collection Origins

This collection was assembled by Benjamin P. Lamberton (1844–1912), Rear Admiral in the U.S. Navy, from a variety of sources. The collection includes Lamberton's official and personal correspondence; correspondence and records of his father, James Lamberton; and correspondence of several other family members including Benjamin Lamberton, Jr., and Robert Lamberton (1834). There are also correspondence and materials relating to Sterrett Ramsey, a U.S. Naval purser from 1839 to 1840 and 1844 to 1848.

Benjamin P. Lamberton graduated from the U.S. Naval Academy in 1864. He served as a chief of staff under George Dewey in Manila in 1898. Lamberton later commanded Dewey's flagship *Olympia* from 1898 to 1899. In 1903 Lamberton was made a Rear Admiral. He retired in 1906.

Physical Description

There are 23 albumen cartes-de-visite. Other materials are correspondence.

Subjects

The photographs are portraits of Benjamin P. Lamberton and his family (between 1834 and 1917); and his U.S. Naval Academy classmates (circa 1860 to 1864).

Arranged: First by medium, then by creator, and then by date.

Captioned: Some with name and date.

Finding Aid: No.

Restrictions: No.

AF·6

Military and War Poster Collection

Dates of Photographs: Circa 1840s–Present

Collection Origins

This collection was assembled by division staff from diverse sources (including the U.S. War Department) to illustrate American military poster art.

Physical Description

There are 400 photographs, including color dye coupler slides and phototransparencies, and silver gelatin photoprints. Other materials include recruitment literature.

Subjects

The photographs reproduce military and war posters which are or once were in the division holdings. The photographs document posters used for bond drives; labor and war production; loan drives; military recruitment; morale; and propaganda purposes in Canada, Denmark, France, Germany, Italy, Mexico, the Netherlands, Poland, Russia, Spain, the United Kingdom, and the United States during World Wars I and II. There are also photographs of Civil War posters.

Arranged: By topic or war, and then by country or region.

Captioned: With general subject information.

Finding Aid: There is a finding aid to the collection objects, not specifically to the photographs, arranged by five subject categories. 1) World War I (U.S. recruiting). 2) World War I (foreign by country). 3) World War II (U.S.). 4) World War II (foreign). 5) Post–World War II. Each card includes caption information, negative number, and catalog/accession number of the objects shown.

Restrictions: No.

AF·7

Military Artifacts Collection

Dates of Photographs: 1930s–Present

Collection Origins

This collection was assembled by division staff to document significant artifacts in military history. The collection primarily contains materials which have been copied from other repositories.

Physical Description

There are 5,500 photographs, including collodion wet plate photonegatives; color dye coupler photoprints, phototransparencies, and slides (Ektachrome and Kodachrome); silver gelatin dry plate photonegatives; and silver gelatin phototransparencies.

Subjects

The photographs document world military and ordnance artifacts, with an emphasis on combat equipment for World Wars I and II. Many images document U.S. military materials between 1900 and the present. Some military artifacts from Austria, Canada, England, France, and Germany are also illustrated. Specific artifacts illustrated include equipment, footwear, headgear, insignia, medals, and uniforms.

Arranged: Chronologically, and by subject heading.

Captioned: Some with subject headings.

Finding Aid: No.

Restrictions: No duplication allowed.

AF·8

Military History Information File

Dates of Photographs: 1930s–Present

Collection Origins

This collection was assembled by the Military History staff of the Division of Armed Forces History as primary source research documentation for military and firearms history. The materials came from private donors and purchases.

Physical Description

There are 1,000 photographs, including color dye coupler slides and silver gelatin photoprints. Other materials include articles, correspondence, graphic prints, manuals, notes, pamphlets, and reports.

Subjects

The photographs document United States military history from the 1700s to the present, including Army basic training; Army field maneuvers; Army installations (such as, auditoriums, barracks, and mess halls); Army personnel (in and out of uniform); and promotional material (for enlistment). There are also images of Canada, England, France, and Germany.

Arranged: Into six series. 1) General documents. 2) Oversize documents. 3) Citations and commissions. 4) Enlistment and discharge papers. 5) Maps. 6) Graphics. Most photographs in this collection are in series 6, a few are in series 2.

Captioned: Some, with the last name of the individual shown, the date, and rank.

Finding Aid: 1) An accession card file which is alphabetically arranged by the last name of the donor. 2) A cross-referenced accession card file which is alphabetically arranged by subject.

Restrictions: No.

AF·9

Mordecai Collection of Ordnance Engraving Plates

Dates of Photographs: 1963–Present

Collection Origins

This collection was assembled by division staff from photographs created by OPPS to reproduce a collection of 140 plates made by Alfred Mordecai.

The original Mordecai plates were used as illustrations in his work *Artillery for the Land Services of the United States*. Washington, 1858. The plates came to the division from the War Department.

Physical Description

There are 145 silver gelatin photoprints.

Subjects

The photographs reproduce original Alfred Mordecai book illustrations of the following U.S. military artifacts: ammunition; barbette carriages; casement carriages; field carriages and equipment; harnesses; implements and equipment; instruments; machines; mortar beds; mountain artillery; ordnance weapons; siege carriages; and tools.

Arranged: In original book plate order.

Captioned: With drawing title, plate numbers, and an OPPS negative number.

Finding Aid: List of illustrations (in the order that they appear in Mordecai's book) with the corresponding OPPS negative number noted.

Restrictions: No.

AF·10

Naval History Art Collection

Dates of Photographs: 1957–1987

Collection Origins

This collection was assembled by division staff from photographs taken by OPPS and the Division of Conservation. The photographs were taken to document works of art with naval themes. The art objects reproduced were found in several sources, including objects in the Division of Armed Forces History Naval History Section art holdings.

Physical Description

There are 120 silver gelatin photoprints.

Subjects

These photographs reproduce ink drawings, lithographs, oil paintings, pastels, poster art, and watercolors documenting naval history. There are photographic reproductions of drawings of ships; portraits of men prominent in naval history; and recruitment posters.

Arranged: Chronologically.

Captioned: With OPPS negative number.

Finding Aid: No.

Restrictions: No.

AF·11

Ordnance and Weapons Collection

Dates of Photographs: 1960s–Present

Collection Origins

This collection was assembled by division staff from photographs made by OPPS. The photographs were created to serve as a reference file documenting the division's weapons and ordnance collection.

Physical Description

There are 7,000 silver gelatin photoprints.

Subjects

The photographs document American, Asian, British, and other European ceremonial and military weapons (including edged weapons, firearms, and ordnance), in the division's object holdings.

Arranged: By subject heading.

Captioned: With the finding aid index printout entries.

Finding Aid: Index printout dating from 1969 and 1970. It lists the catalog number of the object; the accession number; make; caliber; model; patentee; type of mechanism; date of manufacture; serial number; negative number; and location of the original object.

Restrictions: No duplication allowed.

AF·12

Philadelphia Gun Boat Collection

Dates of Photographs: 1935

Collection Origins

The Revolutionary War gun boat, the *Philadelphia*, was raised from Lake Champlain in 1935. It came to the Smithsonian in 1961, with attendant photographic documentation of its raising.

Physical Description

There are 70 silver gelatin photoprints.

Subjects

The photographs document the raising of a Revolutionary War gun boat, the *Philadelphia*, from Lake Champlain in 1935. The images document each step of the raising.

Arranged: In chronological order (of the raising).

Captioned: With OPPS negative numbers.

Finding Aid: Catalog card file.

Restrictions: No.

AF·13

Charles Johnson Post Collection

Dates of Photographs: 1953–1966

Collection Origins

This collection was assembled by Phyllis Post, daughter of artist and author Charles Johnson Post (1873–1956). Post's sketches, watercolors and writings appeared in a variety of American magazines and newspapers.

The original watercolors by Charles Johnson Post were created in Puerto Rico and Cuba during the Spanish-American War. The original photographs of the watercolors were made for the artist's portfolio. Some were later copied by OPPS.

Physical Description

There are 10 photographs, including color dye coupler phototransparencies and slides, and silver gelatin photoprints. Other materials include clippings, copies of Post's articles, correspondence, and watercolors.

Subjects

The photographs reproduce Charles Johnson Post's watercolors of the Spanish-American War. Major topics depicted include the Rough Riders of the Spanish-American War and military life in Cuba and Puerto Rico. Also included are portraits of individuals involved in these activities.

Arranged: By type of material.

Captioned: Some with the name of the individuals shown, the date, and the location.

Finding Aid: A card catalog arranged: 1) alphabetically; 2) by accession number; and 3) by catalog number (includes OPPS negative number).

Restrictions: No.

AF·14

Quarter Master Photograph Collection

Dates of Photographs: 20th Century

Collection Origins

These photographs were prepared and maintained by the War Department Quarter Master Museum to illustrate U.S. Army enlisted men's uniforms in the 1860s. They were later donated to the division.

Physical Description

There are 80 photographs, including silver gelatin photonegatives and photoprints.

Subjects

The photographs document U.S. Army enlisted men's uniforms in the 1860s. Included are images of full dress uniforms, fatigues, field dress, great coats, ponchos, and stable frocks for the cavalry, engineers, foot artillery, hospital stewards, infantry, light artillery, musicians in the artillery, ordnance, and soldiers.

The dress of corporals, first sergeants, ordnance sergeants, privates, quarter masters sergeants, sergeant majors, and sergeants are also illustrated.

Arranged: Into two series. 1) Photonegatives, arranged by negative number. 2) Photoprints, arranged by subject.

Captioned: With OPPS negative number and subject information.

Finding Aid: A list, "Smithsonian Institution U.S. National Museum List of Official Quartermaster Photographs of Civil War Period, Illustrating Enlisted Men's Uniforms, Arms, and Equipment, in the Collections of United States National Museum. 5/52.", is arranged by OPPS negative number, and gives narrative subject descriptions of the uniformed men shown.

Restrictions: No.

AF·15

A.H. Russell World's Columbian Exposition Ordnance Exhibit Photographs

Dates of Photographs: 1893

Collection Origins

This collection consists of an album entitled *Government Exhibit of Guns and Ammunition at the*

World's Columbian Exposition, Chicago, Ill. 1893, Under Charge of Captain Andrew H. Russell, United States Army also Reports by W.C. Dodge.

Physical Description

There are 300 silver gelatin photoprints in an album.

Subjects

The photographs document the ordnance exhibit of the World's Columbian Exposition of 1893 which was held in Chicago.

The photographs document an exhibition of ordnance including: cannons; guns (including flint locks, machine guns, volleys, and wheel lock guns); and swords. There are also several general views of the exposition.

Arranged: By subject.

Captioned: Album pages are labeled with subject headings.

Finding Aid: 1) A list gives the exhibit number, the title of the exhibit, and the negative number as assigned by Russell. 2) The album is annotated with OPPS negative numbers.

Restrictions: No.

AF·16

Ship Drawings and Plans Collection

Dates of Photographs: 1930s–Present

Collection Origins

This collection was assembled by Howard I. Chapelle, naval architect and historian, for his book *The History of the American Sailing Navy.* New York: Norton, 1949.

Note: The collection also includes plans drawn by George F. Campbell; Merritt A. Edson, Jr.; William E. Geoghegan; Howard Hoffman; Ernest W. Peterkin; Harold A. Underhill; and Dana Wegner. Photographic reproductions of original plans from the National Maritime Museum in Greenwich, England; the U.S. National Archives; and the U.S. Navy were later added to the collection by division staff.

Physical Description

There are 500 silver gelatin photoprints. Other materials include blueprints, ordnance drawings, and ships's plans (copies on mylar and originals).

Subjects

The photographs reproduce ordnance drawings, ship drawings (American and European), ship models, and ship plans from the mid-18th century to the present.

The photographs show the following ship models: the *Albermarle* (an ironclad ram built by Kenneth Foote); the *Alexander Hamilton* (a revenue cutter built by Boucher-Lewis Precision Models, Inc.); the *Argus* (a brig built by Alfred S. Brownell); the *Bear* (an arctic rescue ship and Coast Guard cutter built by Boucher-Lewis Precision Models, Inc.); the *Boston* (a frigate built by Robert V. Bruckshaw); the *Carondlet* (an ironclad river gunboat built by Thomas E. Tragle); the *Confederacy* (a frigate built by Robert Bruckshaw); and the *Congress*.

Also included are the *Constellation* (a frigate built by Arthur G. Henning); the *Constitution* (a frigate built by Bassett-Lowke Ltd.); the *Delaware* (a ship of the line built by Arthur G. Henning); the *Demologos* (a catamaran steam frigate built by Thomas E. Tragle); the *Fredericksburg* (an ironclad ram built by J.E. Beach); a galley gunboat (built Boucher-Lewis Precision Models, Inc.); and the *Hartford* (a screw sloop of war built by Bassett-Lowke).

Also included are the *Niagara* (a brig built by Boucher-Lewis Precision Models, Inc.); the *Philadelphia* (a gunboat built by Howard P. Hoffman); the *Prince de Neufchatel* (a privateer built by Jay Hanna); the *Raleigh* (a frigate built by Robert Bruckshaw); the *Rattlesnake* (a privateer built by Alfred S. Brownell and Merritt A. Edson, Jr.); and the *Vincennes* (a sloop of war built by Arthur G. Henning).

Arranged: In accession number order of the original plans and blueprints.

Captioned: Some with ship name.

Finding Aid: Three, to portions of the collection. 1) A card index in alphabetical order by the name of the ship. 2) A register of drawings, listed in order of accession. 3) Approximately 150 photoprints are listed in the guide to the collection entitled, *The Smithsonian Collection of Warship Plans: A Catalogue of Warship Plans, Ordnance Drawings, and Ship Model Photographs Available from the Division of Naval History, National Museum of American History.* This last guide was written by Phillip W. Snyder and published by the Smithsonian in 1982.

Restrictions: No.

AF·17

Ship Photograph Collection and Information File

Dates of Photographs: 1930s–Present

Collection Origins

This collection was assembled by the Naval History section of the Division of Armed Forces History for staff reference and research purposes.

Physical Description

There are 600 silver gelatin photoprints. Other materials include clippings, correspondence, mimeographs, notes, reprints, and xerographic copies.

Subjects

The photographs document both U.S. and foreign ships, dating from the 18th through 20th centuries, such as, the *Boston*, the *Cairo*, the *Etna*, and the *Galveston*.

    Types of ships documented include: adriatic luggers, arctic exploration ships, arctic rescue ships, barges, bomb vessels, brigantines, coast guard cutters, cruisers, frigates, galleys, galley gunboats, gondolas, iron clad river gunboats, lighters, powder boats, privateers, protected cruisers, revenue cutters, schooners, ships of the line, side-wheel steamers, sloops, steam cutters, store ships, submarines, and trabacolos.

Arranged: By ship name.

Captioned: Some with type of ship; ship name; date completed; country of origin, remarks on the size or special features of the ship; and OPPS negative number.

Finding Aid: No.

Restrictions: No.

AF·18

Weems Memorial Library Collection

Dates of Photographs: 1964

Collection Origins

This collection was assembled by Captain Phillip van Horn Weems during his career in the U.S. Navy. Weems was a navigator and pilot from World War I to 1942. He developed the Weems system of navigation. This collection documents Weem's interest in navigation instruments. The collection was later added to by division staff. The photographs were taken by OPPS on behalf of division staff.

Physical Description

There are 250 silver gelatin photoprints. Other materials include books, letters, manuscripts, and navigation instruments.

Subjects

The photographs are multiple views of naval navigation instruments developed by Weems.

Arranged: By subject.

Captioned: With OPPS negative number.

Finding Aid: No.

Restrictions: No.

AF·19

World War I Art Collection

Dates of Photographs: 1950s–1960s

Collection Origins

This collection was assembled by division staff from original art work created for the War Department and photographic reproductions of the art work created by OPPS. The original art work was created by artists, commissioned as officers, in the U.S. Army. The scenes were sketched on the battlefields of World War I.

Physical Description

There are 500 photographs, including color dye coupler phototransparencies and slides, and silver gelatin photonegatives and photoprints.

Subjects

This collection contains photographic reproductions of drawings, paintings, and sketches of the military actions and life of U.S. Army soldiers during World War I. Most of the scenes shown are in Austria, England, France, and Germany between 1917 and 1920.

There are images of barracks life; the front; mess halls; military accommodations on the road; police duty (comic); and wounded soldiers.

Arranged: By the last name of the artist who created the original work of art, then by catalog number.

Captioned: With the negative number, accession number of the original art work, title of the original art work, artist's last name, and date.

Finding Aid: Item-level inventory arranged by last name of artist which includes the title of the painting, whether in black-and-white or color, negative or slide number, and a catalog number.

Restrictions: No.

CG

Division of Ceramics and Glass

Division of Ceramics and Glass
National Museum of American History
Smithsonian Institution
Washington, D.C. 20560
Sheila Alexander, Museum Specialist (Glass)
Regina Blaszczyk, Museum Specialist (Ceramics)
(202) 357-1786
Hours: Monday—Friday, 9 a.m.—5 p.m.

Scope and Focus of the Collections

There is one photographic collection with approximately 18,200 images in the Division of Ceramics and Glass.

Focus of the Collections

These photographs document American and European ceramic and glass artifacts and traditional glassworkers and potters from the 18th century to the present. There are also a limited number of images documenting Anglo-American archeological kiln sites, commercial ceramics and glass, glass and ceramic objects in exhibitions, production procedures, and production shops.

Photographic Processes and Formats Represented

The collection consists of standard 20th century slide, photoprint, and photonegative processes, such as, color dye coupler slides and silver gelatin photonegatives and photoprints.

Other Materials Represented

This division also collects ceramic and glass artifacts and materials related to their manufacture and distribution. Ceramic collections include American art pottery, late 19th and early 20th centuries; American china-decorated wares, late 19th and 20th centuries; American commercial ceramics, including earthenware, porcelain, and bone china, 18th through 20th centuries; and traditional American earthenware and stoneware, 17th through 20th centuries.

The division's ceramic collections also include American and English tiles, largely 19th and 20th centuries; contemporary American studio ceramics; Continental European porcelain and Oriental prototypes, 18th century; English earthenware and stoneware, 18th and 19th centuries, particularly types used in America, such as, refined salt-glazed stoneware, creamware, pearlware, lusterware, ironstone, and transfer-printed earthenware; and English porcelain and bone china, 18th and 19th centuries.

Glass artifacts include early American glass; American commercial and studio glass, 20th century; American pressed glass, cut glass, and art glass, 19th and 20th centuries; and European and other glass marketed in the United States. The division has a small historical archeology collection relating to 18th and 19th century American domestic and manufacturing sites.

Also included in the division's holdings are examples of advertising literature; articles and notes clipped from secondary sources; business records; glass formulas; and trade publications. Additional business records and advertising materials related to ceramics and glass are housed in the Archives Center.

Access and Usage Policies

This collection is open to the public by appointment. Special restrictions may apply to certain materials within the collection. The existing finding aid lists subject categories only.

Publication Policies

In addition to obtaining permission from the Smithsonian Institution to reproduce a photograph, researchers may have to obtain permission from the copyright holder. The Smithsonian Institution is not necessarily the copyright holder. The preferred credit line is: "Courtesy of the Division of Ceramics and Glass, National Museum of American History, Smithsonian Institution." The division also asks that researchers credit donors when applicable.

Note: The "Other Materials Represented" portion of this Introduction is courtesy of division staff.

CG·1

Division of Ceramics and Glass Photographic Reference File

Dates of Photographs: 20th Century

Collection Origins

This collection was assembled by division staff from diverse sources (such as the Corning Museum of Glass and the Henry Ford Museum) to document object accessions and related outside materials.

Richard Hofmeister of OPPS created many of these images in the 1960s. Other photographers and studios represented include Rolfe Baggett, Brenda Gillmore, the Helga Photo Studio, Eric Long, Dane Penland, Jeff Ploskonka, and the firm of Taylor and Dull.

Some of the photographs were used as illustrations in:

1) Paul V. Gardner. *American Glass.* Washington, D.C.: Smithsonian Institution Press, 1977. 2) J. Jefferson Miller II. *18th Century English Porcelain: A Brief Guide to the Collection in the National Museum of History and Technology.* Washington, D.C.: Smithsonian Institution Press [for sale by the Superintendent of Documents, U.S. Government Printing Office], 1973. 3) J. Jefferson Miller II. *English Yellow-Glazed Earthenware.* Washington, D.C.: Smithsonian Institution Press, 1974. 4) Susan H. Myers. *The John Paul Remensnyder Collection of American Stoneware.* Washington, D.C.: Smithsonian Institution Press, 1978. 5) Hans Syz, J. Jefferson Miller II, and Rainer Ruckert, *Catalogue of the Hans Syz Collection,* Volume I. Washington, D.C.: Smithsonian Institution Press, second edition, 1979.

Physical Description

There are 18,200 photographs, including color dye coupler phototransparencies and slides and silver gelatin photoprints.

Subjects

Most photographs document the ceramic and glass artifacts in the division's holdings. They are images of division exhibitions; and photographic reproductions of historic engravings, etchings, and other graphic materials. There are also images of ceramic objects, and glass objects found at historical archaeological sites.

A small section of the collection illustrates the work of potters and glass workers, such as, gaffers, from the 1700s to the present. Work is shown in arts and crafts studios, in factory settings, and in traditional shops. Also documented are ceramics and glass advertisements, sales shops, and technology.

Arranged: There are two major series. 1) Silver gelatin photoprints in binders. 2) Color dye coupler slides. Photoprints are arranged according to the following major subject categories. 1) Traditional American earthenware and stoneware. 2) American commercial wares, art pottery, and studio ceramics. 3) English traditional and commercial ceramics. 4) Hans Syz Collection of 18th-century European and Oriental porcelain. 5) Miscellaneous European ceramics. 6) Historical archaeology. 7) Glass. 8) Ceramics and glass technology, marketing, and use. 9) Miscellaneous furniture and decorative arts from the Alfred Duane Pell Collection. 10) Exhibits.

The color slides are arranged according to the following categories. 1) Traditional American earthenware and stoneware. 2) American commercial wares, art pottery, and studio ceramics. 3) Historical archaeology. 4) English ceramics. 5) Continental European ceramics. 6) Chinese and Japanese export porcelain. 7) Hans Syz Collection. 8) Glass. 9) Ceramics and glass technology, marketing, and use.

Each binder deals with a single topic, which may be further divided by subtopics. Items in the glass photoprint and slide categories are further broken down as follows: American, Chinese, and European ceramics and glass; American and English bottles; American studio glass; ledger of the Manhein Glasshouse; paperweights; and miscellaneous and specialty items.

Captioned: Photoprints with subject categories on their reverse; most slides with catalog number, maker, date, and country of manufacture.

Finding Aid: An annotated listing of subject headings issued by the division and entitled "Division of Ceramics and Glass Photographic Reference Files, February 1984."

Restrictions: Portions are restricted.

CL

Division of Community Life

Division of Community Life
National Museum of American History
Smithsonian Institution
Washington, D.C. 20560
Richard Ahlborn, Curator
(202) 357-2385
Hours: Monday–Friday, 10 a.m.–4 p.m.

Scope of the Collections

There are 17 photographic collections with approximately 41,000 images in the Division of Community Life.

Focus of the Collections

These photographs document American cultural history and everyday 19th and 20th century American life outside of the home. Research materials deal with the history of business; education; entertainment; fraternal organizations; popular culture; professional organizations; religious life; sports; urban life; and trades and labor. These topics are augmented by materials on American ethnic groups, particularly Spanish-American and Afro-American cultures. There are also some holdings on European and Latin American cultures.

Greater emphasis in division photo collections is placed on American folk art; amusement parks; carved gravestone markers; child labor; education; entertainment; immigration; Polish folk architecture and crafts; religion; slavery; and urban life.

Photographic Processes and Formats Represented

In addition to standard 20th century slide, photoprint, and photonegative processes there are early photographic processes, such as, albumen photoprints, cyanotypes, a pannotype, and tintypes.

Other Materials Represented

This division also collects advertising cards (such as, bubble-gum and cigarette cards); booklets and prints; catalogs; clippings; correspondence; decorative handwriting; drawings; graphics; gravestone rubbings; images of saints; immigration and naturalization records; legal documents; newspapers; phonograph records; photomechanicals; posters; set designs; sheet music; sports trading cards; tickets and programs; as well as trade literature. Other artifactual materials include baskets; ceramics; costumes; decorated horse gear; some decorative arts materials; furniture; games; hand tools; metalwork; postcards; toys; and wooden panels.

Access and Usage Policies

Researchers interested in viewing these collections should contact Curator Richard Ahlborn in the Division of Community Life at least 48 hours in advance of their proposed visit. Partial finding aids exist to several collections.

Photographic copies of these photographs are available from OPPS at the prevailing rate. The photonegative number may be obtained from the division. If no photonegative exists the researcher must pay to have one produced from the original artifact.

Publication Policies

In addition to obtaining permission from the Smithsonian Institution to reproduce a photograph, researchers may have to obtain permission from the copyright holder. The Smithsonian Institution is not necessarily the copyright holder. The preferred credit line is: "Courtesy of the National Museum of American History, Smithsonian Institution, Division of Community Life, [Collection Name]."

CL·1

American Community Life Information File

Dates of Photographs: 1960s–Present

Collection Origins

This collection was assembled by division staff from diverse sources, including corporate and private donors, exchanges with other institutions, materials copied from other collections, and purchases.

The collection was created to document division exhibits, such as, the "Buckaroos in Paradise Exhibit" (1980); the "Horsemen of the Spanish Borderland Exhibit"; and the "Spanish-New Mexico Textile Exhibit."

Physical Description

There are 11,200 photographs, including color dye coupler slides and silver gelatin photoprints. Other materials include articles, clippings, conservation laboratory findings, correspondence, lists, memos, notes, pamphlets, reports, reprints, and work requests.

Subjects

The photographs primarily document cultural, ethnic, and occupational groups in the United States and their contributions to American culture.

Among the culture groups documented are Afro-Americans and Hispanic Americans. Among the occupational groups documented are cowboys, explorers, laborers, pioneers, politicians, publishers, and scientists. Activities documented include theater and travel. Objects documented include folk art, inventions, maps, and religious objects. There are also photographs of American architecture; cityscapes; landscapes; and the Old West.

Arranged: Into six series. 1) General ethnic reference files. 2) General subject file. 3) Afro-American history project. 4) Afro-American photographic file. 5) Divisional exhibition files. 6) A file of reports from the Conservation Analytical Laboratory on objects in the division collections.

Captioned: No.

Finding Aid: Item-level finding aid to part of this collection.

Restrictions: Some for reference only. No duplication allowed.

CL·2

American Community Life Photograph Collection

Dates of Photographs: ND

Collection Origins

This collection was assembled by division staff from diverse published and unpublished sources. About 16 of the autographed photographs appear to have been donated by Ken Sparwin. There are also 40 autographed photographs which were originally in the collection of Ed Rowlands of Pittsburgh, Pennsylvania.

Photographers represented include Jack Hillier of Alexandria, Virginia (autographed images).

Physical Description

There are 150 photographs, including color dye coupler photoprints (oversized and mounted); and silver gelatin photoprints (some oversized or autographed) and radiographs.

Subjects

The photographs document illustrious individuals associated with American civil rights, education, motion pictures, music, sports, and theater.

There are portraits of Sue Carol, Walt Disney, Beth and Betty Dodge, Father Edward Joseph Flanagan, Martin Luther King, Jr. (two portraits from 1960), Little Jack Little, Una Merkel, Ken Murray, Paderewski, Lily Pons, Babe Ruth, Kate Smith, Harold Stein, Nick Stuart, and J. Termini.

There are also radiographs (2) of a Mexican saddle and of an 18th century statue (labeled "Santiago Major of San Xavier Del Bac Mission," now in the Arizona State Museum); and images of an unidentified American school.

Arranged: No.

Captioned: Some photographs are autographed.

Finding Aid: No.

Restrictions: No.

CL·3

American Hand Tool Photograph Collection

Dates of Photographs: 20th Century

Collection Origins

This collection was assembled by division staff from diverse sources to document American hand tools in the division's accessioned object holdings, such as, the John R. Gerwig hand tool collection.

Photographers and studios represented include the General Electric Company; John R. Gerwig, Jr., of Baltimore, Maryland; Richard Muzzrole; and the Folklife Festival of the Smithsonian Institution.

Physical Description

There are 2,350 photographs, including color dye coupler slides and silver gelatin photoprints.

Subjects

The photographs primarily document American hand tools of the 18th and 19th centuries, including: gauging and measuring tools; gripping and holding tools; heating and modeling tools; mechanized tools; planing tools; rotary and screw tools; slicing tools; and striking tools. Note: There are a few 20th century images, for example, World War II hand tool use at the General Electric Company.

Other types of tools illustrated include: ancient hand tools; architectural tools (for items such as moldings); chisels; cooper's tools; cutlery; engraver's tools; hammers; hatchets; lathes; monkey wrenches; planes; power hand tools; and spiral screwdrivers.

Photographs of tools for the following trades a included: blacksmithing; brazing; carpentry; ca

riage making; coopering; forging; sail making; shingle making; soldering; stoneworking; tanning; and welding.

Arranged: By series. 1) John R. Gerwig hand tool collection (then by type of tool). 2) Potential hand tool accessions (arranged by last name of potential donor). 3) Hand tool research files (alphabetical by subject heading). 4) Miscellaneous prints (arranged by OPPS negative number).

Captioned: Some with subject headings, donors, or negative numbers.

Finding Aid: No.

Restrictions: Series 2 of the collection is for reference only and may not be duplicated.

CL·4

Community Life Entertainment Vertical File

Dates of Photographs: 20th Century

Collection Origins

This collection was assembled by the division staff from a variety of donations and sources. The photographs illustrate entertainment related topics from the 19th and 20th centuries in the United States.

Physical Description

There are 600 silver gelatin photoprints. Many are duplicate studio photographs distributed for public relations purposes. Other materials include biographical information, clippings, handwritten notes, and some reprints.

Subjects

Most of the photographs illustrate entertainment related topics from the 19th and 20th centuries in the United States, including auctions, bands, campus fads, Christmas tree ornaments, circuses, computers, dances and dancing, disasters, games, mass media, music and songs (jazz, and rock and roll), sports, and toys.

American places documented include amusement parks (such as Coney Island), country and general stores, and the 1876 Centennial Exposition in Philadelphia.

There are also photographs of games and sports including billiards, bingo, bowling, boxing, card playing, the D.C. lottery, fishing, golfing, horse racing, hunting, and jousting.

There are still photoprints from motion pictures, such as, *Das Boot, The Empire Strikes Back, Showboat, Wizard of Oz,* and *Woodstock 1969*; and television still photoprints documenting shows, such as, "All in the Family," "Barney Miller," "The Honeymooners," "Leave It To Beaver," "Lou Grant," "Meet the Press," "The Newlywed Game," "Saturday Night Live," and "Sesame Street."

The biographical files include the following individuals: Fred Allen; Amos & Andy; Mary Astor; Gene Autry; John Barrymore; Ray Charles; Bing Crosby; Jessica Dragon; Duke Ellington; Clark Gable; Greta Garbo; Buster Keaton; Frederick March; Pola Negri; Elvis Presley; Norma Shearer; Gloria Swanson; and Rudy Vallee.

Arranged: By series. 1) General American entertainment section. 2) American popular culture (stage, radio, and screen). 3) Biographical file on American entertainers. 4) Sports and recreational events. 5) Biographies of sports figures. Then, alphabetically by subject heading (or last name of individual or group).

Captioned: Some are autographed.

Finding Aid: No.

Restrictions: No.

CL·5

Community Life Sports Card Collection

Dates of Photographs: 1920s

Collection Origins

This collection was assembled by division staff from diverse sources. The original sports cards were sold as enclosures in bubble-gum or cigarette packets. They were popularly collected. Hassan Cigarette Company and the Mecca Cigarette Company produced most of the sports cards in the collection.

Physical Description

There are 90 silver gelatin photoprints. Other materials include 2,630 photomechanicals. Note: These cards are printed on board with a color print of a team on one side and extensive biographical and statistical information on the other side.

Subjects

The photographs document sports figures in the fields of baseball, basketball, billiards, boxing, discus throwing, football, hockey, pool, running, and various other sports; as well as some teams and groups of sports heroes.

Arranged: Into six subunits. 1) Football cards (300). 2) Basketball cards (300). 3) Boxing cards (40). 4) Hockey cards (30). 5) Baseball cards (2,000). 6) Miscellaneous cards (50).

Captioned: Most of the cards include name of the player shown; team or affiliation of the player (where applicable); biography of the player; record or statistics of the player; and a review of his position and scoring record and "style."

Finding Aid: There is a one-page hand-lettered description of the arrangement of the basketball and baseball cards.

Restrictions: No.

CL·6

Conwell Family Papers

Dates of Photographs: 1860s–1954

Collection Origins

This collection was assembled by James S. Conwell, his wife Mae Hopkinson Conwell (1868–1957), and their daughters Valentine L. and Delsey D. Conwell of Los Angeles, California.

There are also some letters of other family members including 23 from Nathaniel G. Hopkinson, ancestor of Mae Hopkinson Conwell, written to his family between 1836 and 1844.

Physical Description

There are 40 photographs, including albumen photoprints; cyanotypes; a pannotype (a gem portrait); silver gelatin photoprints; and tintypes (including a 1″ circular "gem" tintype). Other materials include correspondence, clippings, a notebook, and tinted postcards.

Subjects

The photographs are studio portraits of Conwell family members, including James S. Conwell, his wife Mae Hopkinson Conwell, and their two daughters Valentine L. and Delsey D. Conwell.

There is also a studio portrait of a young girl on a bicycle labelled "Miss Conwell, aged three years—the youngest cyclist in the world," which was used for advertising purposes on July 22, 1895, in San Francisco.

Arranged: No.

Captioned: No.

Finding Aid: No.

Restrictions: No.

CL·7

Gregory and Kay Day Afro-American Photographic Collection

Dates of Photographs: 1970s

Collection Origins

Gregory Day and Kay Young Day of Takoma Park, Maryland, researched Afro-American basket-making, conch fishing, shrimping, and subsistence fishing in the coastal region of South Carolina for a planned publication.

Kay and Gregory Day have copyrighted these materials. Researchers are held responsible for obtaining permission to copy or publish these photographs directly from the Days.

Physical Description

There are 75 photographs, including color dye coupler slides, and silver gelatin photoprints. Other materials include item accession sheets, object inventory sheets, and an oral history interview transcript (about Afro-American rice cultivation in South Carolina).

Subjects

The photographs document Afro-American subsistence activities and occupations in the American South, particularly in coastal communities in the Carolinas. There are photographs of coil basket production; conch fishing and shrimping; constructing a mortar and pestle; and subsistence fishing.

Arranged: No.

Captioned: With an assigned item number.

Finding Aid: Individual object inventory sheets which list the museum catalog number of the object illustrated, the item number, a description of the object, and the price paid for the item. There is also an item accession sheet that lists additional information about the collection, such as, amount of time needed to create objects, dimensions, decorative details, and materials.

Restrictions: For reference only. No duplication allowed.

CL·8

Eleanor Dickinson Photographic Collection on the American Protestant Revival

Date of Photographs: Circa 1972

Collection Origins

Eleanor Dickinson is a photographer who worked near Knoxville, Tennessee. She later became curator of the Tennessee State Museum. There she developed an exhibit and exhibit catalog on the American Protestant Revival movement entitled "Revival." These images were originally used in that work.

Dickinson has copyrighted the images. Researchers are held responsible for obtaining permission to copy or publish these photographs directly from Dickinson.

Physical Description

There are 60 silver gelatin photoprints (matted).

Subjects

These photographs document the revival of American Protestantism which took place in the vicinity of Knoxville, Tennessee, around 1972.

There are photographs of churches; people practicing religious blessing and healing activities (including the laying on of hands); religious signs (including meeting announcements); revival services; and tent meetings.

Arranged: No.

Captioned: No.

Finding Aid: No.

Restrictions: For reference only. No duplication allowed.

CL·9

German Institute Polish Photograph Collection

Dates of Photographs: 1940–1945

Collection Origins

This collection was assembled by division staff from images created by the German Institute of Zakopane, Poland.

Richard Ahlborn, curator of the division, describes the institute as a Nazi organization which documented the Jewish and Gypsy peoples of Poland between 1940 and 1945, possibly with the intent of anthropological and physical studies.

The division staff believes that this collection may have been given to the Smithsonian Institution by the United States Information Agency immediately following World War II. The collection was divided into several parts at that time. This is one part of the original accession.

Physical Description

There are 360 photographs, including color dye coupler slides and silver gelatin photoprints.

Subjects

The photographs document Polish architecture, artifacts, and people (particularly children, Jewish people, and Gypsies) between 1940 and 1945.

Many of the individuals shown are in local costume. A number of the children and adults are shown both from the front and in profile in "mug shot" fashion.

The buildings shown are folk architecture. They include many farms, houses, log buildings, and religious structures. There are also photographs of Polish artifacts, such as, ceremonial vessels, furniture, pottery, sculpture, textiles, weaving, and wooden serving ware.

Arranged: No.

Captioned: No.

Finding Aid: No.

Restrictions: No.

CL·10

Edith Halpert Papers

Dates of Photographs: 1953–1966

Collection Origins

This collection was assembled by Edith Halpert (1900–1970), an art gallery director and folk art dealer who was involved with the production and sale of weather vane reproductions. These reproductions of weather vanes were made from original 19th century weather vane molds.

Photographers represented include Nathan C. Baum; Howard Chase; and George Karfiol, New York City.

Physical Description

The collection contains ten silver gelatin photoprints. Other materials include catalogs (for weather vanes), clippings, correspondence, notes, and records.

Subjects

The photographs document 19th century American weather vanes in the shapes of fire engines, fishes, foxes, horses, oxen, peacocks, pigs, plows, roosters, sheep, ships, and squirrels.

Arranged: No.

Captioned: No.

Finding Aid: No.

Restrictions: No.

CL·11

Allan I. Ludwig and Saul Ludwig Papers

Dates of Photographs: Circa 1960s

Collection Origins

Allan I. Ludwig is an author and art historian who wrote his doctoral dissertation at Yale University on "Gravestones of New England." He was assisted by his brother, Saul Ludwig.

Physical Description

There are 400 silver gelatin photoprints in six albums. Other materials include identification sheets.

Subjects

The photographs document New England gravestones of the 17th through 19th centuries.

Arranged: By assigned numbers.

Captioned: With an assigned number; date; site; artist's name; and the name of the deceased individual.

Finding Aid: An identification sheet arranged by the assigned number of the photograph. It lists the name of the individual buried and their birth and death dates; the location and size of the gravestone; the material of the gravestone; the attribution of the carver; and the carver's life or work dates.

Restrictions: No.

CL·12

Francis M. Misklea Collection
A.K.A. Allan Herschel Company Collection

Dates of Photographs: Circa 1879–1956

Collection Origins

This collection was assembled by Francis M. Misklea, an employee of the Allan Herschel Company, to document manufacturers of amusement park rides including the Allan Herschel Company; the Herschel-Spillman Company; W.F. Mangels Company; Philadelphia Toboggan Company; Spillman Engineering Corporation; and Rudolph Wurlitzer Company.

The Herschel Company manufactured carousels and amusement park rides in North Tonawanda, New York, from 1879 to 1956.

Physical Description

There are 700 silver gelatin photoprints in 11 albums. Other materials include advertisements, articles, brochures, catalogs, clippings, correspondence, a monograph (William F. Mangels. *The Outdoor Amusement Industry*. Vantage Press, 1952), phonograph records, postcards, and sales records.

Subjects

The photographs document amusement park rides (particularly carousels) from the 1870s until the middle 1950s, primarily in New York state.

Among the rides shown are chariots; Hop on a Magic Carpet; Hurricane; the kiddie auto rides; the Looper; merry-go-rounds; Model "A"; Over the Jumps; Rocket; Spillman's auto speedway; Water Scooter; and the Whip.

Arranged: Into 36 series by accession number (modified by decimals to designate corporate name).

Captioned: No.

Finding Aid: A brief inventory listing.

Restrictions: No.

CL·13

Motion Picture Still Photograph Collection

Dates of Photographs: 1930s–1960s

Collection Origins

This collection was assembled by an unidentified Danish museum in Copenhagen to document films made at American film studios. It was later given to the Smithsonian Institution.

Physical Description

There are 24,000 silver gelatin photoprints. Other materials include brochures, captions (and cutlines), handouts, and posters.

Subjects

The photographs are publicity still images taken from American commercial motion pictures (films) made in the 1930s through the 1960s. The films were made at 20th Century Fox, United Artists, and Warner Brothers. The photographs were taken for advertising purposes.

Among the films represented are *Operation Mad Ball; Rear Window; The Sea Hornet; Stop, You're Killing Me; Terror of the Town; Up Periscope;* and *Vertigo.*

Arranged: No.

Captioned: In Danish.

Finding Aid: No.

Restrictions: No.

CL·14

Perkins Studio Collection

Dates of Photographs: 1890–1900s

Collection Origins

The Perkins Studio (of unknown location) took these formal studio portraits to document stage productions and theatrical personalities for commercial purposes.

Physical Description

There are 220 silver gelatin photoprints (some are autographed).

Subjects

The photographs are formal studio portraits of theatrical personalities and images of stage productions.

Among the actors and actresses portrayed are William Terriss (as King Henry II), Ray Thomas, Isabelle Urquhart, and Francis Wilson.

Arranged: No.

Captioned: Some are autographed.

Finding Aid: No.

Restrictions: No.

CL·15

Robert L. Sardino Collection of Theatrical Lantern Slides

Dates of Photographs: 1914–1975

Collection Origins

This collection was assembled by Robert L. Sardino who worked in Syracuse, New York, theaters as a projectionist from about 1914 until he retired in 1975 at age 75. Sardino assembled movie theater lantern slides used for projection during pauses between films and before and after showings.

Physical Description

There are 310 photographs, including tinted silver gelatin dry plate lantern slides and photonegatives.

Subjects

These photographs are movie theater lantern slides, which were used as backdrops during performances or as entertainment during pauses between feature films. They include: headers; motion picture advertising slides; motion picture studio logos and trademarks; news slides; trailers; and vaudeville backdrops (including holiday scenes, interiors, and landscapes).

Among the news slides of the 1920s and 1930s are "The Arrival of the Aquitania," "Ceremonies Honoring 1861 Veterans," "Dr. Langley's Airplane at the Smithsonian Institution," "England's Militant Suffragettes," "Jack Johnson's Airplane Flight," "Mine Strike in Colorado headed by J.W. Brown," "The Panama Canal," "President Wilson's 1914 Mexican War," and "Teddy Roosevelt at the Smithsonian Institution." Note: The text in quotes is from the slide labels.

Among the motion picture advertising slides are stills for *Buried Alive; The False Bride; The Lamb, the Woman, the Wolf; Lucille Love; Out of the Far East; The Romance of An Actor; Treasure Hunters Lost in Africa;* and *The Yanqui Revenge.*

Motion picture distributor, film studio name, or trademark slides are included for the following studios: Eclair; Gold Seal; Imp Stock Company; Nestor; 101 Bison; Powers; Rex; and Victor.

Arranged: No.

Captioned: Some with subject information.

Finding Aid: No.

Restrictions: No.

CL·16

Sweet Caporal Cigarette Card Photograph Collection

Dates of Photographs: 1890s

Collection Origins

This collection was assembled by a private donor and later given to the division. The photographs were originally offered as "bonuses" inside cigarette packages of Sweet Caporal Cigarettes in the 1890s. Much like sports cards, these images were popular collectors items.

Physical Description

There are over 300 albumen photoprints mounted on small pieces of cardboard (cigarette cards).

Subjects

The photographs are portraits (bust and full-length shots) of well-known actresses of the 1880s and 1890s. Many of the women are in costume.

Among the actresses shown are Mademoiselle Besoin, Amelia Clover, Sadie Kirby, Bertha Ricci, Mademoiselle Royer, and Emmie Weathersby.

Arranged: No.

Captioned: Most of the photographs are embossed with the name of the actress illustrated. The backs of the cards are labeled "Sweet Caporal Cigarettes."

Finding Aid: No.

Restrictions: No.

CL·17

Van Alstyne Folk Art Photograph Collection

Dates of Photographs: 20th Century

Collection Origins

This collection came to the Division of Community Life from the Division of Domestic Life, where it formed part of the American Domestic Life Photograph Collection. Most of the objects shown are in the museum's collections.

The collection was used in Peter Welsh's exhibit catalog entitled *American Folk Art: The Art and Spirit of a People*. Washington, D.C.: Smithsonian Institution, 1965.

Physical Description

There are 300 silver gelatin photoprints in three albums.

Subjects

The photographs document American folk art objects, particularly metal and wood sculpture of the 18th through the 20th centuries. There are photographs of carousel animals, cigar store figures, circus figures, folk carvings, and weather vanes.

Arranged: By the accession number of the object shown in the print.

Captioned: No.

Finding Aid: An inventory list arranged by the object accession number which also gives a brief description of the object.

Restrictions: No.

CN

Division of Conservation

Division of Conservation
National Museum of American History
Smithsonian Institution
Washington, D.C. 20560
J. Scott Odell, Head Conservator
(202) 357-1735
Hours: Monday–Friday, 9 a.m.–5 p.m.

Scope and Focus of the Collections

There are three photographic collections with approximately 6,200 images in the Division of Conservation.

Focus of the Collections

These photographs are used primarily as research material to illustrate conservation problems, restoration techniques, and preservation activities in the field of artifactual conservation. Division collections illustrate the restoration of machinery; musical instruments; paper; textiles; and other objects.

Photographic Processes and Formats Represented

Division collections contain standard 20th century photonegative, photoprint, and phototransparency processes, such as, color dye diffusion transfer photonegatives, photoprints, and phototransparencies; and silver gelatin photoprints.

Other Materials Presented

This division also collects treatment reports and work request forms in notebooks.

Access and Usage Policies

These collections are restricted for use by Division of Conservation staff and other SI staff members. Images of restricted materials may not be reproduced. Online finding aids are in preparation for some of these collections.

Publication Policies

In addition to obtaining permission from the Smithsonian Institution to reproduce a photograph, researchers may have to obtain permission from the copyright holder. The Smithsonian Institution is not necessarily the copyright holder. The preferred credit line is: "Courtesy of the Division of Conservation, National Museum of American History, Smithsonian Institution."

CN·1

Conservation Division Musical Instrument Treatment File

Dates of Photographs: 1970s–1980s

Collection Origins

This collection was assembled by J. Scott Odell, Head Conservator of the Division of Conservation, to document his restoration work on musical instruments and his travels to musical instrument restoration facilities around the world. This collection is a part of Odell's personal papers.

The photographs in this collection also illustrate some material samples, such as, wood samples, and restoration work done by Odell or his colleagues.

Photographic studios represented include the Metropolitan Museum of Art, New York City; the National Museums of Budapest and Prague; and the Pushkin Museum, Moscow.

Physical Description

There are 3,200 photographs, including color dye coupler slides, and silver gelatin photonegatives and photoprints.

Subjects

The photographs document the conservation treatment and physical condition of musical instruments in collections worldwide. The photographs show technical details, such as, bridges and bows, as well as damage and restoration activities. Instruments documented include brass, keyboard, strings, and woodwinds.

There are several photographs of unrelated materials, such as, wood samples or textile restoration activities on the "Star Spangled Banner."

Arranged: Two major series, both arranged by Division of Conservation log number. 1) Color slides. 2) Silver gelatin photonegatives and photoprints.

Captioned: No.

Finding Aid: 1) The photographer's log books arranged by the Division of Conservation job number.

2) A card index, arranged by: a) the instrument maker's name; b) the species of the wood materials used in repairing or making the instrument; and c) the donor or owner of the instrument. The cards list museum accession number, catalog number, donor's name, museum name, negative number, and conservation job number.

Restrictions: No access.

CN·2

Conservation Lecture Series Slide Collection

Dates of Photographs: 1970s–Present

Collection Origins

This collection is being assembled by division staff from a variety of donors to illustrate conservation problems, restoration techniques, and preservation activities. The collection is growing. These images are stored in an OPPS cold storage vault. At present, the major sources of images are slide collections from conservation colleagues within the United States and Canada.

Physical Description

There are 1,000 photographs, including color dye coupler slides and silver gelatin slides. Most are copy images.

Subjects

The photographs document damage to artifact collections (within the Smithsonian Institution); group salvage activities; preservation activities; restoration procedures; and worldwide disaster documentation.

Conservation procedures, tools, and work stations are documented, as are materials used in restoration. Most of the images were taken of conservators and curators in the Washington, D.C., area.

Arranged: No.

Captioned: No.

Finding Aid: The division is planning to produce an online finding aid to this collection.

Restrictions: No access.

CN·3

Conservation Treatment Report File

Dates of Photographs: 1979–1985

Collection Origins

Since the founding of the division in 1979, the staff has taken photographs of the objects which have undergone restoration. At present, three shots of each item are taken both before and after treatment. Approximately 500 to 600 objects undergo treatment annually.

In the future, image documentation will be kept online and all original negatives will remain in cold storage at OPPS.

Physical Description

There are 2,000 photographs, including color dye coupler slides, and silver gelatin photonegatives and photoprints. Other materials include typed reports.

Subjects

The photographs document objects treated in the conservation laboratories in the National Museum of American History. The objects include calculators and computers; chemical apparatus; clocks and watches; coins and money; costumes; documents; electric motors and appliances; eyeglasses; food or fuel processing equipment; furniture; glass and ceramic objects; hand tools; jewelry; machine tools; medical instruments; musical instruments; patent medicines; photographs; quilts; railroad engines; signs; stamps; and trade catalogs.

Arranged: In increasing numerical order by assigned conservation job log number.

Captioned: With job numbers, object catalog number, and descriptive information about the object.

Finding Aid: 1) Quarterly treatment report summary lists enumerate the job log number; object name or description; museum accession; catalog and negative number; and conservation work hours spent. They are arranged alphabetically by the name of the department and division of the National Museum of American History. 2) Conservation work request forms list the name and location of the requestor; object description; accession, negative, and catalog numbers; exhibition title and deadline; lender's name; and conservation work done.

Restrictions: No access.

CS

Division of Costume

Division of Costume
National Museum of American History
Smithsonian Institution
Washington, D.C. 20560
Claudia Kidwell, Curator
(202) 357-3185
Hours: Monday—Friday, 10 a.m.—4 p.m.

Scope of the Collections

There are six photographic collections with approximately 25,000 images in the Division of Costume.

Focus of the Collections

These photographs are used primarily as research material to document the garments and accessories worn by Americans between the 17th and 20th centuries. Also documented are grooming aids; the personal appearance of men, women, and children of all socio-economic levels of American society; and tailoring and dressmaking equipment.

Photographic Processes and Formats Represented

These collections include standard 20th century slide, photoprint, and photonegative processes, such as, color dye coupler slides and silver gelatin photonegatives and photoprints.

Other Materials Represented

This division also collects body care accessories, such as, cosmetics and hair care items; clothing manufacturing equipment and tools, such as, pleating and cutting devices; fashion journals; fashion sketches; garments (including outerwear and underwear); jewelry; lithographic or engraved fashion plates; personal accessories (such as, card cases, fans, and footwear); satiric cartoons on fashions and fads; store mannequins; and trade catalogs.

Access and Usage Policies

The division is open to the public by appointment only. Partial finding aids exist to several collections. Restricted materials within the division may not be reproduced.

Publication Policies

In addition to obtaining permission from the Smithsonian Institution to reproduce a photograph, researchers may have to obtain permission from the copyright holder. The Smithsonian Institution is not necessarily the copyright holder. The preferred credit line is: "Courtesy of the Division of Costume, National Museum of American History, Smithsonian Institution."

CS·1

Costume Photograph Collection

Dates of Photographs: 19th and 20th Centuries

Collection Origins

This collection was assembled by division staff for exhibition, publication, reference, and research purposes.

Images from the collection are in the following Smithsonian publications: 1) Claudia B. Kidwell. *Women's Bathing and Swimming Costume in the United States.* United States National Museum Bulletin 250. Washington, D.C.: Smithsonian Institution Press, 1968. 2) Claudia B. Kidwell and Margaret C. Christman. *Suiting Everyone: The Democratization of Clothing in America.* Washington, D.C.: Smithsonian Institution Press, 1974. 3) Claudia B. Kidwell. *Cutting a Fashionable Fit: Dressmakers' Drafting Systems in the United States.* Smithsonian Institution Studies in History and Technology, no. 42. Washington, D.C.: Smithsonian Institution Press, 1979.

Physical Description

There are 20,250 photographs, including albumen photoprints (some cartes-de-visite); color dye coupler slides; daguerreotypes; and silver gelatin photoprints.

Subjects

The photographs document American apparel from the 17th century through the present, including the artifactual holdings of the division. They illustrate children's, men's, and women's accessories, clothing, and jewelry. Also shown are apparel advertising; clothing care items; clothing sales materials; devices for creating accessories and clothing; grooming items; and patent models of apparel manufacturing devices.

There are photographs of card cases; cosmetics; display mannequins and windows; fans; haircare and shaving equipment; handbags; handkerchiefs; jewelry; machinery and tools (for handsewing and for business manufacture of clothing); neckwear (such as, ties and cravats); parasols and umbrellas; smoking jackets; sport clothing (for tennis, croquet, and swimming); and underwear.

Photographic reproductions of art work, such as, cartoons, graphics, and paintings which illustrate apparel are included. Also included are photographs of apparel conservation; non-National Museum of American History exhibitions; and special exhibitions.

Arranged: Into five series. 1) Original photographs. 2) Drawers of slides (arranged by catalog number of the object shown). 3) Slide notebook browsing files (arranged by topic). 4) Copy print/contemporary print photograph file (arranged first by subject, then date). 5) Print notebook browsing file (arranged by subject, then by date of subject).

Captioned: Photoprints give the object name; a description; object date; OPPS negative number; and the object catalog or accession number. The slide captions give the name and a catalog or accession number of the object shown.

Finding Aid: No.

Restrictions: No.

CS·2

Evan Picone Collection

Dates of Photographs: 1977–1979

Collection Origins

This collection was assembled by division staff to document the Evan Picone company, and the company's 1978 and 1979 product line and sales season.

Physical Description

There are 300 silver gelatin photoprints in three albums.

Subjects

The photographs document the design, production, and retail and wholesale display of the 1978 and 1979 Evan Picone women's clothing line.

There are images of buyers; designers; design rooms; display racks; factory floors; models; pattern makers; production staff; and sales staff.

Views include the Evan Picone showroom, New York; the New Jersey production plant; and Saks Fifth Avenue and Garfinckel's department stores sales rooms in Chevy Chase, Maryland.

Arranged: There are three loose-leaf notebooks in this collection, arranged in chronological sequence of creating, designing, and selling the garments.

Captioned: Many with the name and title of the individual shown or with a subject description.

Finding Aid: No.

Restrictions: No.

CS·3

Fashion Plates Collection

Dates of Photographs: 1960–1980s

Collection Origins

This collection was assembled by the division staff for use in dating and identifying division costume collections. Most images were taken by OPPS at the request of division staff. Several images document materials in other repositories such as the Library of Congress.

The collection was used in the publication of 1) Claudia B. Kidwell. *Women's Bathing and Swimming Costume in the United States.* United States National Museum Bulletin 250. Washington, D.C.: Smithsonian Institution Press, 1968; and 2) Claudia B. Kidwell and Margaret C. Christman. *Suiting Everyone: The Democratization of Clothing in America.* Washington, D.C.: Smithsonian Institution Press, 1974.

Physical Description

There are 4,500 photographs, including color dye coupler slides and silver gelatin photoprints. Other materials include engraved and lithographic fashion plates (published).

Subjects

The photographs reproduce fashion plate illustrations (engraved and lithographic plates) of accessory and clothing styles, published from the 1790s to the 1890s in American, English, French, and German fashion magazines. Most plates show women's fashions.

Among the original magazine sources of the plates are *Allegmeine Modenzeitung, La Belle Assemblee, Le Bon Ton, Demorest's Monthly Magazine, Godey's Ladies Book, Graham's Magazine, Journal Desmoiselles, Le Moniteur de la Mode United, Peterson's Magazine, Le Petit Messager, Repository of the Arts, Young Englishwoman,* and *World of Fashion.* In all, nearly 40 magazine titles of the 19th century are included.

Arranged: Into two series. 1) The fashion plates (chronologically by date). 2) The photoprints (chronologically by decade).

Captioned: With the image source and garment date.

Finding Aid: 1) A card catalog to the fashion plates. 2) A subject index to the fashion plates. No separate finding aid to the photographs.

Restrictions: No duplication allowed.

CS·4

Hart, Schaffner and Marx Records

Dates of Photographs: Circa 1898–1910; 1958

Collection Origins

Harry Hart and Brother was founded in Chicago, Illinois, in 1872 and rapidly became the largest men's clothing manufacturer in the United States. In 1878 the firm changed its name to Hart, Abt and Marx, and in 1887 it became Hart, Schaffner and Marx.

Note: Most of the collection (the nonphotographic material) was created between 1901 and 1972.

Physical Description

There are 58 silver gelatin photoprints. Other materials include annual reports; cash books; catalogs; correspondence; cost estimates; earnings and hours records; general orders on tailoring methods; inspection reports; press releases; remittance forms; shop price lists; a xerographic copy (of a 1920 booklet); and trade literature.

Subjects

These photographs reproduce advertisements for Hart, Schaffner and Marx men's suits (circa 1898–1910) and document the production process of creating and finishing a suit within the Rochester, Indiana, plant of the firm. There are many shots of the plant interior.

Suit production activities shown include basting; cutting; facing; inspection; invisible stretching; joining; pattern fitting; pocket making; pressing; sewing; sleeve setting; tacking; and testing. Note: Most production images date from 1958.

Arranged: By subject into two series. 1) 16 unarranged photographs of advertisements. 2) 42 photoprints documenting men's suit production in chronological sequence corresponding to actual suit production order.

Captioned: The 42 photographs of suit production are captioned with the location and a brief description of the activity.

Finding Aid: No.

Restrictions: No.

CS·5

Jantzen, Inc. Collection

Dates of Photographs: Circa 1925–1973; 1976

Collection Origins

The collection was assembled by the Jantzen Knitting Mills and its successor, Jantzen, Inc.

Note: John A. Zehntbauer created the company history and the autobiography in this collection.

Images from the collection were used in the following Smithsonian publication: Claudia B. Kidwell. *Women's Bathing and Swimming Costume in the United States.* United States National Museum Bulletin 250. Washington, D.C.: Smithsonian Institution Press, 1968.

Physical Description

There are 75 silver gelatin photoprints housed in two albums.

Subjects

The photographs document Jantzen's advertisements, clothing (swimsuit) manufacturing facilities, physical plants, products, and staff worldwide.

Many photographs illustrate men's and women's swimsuits as worn by models and by actors and actresses in pinup pictures—including Irene Bennett, Joan Blondell, Berenice Claire, Jimmy Ellison, and Alice White.

Among the Jantzen S.A. Textile facilities shown are those in Buenos Aires, Argentina; Lidcomb, New South Wales, Australia; Vancouver, British Columbia, Canada; Brenford, Middlesex, England; and Portland, Oregon.

There are photographs of Jantzen sales conventions in Chicago and Paris and images of various Jantzen advertisements and shop signs.

Arranged: By type of material.

Captioned: Some with the model's name, the name of the swimsuit, and a brief description of special features of the swimsuit.

Finding Aid: No.

Restrictions: No.

CS·6

Dorothy Shaver Papers

Dates of Photographs: Circa 1928

Collection Origins

Dorothy Shaver (1897–1959) was the president of the Lord and Taylor department store. She joined the store in 1924 as head of the comparison shopping department. During the following years, she served as a member of the board of directors (1927) and then as president (1945). Shaver was also active in philanthropic, social, and war advisory activities.

Shaver is noted for her role in recognizing the contributions of American fashion designers. She also made innovative use of artists in creating advertising layout and window displays, and was a leader in the decentralization of Lord and Taylor through the establishment of suburban branches.

Physical Description

There are 50 silver gelatin photoprints in an album. Other materials include awards, award programs, correspondence, memorabilia, newspaper clippings, notes, obituaries, programs, phonograph recordings, and travel materials.

Subjects

The photographs portray Lord and Taylor president Dorothy Shaver (circa 1928) and document Lord and Taylor's "Modern Decorative Arts Exhibition" held in Paris in 1928.

The exhibition photographs show primarily art deco (art moderne) rooms decorated by the following French designers: Chareau; Vera Chouchaeff; Madame Cuttoli of Myrbor; Jean Dunand; D.I.M.; Sue et Mare; Jourdain; and Ruhlmann.

There are also photographs illustrating house interiors and shop display windows (mostly art deco/art moderne style); and several portraits of celebrities.

Arranged: In five series. 1) Oversize material. 2) Phonograph records. 3) Notebooks. 4) A scrapbook. 5) Memorabilia, articles, correspondence, and photographs. Then alphabetically by subject.

Captioned: No.

Finding Aid: An item-level index arranged by subject heading which lists box and folder numbers.

Restrictions: No.

DL

Division of Domestic Life

Division of Domestic Life
National Museum of American History
Smithsonian Institution
Washington, D.C. 20560
Ann Serio, Museum Specialist
(202) 357-2308
Hours: Monday–Friday, 10 a.m.–4 p.m.

Scope of the Collections

There are nine photographic collections with approximately 14,000 images in the Division of Domestic Life.

Focus of the Collections

These photographs are used primarily as research material to document daily life in the American home between the 17th century and the present. The images are of the division's exhibitions and accessioned household objects, such as, bibelots; cookware; furniture; heating devices; household furnishings; lighting devices; metalware; silverware; toys; and woodenware.

Photographic Processes and Formats Represented

Photographic holdings include standard 20th century slide, photoprint, and photonegative processes.

Other Materials Represented

These collections include a few examples of floor plans, graphic prints, household artifacts, related items on paper, as well as scrapbooks.

Access and Usage Policies

These collections are open to researchers. Due to space limitations, the Division of Domestic Life requests that all researchers write for an appointment one month in advance. Finding aids exist to some collections within this division.

Photographic copies are available from OPPS at the prevailing rate. There is a charge for bulk xerographic orders.

Publication Policies

In addition to obtaining permission from the Smithsonian Institution to reproduce a photograph, researchers may have to obtain permission from the copyright holder. The Smithsonian Institution is not necessarily the copyright holder. The preferred credit line will vary, but will always include at least the following: "Courtesy of the National Museum of American History, the Smithsonian Institution, Division of Domestic Life, [Collection Name]." It may also include a collection or donor statement. Please check with the division prior to publication.

DL·1

American Domestic Interiors Pictorial Collection

Dates of Photographs: 20th Century

Collection Origins

This collection was assembled by the division staff and includes a variety of photographs produced for and collected by the division. Many are photographic reproductions of fine arts objects, such as, oil paintings and prints.

Physical Description

There are 400 photographs, including color dye coupler slides and silver gelatin photoprints. Many photographs are copy or duplicate photoprints. Other materials include data sheets and xerographic copies.

Subjects

The photographs reproduce interiors of American homes as they are shown in paintings, photographs (more rarely), and prints.

The images also document architecture, decorative and functional interior accessories, furniture, and interior design. Some images include portraits of unidentified individuals.

Arranged: Into four series. 1) Alphabetically by artist or title. 2) Alphabetically by original picture owner. 3) Works by anonymous artists arranged by subject matter. 4) Chronologically.

Captioned: No.

Finding Aid: 1) An authority file of the artists represented in the collection lists the artist's name and dates; title of his or her pictures; and the subject categories in which the artist's work appears. 2) A bibliography (on catalog cards) of copied illustration sources lists the title of the book, author, publisher, date, and city of publication. 3) "View of Interiors" data sheets which include artist; title; medium; date; owner; people depicted; geographic location; room depicted; sitter with furniture only; chair (painted, unpainted, upholstered); table (cov-

ered, uncovered, painted, unpainted); and other accessories. 4) A subject authority file in card catalog format lists the subject headings used in these files.

Restrictions: For reference only. No duplication allowed.

DL·2

American Domestic Life Photographic Collection

Dates of Photographs: Circa 1950–Present

Collection Origins

This collection was assembled by division staff to document several division exhibits and to serve as a source of appropriate images for potential future exhibits. The photographs were created by division staff, OPPS, and outside sources.

Physical Description

There are 3,000 photographs, including color dye coupler photonegatives and slides; and silver gelatin photonegatives and photoprints. The photoprints are housed in 21 albums.

Subjects

The photographs document division exhibits and topics of interest for potential future exhibits. Among the exhibits documented are "After the Revolution: Life in America 1790–1800"; "Everyday Life in Early America"; and "The Growth of the United States."

Other research topics illustrated include architecture (primarily exteriors and interiors of historic houses, such as, the Cowing House, Hart House, and Hovey House); diet; drink; expositions; furniture makers; historic interior design (period rooms); law and the courts; living standards; money; recreation; status as shown in material culture; and warfare.

Arranged: Into six series based on exhibition or component name. 1) Growth of the United States,

20 albums. 2) "Everyday Life in Early America," one album. 3) "Everyday Life in the American Past," two albums. 4) Components including: a) Cowing House, one album, b) Hart House, one album, c) Hovey House, d) Various period rooms, two albums. 5) "After the Revolution: Life in America 1790–1800," 25 albums. 6) Temporary Exhibits, one album.

Captioned: No.

Finding Aid: No.

Restrictions: No.

DL·3

Division of Domestic Life Object Photograph Collection

Dates of Photographs: Circa 1950s–Present

Collection Origins

These photographs were assembled by division staff from OPPS-produced images to document division collections. The folk art photographs included were copied from images in the Van Alstyne American Folk Art Collection.

The object photographs are used primarily by the staff for administrative and research purposes, and by researchers seeking photographs of objects in the division's collection.

Physical Description

There are 4,500 photographs, including color dye coupler slides and silver gelatin photoprints in albums.

Subjects

The photographs document the division's American and Anglo-American artifacts dating from the 17th through the 20th centuries. The artifacts illustrated are domestic furniture and furnishings, including kitchenware, lighting devices, smoking equipment, and toys.

There are photographs of advertisements, architecture, dolls, folk art objects, furniture, heating devices, lighting devices, metalware, paintings, and toys.

Arranged: By subject heading.

Captioned: With the appropriate subject heading; object name; negative number; catalog number; a brief description; source; division name; photographer; and date photographed.

Finding Aid: A master authority file of terms, used for the majority of this collection.

Restrictions: No.

DL·4

Division of Domestic Life Record Photographs

Dates of Photographs: 1970s–Present

Collection Origins

In the 1970s the Divison of Domestic Life staff began to photograph each artifact within division holdings as part of the artifact cataloging process. These photographs were taken by division staff and printed by OPPS. They are interfiled with 4,000 catalog cards which describe the artifacts. Most of the photographs date from the 1970s, when the staff first began taking record shots.

Physical Description

There are 2,500 photographs, including silver gelatin photonegatives and photoprints. Other materials include 4,000 catalog cards.

Subjects

The photographs document division accessions, including furnishings and house accessories (metal or wood); and objects associated with childhood. Most of the objects in this division are from the North American continent, or from England, Ireland, Scotland, and Wales.

Objects illustrated include beds, chairs, cleaning equipment, dollhouses, drinking and eating utensils, floor coverings, folk art games, heating devices, lighting accessories, metalware (gold, iron, pewter, and silver), smoking devices, tables, and toys.

Arranged: By series. 1) Actual cultural history card/photoprint file, arranged by object catalog number. 2) Matching file of photonegatives arranged by division negative numbers.

Captioned: No.

Finding Aid: Other division collections, such as, the Division of Domestic Life Object Photograph Collection and the American Domestic Life Photograph Collection can serve as subject indexes to this collection. They are arranged by subject heading and include the object catalog number.

Restrictions: No.

DL·5

Division of Domestic Life Vertical Files

Dates of Photographs: 19th and 20th Centuries

Collection Origins

This collection was assembled by division staff from diverse sources. Division scholars use it as a reference collection.

Physical Description

There are 1,500 photographs, including albumen photoprints and stereographs (1%), and silver gelatin photonegatives and photoprints (99%). Other materials include advertisements, articles, clippings, donor-related correspondence, notes, pamphlets, published illustrations, and reports.

Subjects

The photographs document architecture, dolls, folk art, furniture, heating devices, lighting devices, museum installations, and silver artifacts. Most images

document objects from North America. Most images are photographic reproductions of works in other media.

Arranged: By subject heading.

Captioned: No.

Finding Aid: No.

Restrictions: No.

DL·6

Edgerton House Collection

Dates of Photographs: 1916 and 1963

Collection Origins

The Brewster family assembled this collection to document the construction, design, and furnishings of their house "Edgerton."

Mr. and Mrs. Frederick F. [Osler] Brewster, of New Haven, Connecticut, had the house built in 1908. The architect was Henri Stephenson, of the firm of Stephenson and Wheeler of New York City. The house was furnished by W. and J. Sloane of New York City. The house was demolished in 1964. The grounds were given to New Haven as a park.

The collection was donated to the division for research purposes. It is used by both museum staff and outside researchers.

Physical Description

There are 110 silver gelatin photographs in two albums.

Subjects

The photographs document the exterior and interior architecture, the furnishings, and the grounds of a Jacobean Revival style house. The house, called "Edgerton," was built in 1908 in New Haven, Connecticut. It was designed by architect Henri Stephenson.

Arranged: Into two series. 1) Grounds and buildings. 2) Interiors and exteriors.

Captioned: No.

Finding Aid: No.

Restrictions: No.

DL·7

Harral-Wheeler House Collection

Dates of Photographs: 1840s–1957

Collection Origins

This collection was assembled by the Harral and Wheeler families of Bridgeport, Connecticut, to document themselves and a family house. The house was razed in 1957.

The collection was later donated to the division for use by staff and outside researchers.

Physical Description

There are 60 silver gelatin photoprints.

Subjects

The photographs document the exterior and interior architecture, the furnishings, the grounds, and the outbuildings of a Gothic revival style house called the Harral-Wheeler House in Bridgeport, Connecticut; and members of the Harral and Wheeler families.

Arranged: Into series. 1) Photographs of the house, outbuildings, and grounds. 2) Photographs of family members.

Captioned: With unidentified numbers.

Finding Aid: No.

Restrictions: No.

DL·8

Otis Family Scrapbooks

Dates of Photographs: 1904–1909, 1911–1929

Collection Origins

These scrapbooks were assembled by members of the Otis family of Winnetka, Illinois, to document the architecture, family, and professional activities of architect William A. Otis.

Physical Description

There are 150 silver gelatin photoprints in 9 scrapbooks. Other materials include articles, clippings, correspondence, pamphlets, postcards, and theatre programs.

Subjects

These photographs document the community of Winnetka, Illinois, in the early 20th century, with particular emphasis on local architecture, and the William A. Otis family.

Architecture in the midwestern United States during the early 20th century is also documented.

Arranged: Chronologically.

Captioned: No.

Finding Aid: No.

Restrictions: No.

DL·9

Harry T. Peters' *America on Stone* Lithography Collection

Dates of Photographs: 1960–1980

Collection Origins

Harry T. Peters was a collector and researcher who published three major works on American lithographs. Peters's collection of 1,700 lithographs formed the basis of his book, *America on Stone*. New York: Arno Press, 1931. The lithographs were given to the division by Peters's family after his death.

These photographic reproductions of the Peters lithographs were taken by OPPS at the request of the division.

Physical Description

There are 1,725 photographs, including color dye coupler slides and silver gelatin photoprints in 29 albums. The prints and slides are of the same views.

Subjects

Images are individual views of American lithographs which appear in the book *America on Stone* by Harry T. Peters.

Arranged: By catalog number of the lithograph in groupings and by subject headings.

Captioned: No.

Finding Aid: 1) Card catalog arranged by catalog number with a description of each lithograph. 2) Maker's index, listing each print by artist, lithographer, and/or lithography firm; publishers; and printer. 3) Subject index, divided into 36 major categories, such as, advertising, architecture, and flowers.

Restrictions: No.

EL

Division of Electricity and Modern Physics

Division of Electricity and Modern Physics
National Museum of American History
Smithsonian Institution
Washington, D.C. 20560
Elliott N. Sivowitch, Museum Specialist
(202) 357-1840
Hours: Monday–Friday, 10 a.m.–4 p.m.

Scope of the Collections

There are 11 photographic collections with approximately 8,700 images in the Division of Electricity and Modern Physics.

Focus of the Collections

These photographs are used primarily as research material to document the history of electric generators; electric meters; electric motors; electrostatics; physics, from 1900 to the present; radio; telegraphy; telephony; and television. The collections are particularly rich in materials on the history of the laying of the Atlantic communications cable, particle accelerators and detectors, and radios.

Photographic Processes and Formats Represented

Division collections contain standard 20th century slide, photoprint, and photonegative processes including silver gelatin photonegatives and photoprints.

Other Materials Represented

This division also collects electrical apparatus, as well as, biographies; blueprints; broadsides; cartoons; catalogs; charts; clippings; correspondence; exhibition scripts; graphic prints; legal documents; ledgers; manuals; manuscripts; maps; motion picture film footage; museum analytic studies of specimens; notebooks; pamphlets; patents; portraits; published volumes; reprints, scientific papers; shipping papers; sketches; and work books.

Access and Usage Policies

These collections are open to the public by appointment only. Interested researchers are urged to indicate their specific research topic in their letter of inquiry. There are finding aids to several collections in this division. Photocopies of images can be sent to researchers who are unable to visit the Smithsonian Institution. Restricted materials within the division may not be reproduced.

Publication Policies

In addition to obtaining permission from the Smithsonian Institution to reproduce a photograph, researchers may have to obtain permission from the copyright holder. The Smithsonian Institution is not necessarily the copyright holder. The preferred credit line for photographs within this division is: "Courtesy of the Division of Electricity and Modern Physics, National Museum of American History, Smithsonian Institution."

EL·1

Ralph R. Batcher Papers

Dates of Photographs: 1923–1966

Collection Origins

This collection is scheduled to be transferred to the Archives Center, National Museum of American History, in the near future. The collection could not be surveyed due to asbestos contamination. The Batcher Papers are presently stored at the Silver Hill Facility, Building 17, Suitland, Maryland.

EL·2

Biographical Information Files

Dates of Photographs: 1860s–Present

Collection Origins

This collection was assembled by the division staff during the last thirty years to document major figures in the field of electrical science and technology. Many of the photographs were created by OPPS.

Some of the photographs in this collection were used in the National Museum of American History exhibitions "Person-to-Person" and "Edison: Lighting a Revolution."

Physical Description

There are 315 photographs, including color dye coupler photoprints and slides, and silver gelatin photoprints. Other materials include biographies; blueprints; clippings; patents; reprints; and xerographic copies.

Subjects

This collection consists of portraits of prominent engineers, inventors, scientists, and theoreticians in the fields of electrical science and technology, radio, telegraphy, television, and wireless communication.

Some of the individuals shown are Alexander Graham Bell; Thomas Edison; Michael Faraday; Moses Farmer; John Ambrose Fleming; W.S. Gifford; Guglielmo Marconi; Samuel F.B. Morse; Elihu Thomson; and Thomas Watson.

Arranged: Alphabetically by the last name of the inventor or scientist.

Captioned: With the name of the individual, date, and negative number.

Finding Aid: 1) A June 1974 inventory which lists the negative number(s). 2) A division card catalog (3″ × 5″ cards) that lists the subject's name, the negative number of the item, and, on occasion, the source of the image. The card catalog is arranged in three sections: a) by the name of the inventor or individual shown; b) by the negative number of the image; and c) by the field of scientific study, such as, electrostatics or electromagnetism.

Restrictions: No.

EL·3

Electrical Communications Files

Dates of Photographs: 1920s–1974

Collection Origins

This collection was assembled by Curator Bernard Finn as part of his working papers on electrical communication technology; and to document exhibits in which he has been involved or interested.

Photographers represented include Ian Rowan.

Physical Description

There are 2,570 photographs, including color dye coupler slides; and silver gelatin photonegatives, photoprints, and slides. Most (75%) of the images are slides. Other materials include clippings, drawings, maps, reprints, and xerographic copies of notes.

Subjects

These photographs document worldwide developments in electrical communications technology during the last 150 years.

The photographs are of electrical equipment (including their inventors and manufacturers); exhibits related to electrical communications; the laying of various undersea communications cables (such as, the Atlantic Cable and the Canadian Cable); submarine telegraphy developments; and telephone and telegraph communications developments since the 1850s.

Arranged: No.

Captioned: With the date; name of any equipment; names of people; occasion; negative number; and often, the geographic locale.

Finding Aid: No.

Restrictions: No access.

EL·4

Exhibition Research and Reference Photograph Files

Dates of Photographs: 1900s–Present

Collection Origins

This collection was assembled by division staff as both reference material for exhibits, and as documentation of exhibits between the 1950s and the present.

The collection contains materials donated or copied from outside sources, such as, the American Telephone and Telegraph Corporation; the Library of Congress; the National Archives; World Wide Photos; and various individuals in West Orange, New Jersey (circa 1976), for the exhibits "Person-to-Person" and "Edison: Lighting a Revolution."

Physical Description

There are 400 photographs, including a silver gelatin photonegative and photoprints. Most photo-

prints are copy prints mounted on bond paper. Other materials include cartoons, drawings, patents, and prints (graphic).

Subjects

The photographs document the exhibits on electrical devices and electricity held at the Arts and Industries Building and the National Museum of American History. These (Smithsonian) exhibits centered on Thomas Edison and lighting breakthroughs, telephone communications devices, and related developments.

Specific artifacts or artifact-related sites shown include advertisements for telephones; field telephones; inventions; laboratories; telephone directories; telephone wires; toll boards; United States Army portable telegraphy equipment; and various telephone and telegraph companies.

Among the people illustrated are aerial linemen; Alexander Graham Bell (at the New York end of the circuit to Chicago in 1892); Thomas A. Edison; and unidentified telegraph operators.

Among the activities or events shown are the Arts and Industries Building telephone installations; the first telephone call from New York to Paris; line disasters; switchboards in operation; telephone plant construction; and telephone usage.

Arranged: There are eight series of photographs. 1) From the Library of Congress for the NMAH exhibition, "Person-to-Person," 1976. 2) From the National Archives, also for "Person-to-Person." 3–5) Thomas Edison-related photographs. 6) From American Telephone and Telegraph Corporation. 7) Arts and Industries Building electrical exhibitions photographs. 8) Miscellaneous electrical exhibits at NMAH.

Captioned: With names of individuals shown, source, date of the photograph, and a negative number.

Finding Aid: There is a brief inventory of series 1, 2, and 6. Series 3, 4, 5, 7, and 8 have each been summarized in one or two paragraphs.

Restrictions: Some for reference only. No duplication allowed.

EL·5

History of Electrical Science and Technology Collection

Dates of Photographs: Circa 1862–Present

Collection Origins

This collection was assembled by the division staff from a variety of donations, exchanges, and purchases to document electrical power and its applications.

Photographic studios represented include the Edison Lamp Works; Franklin Institute; General Electric Company; J.W. Swan's Electric Lamp Company; Elihu Thomson; Union Iron Works in San Francisco, California; and many other sources.

Some of the photographs in this collection were used in the National Museum of American History exhibitions "Person-to-Person" and "Edison: Lighting a Revolution."

Physical Description

There are 175 silver gelatin photonegatives and photoprints. Some are copies or duplicates. Other materials include blueprints, broadsides, catalogs, clippings, correspondence, exhibit scripts, manuals, manuscript documents, notes, notebooks, pamphlets, patents, published volumes, reprints, and reports.

Subjects

These photographs document electrical power and its applications in the fields of communications, power, power/lighting, and science.

There are photographs of: alarm systems, communications satellites, electron probe microanalysers, electronic testing apparatus, home appliances, motors and generators, power equipment, power projects, radios, radio astronomy, sound spectrography, telegraphy, the telephone centennial, television, thermoelectricity measuring instruments, and wireless equipment.

Arranged: By subject heading (see above). Some subject headings are further modified by the type of material.

Captioned: With a brief subject description, individual's name, and the date of the photograph. Some also have a negative number.

Finding Aid: An item-level inventory which lists the subject heading category for each box, type of material included, box number, and a date and brief description of each item in the box.

Restrictions: No.

EL·6

Modern Physics Research and Reference Files

Dates of Photographs: 1930s–Present

Collection Origins

This collection was assembled by Modern Physics Curator Dr. Paul Forman as documentation of his acquisitions and museum exhibitions. The collection also serves as a personal research file on atomic clocks, atom smashers, Albert Einstein, and the lives of other physicists and historians of science.

This collection contains official Smithsonian Institution records as well as personal research materials.

Physical Description

There are 1,800 photographs, including color dye coupler photoprints and slides, and silver gelatin photonegatives and photoprints. Most (75%) of the photographs are silver gelatin photoprints. Other materials include articles; biographies, clippings; correspondence; donor records; exhibit documentation; manuals; notes; records on possible future accessions; reprints; scientific papers; shipping papers; and xerographic copies of photographs.

Subjects

The collection documents the division's physics exhibits and object collections.

There are photographs of the Alvarez proton linac; atomic clocks; the Berkeley 27″ cyclotron;

the Betatron; the Brookhaven cosmotron; bubble chambers; detector systems; the Fermi Lab 5F synchrotron; ion counters; the McMillan synchrotron; Pound snider red shift apparatus; roentgen gun x-ray; the Stanford electron linac; and complete x-ray spectrometers.

People illustrated in the collection include Albert Einstein and C.W. Van de Graaff.

Arranged: There are eight major series. 1) Physicists' biographies. 2) Einstein exhibit and research files. 3) General science research laboratories. 4) Biographies of historians of science. 5) General topical files on physics and Division of Electricity and Modern Physics acquisitions. 6) Files on the "Atom Smashers Exhibition." 7) Files on the "Atomic Clocks Exhibition." 8) Files on the "Hall of Nuclear Energy" at the National Museum of American History. The exhibit files usually follow the topical arrangement of the exhibit script, and other files are arranged by subject heading.

Captioned: With the date, individual shown, negative number, and location and source of the image.

Finding Aid: No.

Restrictions: No.

EL·7

Mounted Photographic Reference File

Dates of Photographs: 1950s—Present

Collection Origins

This collection was assembled by division staff from diverse sources for research purposes during the last thirty years. Most of the photographs in the collection were either donations or were created by OPPS.

Some of the photographs in this collection were used in the National Museum of American History exhibitions "Person-to-Person" and "Edison: Lighting a Revolution."

Physical Description

There are 2,000 original and duplicate silver gelatin photoprints (some mounted on boards). Other materials include clippings (of graphics), drawings, and patents.

Subjects

The photographs document the history of science and technology in the United States. There are photographs of lighting and communications uses of electricity in the 19th and 20th centuries, such as, in electric motors, generators, meters, radio, telegraph, telephone, and television. There are also photographs of dynamos, electron microscopes, fuel cells, fuses, lamps, lasers, magnets, masers, microphones, phonographs, photophones, radar, traffic signals, and welding apparatus.

Arranged: By series. 1) Original photographs arranged alphabetically by subject heading. 2) Duplicate unmounted prints filed by negative number.

Captioned: With negative number, date, subject information, and occasionally, the image source.

Finding Aid: A division card catalog which lists the subject, the negative number, and on occasion the source of the image. These cards are filed by 1) last name of the individual shown; 2) negative number of the image; and 3) type of item shown.

Restrictions: No.

EL·8

Pamphlet File

Dates of Photographs: 1930—Present

Collection Origins

This collection was assembled by division staff over the last 40 years from donations, exchanges, and purchases. The collection documents the history of electricity and modern electrical science and manufacturing, particularly in the United States between 1850 and the present.

Physical Description

There are 260 silver gelatin photoprints. Other materials include clippings, pamphlets, reprints, and xerographic copies.

Subjects

The photographs document the history of electricity and modern electrical science and manufacturing, particularly in the United States between 1850 and the present.

Included in this collection are images of inventors who worked on the creation of electrical products, such as, George Barker, W.S. Burroughs, and A.M. Compton; and early corporations, such as, the American Institute of Physics, Bell Telephone, and Hazeltime Service Corporation. There are also photographs of objects, such as, chaff, computers, fluoroscopes, fuel cells, and refrigerator parts.

Arranged: In two series. 1) Materials that deal with major manufacturers of electrical equipment and the inventors who worked for them (arranged by corporation, and thereunder by personal name). 2) Topics and products related to electricity (arranged alphabetically by subject heading).

Captioned: With the date of the photograph; the names of individuals shown; a brief subject description; the name of any firms illustrated; and on occasion, a negative number.

Finding Aid: No.

Restrictions: No.

EL·9

Transformer History Collection

Dates of Photographs: Circa 1870s–1900, 1935–1959

Collection Origins

This collection was assembled by division staff over the last 30 years to document the origins and history of transformer development, primarily in the United States.

Most of the photographs in the collection were either donations or were created by OPPS.

Physical Description

There are 30 photographs, including albumen photoprints and silver gelatin photoprints. Other materials include articles, clippings, patents, and reports.

Subjects

The photographs document apparatus used in the construction of transformers; as well as experimental transformers, transformers, and transformer patent models created or operated between 1856 and 1900, and 1935 and 1959.

Arranged: By type of material into three series. 1) Patents, 1884–1889. 2) Photographs. 3) Articles, reports, and clippings.

Captioned: With negative number, name of the item shown, and, on occasion, the inventor.

Finding Aid: A division card catalog which lists the name of the item or individual shown; the negative number; and, on occasion, the source of the image. The card catalog is arranged by 1) the last name of the individual shown; 2) the negative number of the image; and 3) the type of item shown.

Restrictions: No.

EL·10

Commander Paul G. Watson Collection

Dates of Photographs: Circa 1925–1970

Collection Origins

Commander Paul G. Watson, USNR Retired, donated several hundred radio tubes and this photograph collection to the Smithsonian Institution.

Physical Description

There are 70 photographs, including silver gelatin photonegatives and photoprints. Other materials include books, clippings, manuals, and reprints.

Subjects

This collection documents the early days of radio and radio technology from 1925 to 1970. There are photographs of inventors, naval radio stations, radio station personnel (including sound engineers), and radio tubes.

Arranged: By type of material into four series. 1) Books. 2) Manuals. 3) Photoprints. 4) Photonegatives.

Captioned: With a brief description of the type of radio tube shown, individual's name, and date of the photograph.

Finding Aid: There is a two-paragraph description of the collection which lists the types of material included, and subject matter and sizes of the photographs in the collection.

Restrictions: No.

EL·11

Western Union International Collection

Dates of Photographs: 1866–1961

Collection Origins

This collection contains materials documenting the origin and development of the International Division of the Western Union Telegraph Company in the 1940s.

The collection was donated to the Smithsonian Institution in 1979 by Western Union International.

Physical Description

There are 1,100 images, including silver gelatin photonegatives and photoprints. Other materials include blueprints; charts; ledgers; legal documents

regarding contracts; maps; publications; silver gelatin positive print motion picture footage (approximately 2,000 feet); and work books.

Subjects

The photographs document the development and operation of the International Division of the Western Union Telegraph Company in Battery Park, New York, in the 1940s. Most of the photographs show the laying of underwater cable at different cable stations and various Western Union office buildings worldwide.

There are also photographs of cable-laying ships; canteens; station equipment; telephone rooms; and Western Union personnel.

Arranged: No.

Captioned: With subject and date information.

Finding Aid: A preliminary inventory, taken in February 1982 by Robert Harding, Archivist, Archives Center, Smithsonian Institution, lists box and folder numbers, subjects, dates, and types of materials.

Restrictions: No.

EI

Division of Engineering and Industry

Division of Engineering and Industry
National Museum of American History
Smithsonian Institution
Washington, D.C. 20560
William Worthington, Museum Specialist
(202) 357-2058, 357-2379, 357-3188, 357-2228
Hours: Monday–Friday, 10 a.m.–4 p.m.

Scope of the Collections

There are 154 photographic collections with approximately 160,000 images in the Division of Engineering and Industry.

Focus of the Collections

These photographs document civil and production engineering, heavy machinery, industrial archaeology, and mechanisms. The collections primarily emphasize the North American continent. A further breakdown mirroring the internal structure of the division follows.

The section on heavy machinery includes: 1) power machinery utilizing internal-combustion power (diesel engines, gas, gasoline engines, oil, and turbines), muscle power, steam power (engines and turbines), water power (dams, pressure engines, turbines, and water wheels), wave and tidal power, wind power, and miscellaneous power equipment; 2) air compressing, blowing, and pumping equipment; 3) refrigeration equipment (ice harvesting, mechanical cooling, and natural cooling); and 4) construction machinery for earth moving, excavating, fastening, hoisting, materials handling, and mixing concrete.

The section on civil engineering includes: 1) construction machines, materials, and methods; 2) materials testing; 3) materials production; 4) building and structural mechanical equipment for air conditioning, elevators, escalators, heating, plumbing, and ventilating; 5) aqueducts, bridges, viaducts, and other spanning system construction and equipment; 6) structural engineering; 7) tunnels; 8) waterway engineering including canals, harbor, and river improvements; 9) dam construction and equipment; 10) railroad and highway engineering and construction; 11) water supply engineering and equipment; 12) materials handling and storage; and 13) construction and engineering of miscellaneous structures, such as, chimneys, tanks, and towers.

The production engineering section includes: 1) machinery for precision linear measurement; 2) manufacturing processes and machinery for metal, wood, and other materials and mass production; 3) related processes and equipment; 4) production-efficiency methods; and 5) other industrial processes.

The mechanisms section includes: 1) timekeeping devices; 2) office machines, methods, and systems exclusive of mathematical machines, such as, computers; 3) mechanical security services, such as, locks, safes, and vaults; 4) automata; and 5) mechanical sound recordings.

The industrial archeology section includes: 1) recording; 2) preservation; 3) interpretation; and 4) adaptive reuse documentation.

Photographic Processes and Formats Represented

In addition to standard 20th century slide, photoprint, and photonegative processes, there are also early photographic processes, such as, albumen photoprints (stereograph and carte-de-visite formats); an ambrotype; color screen plate phototransparencies (stereographic autochromes); collodion wet plate lantern slides and photonegatives; cyanotypes; platinum photoprints; and salted paper photoprints.

Other Materials Represented

This division also collects library and archival materials, such as, advertisements; biographical material; blueprints; clippings; diagrams; diaries; drawings; early engineering journals; engravings; etchings; manuscripts; obituaries; photogravures; photomechanical reproductions; posters; price lists; professional papers; published works; reprints; trade literature; and xerographic copies.

Also included are: business records; catalogs; charts; conservation information; contracts; correspondence; cross sections of engines; design competition submissions; engineering designs; field notes; graphs; inventories; lecture notes; legal documents; letterbooks; letterpress books; maintenance pamphlets; maps; memorandums; motion picture footage; notebooks; order books; patents; patent office reports; plans; postcards (photomechanical illustrations); questionnaires; reel-to-reel audio tape; reports; requests for employment; sales information; scripts; service and operators' manuals; stressometer readings; test reports; theses; tracings; work requests; and worksheets for engine orders.

The division collects objects relating to the fields of mechanical and civil engineering and mechanisms, such as, automata; clocks; control devices; equipment; instruments; keys; locks; machine tools; machines; materials; phonographs; robots; samples; typewriters; and watches.

Access and Usage Policies

These collections are open to the public for research. Several collections have partial finding aids. Certain materials may be restricted due to copyright status or preservation conditions. Xerographic copies will be made at no charge. The charge for photographic copies of unrestricted prints is dependent on the prevailing rates of OPPS. Please contact the Division of Engineering and Industry for further information.

Publication Policies

In addition to obtaining permission from the Smithsonian Institution to reproduce a photograph, researchers may have to obtain permission from the copyright holder. The Smithsonian Institution is not necessarily the copyright holder. The preferred credit line is: "National Museum of American History, Smithsonian Institution."

Note: The "Focus of the Collection" portion of this Introduction is courtesy of Robert Vogel, former division curator.

EI·1

Alaskan Railroad and Bridge Construction Collection

Dates of Photographs: 1909–1910

Collection Origins

This collection was assembled by Carl Pollock, a civil engineer involved in early Alaskan railroad construction. His job was to evaluate the condition of public utilities, such as, power distribution systems and power plants.

This collection was given to the Smithsonian Institution in 1966.

Physical Description

There are 80 photographs, including cyanotypes and silver gelatin photoprints dry mounted on white card stock. These photographs are included in a booklet of blueprints titled "Cooper River Bridge near Flag Point. Engineer's Report 1910."

Subjects

The photographs document early Alaskan railroad construction (1909–1910), and the condition of Alaskan public utilities. There are photographs of construction camps near Cordova; Cooper River Bridge; Flag Point; Hot Cake Channel Bridge; and Miles Glacier Bridge in Alaska.

Arranged: No.

Captioned: No.

Finding Aid: No.

Restrictions: No.

EI·2

American Hydraulic Laboratories Collection

Dates of Photographs: Circa 1937

Collection Origins

Professor Leslie J. Hooper assembled this volume in 1937 to document the 50 principal hydraulic laboratories in Canada and the United States for Worcester Polytechnic in Worcester, Massachusetts. Hooper was an engineer for Worcester Polytechnic at the time.

This collection was given to the Smithsonian Institution in 1977.

Physical Description

There are 50 silver gelatin photoprints within one large volume of reports.

Subjects

The photographs document Canadian and U.S. hydraulic laboratories around 1937, including Byron Jackson Pump Company; the California Institute of Technology; Case School of Applied Science; Columbia University; Holyoke Water Wheel Testing Flume; Lowell Locks and Canals; the Massachusetts Institute of Technology; Newport News Shipbuilding and Dry Dock Company; Pelton Water Wheel Company; Princeton University; Purdue University; Rensselaer Polytechnic Institute; S. Morgan Smith Company; the Tennessee Valley Authority; the University of Minnesota; the University of Pennsylvania; and the University of Washington.

Arranged: Chronologically.

Captioned: No.

Finding Aid: No.

Restrictions: No.

EI·3

American Institute of Steel Collection

Dates of Photographs: Circa 1935–1945

Collection Origins

This collection was assembled by the American Institute of Steel (now known as the American Iron and Steel Institute) of Washington, D.C., to document civil engineering projects in the United States.

Physical Description

There are 1,200 silver gelatin photoprints mounted on loose scrapbook pages.

Subjects

The photographs document unidentified civil engineering projects in the United States, such as, buildings; continuous-truss bridges; stadiums; steel dams; and suspension bridges.

Arranged: No.

Captioned: No.

Finding Aid: No.

Restrictions: No.

EI·4

Amoskeag Manufacturing Company Collection

Dates of Photographs: 1850s–1967

Collection Origins

This collection was assembled by the New England Textile Mill Survey of 1967. Some of the images of the Amoskeag Millyard of Manchester, New Hampshire, were taken by the survey staff. Other collection materials were given to the Smithsonian in the 1890s.

The Amoskeag Millyard was the largest American textile mill to operate at one location. It discontinued operations in 1936.

Photographers and studios represented include George L. Durette, the Library of Congress, Randolph Longenbach, and Robert Vogel.

Physical Description

There are 900 photographs, including an albumen photoprint, and silver gelatin photonegatives and photoprints. Other materials include articles; documents; correspondence; drawings; engravings; historical literature; maps; notes; and trade literature.

Subjects

All images are of the Amoskeag Millyard in Manchester, New Hampshire, between the 1850s and 1967.

The photographs document the Amoskeag Millyard boiler house; carding and warping facilities; chemical laboratory; coal pockets; construction work; cotton houses; mechanics row; mill workers (carders, carpenters, spinners, weavers, and slashers); paper mills; power station; river dye houses; turbines; and wrought iron penstocks.

Arranged: By subject.

Captioned: With subject information.

Finding Aid: No.

Restrictions: No.

EI·5

James Arthur Collection

Dates of Photographs: 1926–1964

Collection Origins

This collection was assembled by New York University curators from materials gathered to document the clocks and watches owned by James Arthur (1842–1912).

Arthur ran a New York City patent model machine shop and collected clocks, sundials, and watches. He created and assembled some of the materials in the collection to document his artifactual collection. Of particular interest is a watch record book of sales by Ezekiel Jones which dates from 1822 to 1825.

The rest of the correspondence files, documents, manuscripts, and photographs were created by the New York University curators who inherited the object collection. These materials date from 1926 to 1964.

In 1964 the collection was dispersed, along with this archival documentation collection, among three organizations: the National Association of Watch and Clock Collectors' Museum; the Smithsonian's Division of Mechanisms at NMAH; and the Time Museum in Rockford, Illinois.

Physical Description

There are 700 silver gelatin photoprints. Other materials include advertisements; business records; catalogs; inventories; manuscripts; newspaper clippings; patents; publications; and reports.

Subjects

The photographs document timekeeping devices, such as, chronometers, clocks, sundials, and watches dating from the 19th to the 20th centuries.

Arranged: First by type of object, then chronologically by the date of the object.

Captioned: Many with the type of clock or watch, date of the item, New York University index number, and Smithsonian Institution catalog number.

Finding Aid: A card catalog to the objects arranged by the catalog number assigned by the Division of Mechanisms. The New York University index number is also listed. There is no separate index to the photographs.

Restrictions: No.

EI·6

Atlas Imperial Diesel Engine Company Records

Dates of Photographs: Circa 1925–1967

Collection Origins

This collection was assembled by Ralph Lorimar, son of the founder of the Atlas Imperial Diesel Engine Company of Oakland, California. Atlas manufactured marine engines and other machinery. Atlas was absorbed by the White Motor Company in the 1960s. This collection was given to the Smithsonian Institution at that time.

Physical Description

There are 150 silver gelatin photonegatives and photoprints. Other materials include advertisements; articles; correspondence; data; instruction books; proposals; and specifications.

Subjects

Most photographs document items produced by the Atlas Imperial Diesel Engine Company between 1925 and the 1960s, such as, diesel engines, diesel tractors, and engine parts. Other images are of boats and unidentified sales rooms.

Arranged: Into series by subject. 1) Atlas-Superior Diesels. 2) Atlas-Imperial solid-injection and other makers' diesel engines. 3) Ralph Lorimar materials. 4) Atlas-Imperial miscellaneous literature.

Captioned: No.

Finding Aid: No.

Restrictions: No.

EI·7

Anders K. Bak Papers

Dates of Photographs: 1923–1926

Collection Origins

This collection came from the Detroit Edison Company in Detroit, Michigan.

Physical Description

There are 15 silver gelatin photoprints mounted on blueprint paper. Other materials include blueprints, notes, reprints, and xerographic copies.

Subjects

The photographs show the inside of boilers in various stages of deterioration. Also shown are air nozzles, flues, and round burners. (Presumably, the equipment is that of the Detroit Edison Company.)

Arranged: No.

Captioned: No.

Finding Aid: No.

Restrictions: No.

EI·8

Baltimore & Ohio Railroad Collection

Dates of Photographs: Circa 1870–1980s

Collection Origins

This collection is composed of the Baltimore & Ohio Railroad company records. Photographers represented include Basil Mann.

Physical Description

There are 10,850 photographs, including collodion wet plate photonegatives; color dye coupler photoprints (including an oversized panorama); cyanotypes (in 3 albums); silver gelatin dry plate photonegatives; and silver gelatin photonegatives (on nitrate) and photoprints (in 3 albums). Other materials include architectural drawings, articles, clippings, correspondence, engineering drawings, financial reports, manuscripts, maps, patents, price lists, requests for employment, sketches, and statements of expenditures.

Subjects

The photographs document the Baltimore & Ohio Railroad equipment and facilities in the eastern and northeastern United States during 1826 to 1943, 1951, and the 1980s. The railroad facilities in Maryland and Pennsylvania are particularly well documented.

There are images of bridges; construction work; cranes; railroad stations; railroad yards and equipment; trackage; tunnels; viaducts; and most other aspects of railroad civil engineering. Also included are several Baltimore & Ohio repair shops (1910–1940).

There are also photographs of the activities and objects in several Baltimore & Ohio Railroad workshops, such as, boiler assembly; bolt-making; boring; erecting; fabrication; frog grinding; horizontal wood boring; locomotive assembly (1930s); locomotive wheel grinding; machine work (1917); an Osrund scoring machine; shop views (1923); and time clocks.

Arranged: A portion of the collection is arranged. 1) The three bound photograph albums are arranged by subject and are titled "Photographic Views of the Baltimore & Ohio Railroad and Its Branches, 1872"; "Baltimore & Ohio Views of Bridge and Buildings, Pittsburgh Division from Cumberland to Pittsburgh and Branches"; and "Baltimore & Ohio Bridge 74 over the Monogahela River at Glenwood (Pittsburgh), Pennsylvania: Replacement of Plan Trusses with Bowstring Trusses." 2) Loose prints of stations are organized alphabetically by location of railroad stations, or subject. 3) Glass negatives are arranged by original negative numbers.

Captioned: Some images with negative number, building, date, and location. Some negative envelopes with subject, date, and negative number.

Finding Aid: 1) An inventory list of all materials in this collection. 2) A finder's guide for the nitrate negatives organized by negative number. 3) An index to prints (dating from 1909 to 1919) arranged by negative number.

Restrictions: No.

EI·9

Greville Bathe Papers

Dates of Photographs: 1897–1967

Collection Origins

This collection was assembled by Greville Bathe, an engineer and historian from Philadelphia, Pennsylvania, to document 19th and 20th century mechanical engineering.

This collection documents machines and models of machines built by Bathe from 1897 to 1955. Some of the models are of much earlier machines.

The collection was given to the Smithsonian Institution in 1968.

Physical Description

There are 200 silver gelatin photoprints. All but 75 photoprints are mounted in an album. Many of the images are heavily retouched. Other materials include an album; correspondence; notebooks; notes for publications; and product catalogs of model makers and manufacturers.

Subjects

The photographs document machines and models built by Greville Bathe from 1897 to 1955, including a condensing steam engine; the Leonardo da Vinci Steam Gun; a Tom Thumb locomotive; and a twin screw boat engine.

Arranged: The album is arranged chronologically. The rest of the photoprints are unarranged.

Captioned: The album is labeled with subject information.

Finding Aid: Documented in the division's Archives Inventory File.

Restrictions: No.

EI·10

P.J. Bier Collection

Dates of Photographs: 1952

Collection Origins

This collection was assembled by Mr. P.J. Bier (1884–   ) who worked for the U.S. Bureau of Reclamation, Denver, Colorado, until his retirement in 1954. Photographers represented include Lukens.

Physical Description

There are 45 silver gelatin photoprints. Other materials include correspondence, personal papers, reprints, test reports, and travel reports.

Subjects

The photographs document Colorado dams and power stations and their elements in 1952. There are photographs of dam intakes; penstocks (including Boysen penstocks, Davis Dam penstocks, and Folsom penstocks); the New River siphon; and an underground power plant. There is also a photographic reproduction of a map which shows the location of power plants in Colorado.

Arranged: First by subject and then by type of material.

Captioned: With subject information.

Finding Aid: No.

Restrictions: No.

EI·11

Blanchard Gunstock Lathe Collection

Dates of Photographs: 1963

Collection Origins

L.C. Eichner constructed a replica of the Blanchard gunstock lathe. These photographs were taken to document that event.

Physical Description

There are 95 photographs, including color dye diffusion transfer photoprints (Polacolor) and silver gelatin photoprints.

Subjects

The photographs document the construction of a replica of the Blanchard gunstock lathe in 1963.

Arranged: No.

Captioned: No.

Finding Aid: No.

Restrictions: No.

EI·12

Wendel Bollman Collection

Dates of Photographs: Circa 1860–1980s

Collection Origins

This collection was assembled by division staff from diverse sources to document the history of Wendel Bollman (1814–1884) and his firms, W. Bollman and Company, and the Patapsco Bridge and Iron Works.

Wendall Bollman worked as a civil engineer in Baltimore, Maryland, from 1850 to 1884. He spe-

cialized in the design and construction of iron structures, especially bridges. Bollman designed the dome of the Baltimore City Hall, the Bollman Truss, several bridges in Chile, and iron bridges at Harpers Ferry. Note: Photographs of Bollman bridges are also in the Baltimore & Ohio Railroad Collection.

Photographers represented include Emory Kemp; Kilburn Littleton & Van Orsdell, Wilmington, North Carolina; and T.F. Parnell, Cumberland, Maryland.

These materials were published in Robert Vogel. *Engineering Contributions of Wendel Bollman.* Smithsonian Institution, 1965.

Physical Description

There are 500 photographs, including photostat negatives and silver gelatin photonegatives (some nitrate) and photoprints. Other materials include articles, correspondence, historical literature, maps, patents, reports, and specifications.

Subjects

The photographs document railroad and highway bridges built by W. Bollman and Company of Baltimore, Maryland, including bridges in Savage, Maryland; Wilmington, North Carolina; Bellaire, Ohio; Glencoe, Pennsylvania; and Harpers Ferry, West Virginia, among others.

Arranged: By construction project and then by type of material.

Captioned: With subject, photographer's name, and date.

Finding Aid: No.

Restrictions: No.

EI·13

Boston Elevated Photograph Album

Dates of Photographs: 1899–1901

Collection Origins

Unknown.

Physical Description

There are 70 photographs, including albumen photoprints and cyanotypes in an album.

Subjects

These photographs document the Boston Elevated railroad from 1899 through 1901, including bridge construction, equipment, and terminals.

Arranged: No.

Captioned: With subject and date.

Finding Aid: No.

Restrictions: No.

EI·14

Boston Waterworks Collection

Dates of Photographs: Early 20th Century

Collection Origins

Unknown.

Physical Description

There are 6,000 photographs, including collodion wet plate and silver gelatin dry plate photonegatives.

Subjects

These photographs document features of the Boston Waterworks, such as, aqueducts, dams, and reservoirs.

Arranged: By negative number.

Captioned: With subject, date, and negative number in gold lettering on the plate.

Finding Aid: No.

Restrictions: No.

EI·15

Uriah Boyden Collection

Dates of Photographs: 1828–1866

Collection Origins

This collection was assembled by an unknown individual to document the career of hydraulic engineer Uriah Atherton Boyden (1804–1879).

Boyden's engineering practice involved work with hydraulic turbines. When Boyden retired from active practice he turned to the study of physics and chemistry.

Physical Description

There are 12 photographs, including silver gelatin photonegatives and photoprints. Other materials include account books; clippings; correspondence; diaries; and handwritten notes on experiments.

Subjects

The photographs reproduce original drawings, patent applications, and sketches produced by Uriah Boyden. The original drawings, patents, and sketches are of canals; dynamometers; electromagnetism; gas heating devices; locks; mills; pneumatic glasses; sound waves; thermometry; and turbines.

Arranged: By type of material into the following series. 1) Handwritten notes. 2) Translations of articles. 3) Clippings. 4) Correspondence. 5) Account books. 6) Diaries. 7) Photographs (arranged by subject).

Captioned: No.

Finding Aid: No.

Restrictions: No.

EI·16

C.P. Bradway Machine Works Collection

Dates of Photographs: July–September 1965

Collection Origins

This collection was assembled by the Smithsonian Institution during an industrial archeology field survey at C.P. Bradway Machine Works in West Stafford, Connecticut, in 1965. Bradway was a former builder of water turbines.

Photographers represented include Robert Vogel and the survey contract photographers (unidentified).

Physical Description

There are 250 photographs, including color dye coupler photoprints and silver gelatin photonegatives and photoprints. Some of the photoprints are mounted in two albums. Other materials include catalogs, correspondence, drawings, field notes, miscellaneous notes, sketches, and xerographic copies.

Subjects

The photographs document the equipment, facilities, principals, products, and tools of the C.P. Bradway Machine Works of West Stafford, Connecticut. There are photographs of machine tools and turbine manufacturing activities. There are also images of the Bradway family and other New England turbine builders.

Arranged: No.

Captioned: With subject information.

Finding Aid: Each album has a contents list.

Restrictions: No.

EI·17

Breweries, Foundries, and Distilleries Miscellaneous Collection

Dates of Photographs: 1889–1910

Collection Origins

The Poole and Hunt photographs in this collection came to the division from the Baltimore Museum of Industry in January 1979.

Physical Description

There are 95 silver gelatin photoprints. Other materials include clippings, correspondence, notes, and xerographic copies.

Subjects

The photographs are of exteriors and interiors of breweries, distilleries, and foundries primarily in the United States between 1889 and 1910 including the American Breweries of Baltimore; the Bement Boring Mill; Hinkle Breweries; and Poole and Hunt.

There are photographs of equipment and facilities, including a drawbridge turntable; a gear shaper; gun barrels; an interior arsenal building with gun batteries; a rolling mill; screw machines; shaft coupling; steam hammers; transmission housing; and wheel lathes.

Arranged: No.

Captioned: No.

Finding Aid: No.

Restrictions: No.

EI·18

Brooklyn Bridge Exhibit Collection

Dates of Photographs: 1869–1970

Collection Origins

This collection was assembled by division staff from diverse sources for a Brooklyn Bridge Centennial Exhibition in 1983.

The Brooklyn Bridge, which spans the East River between Brooklyn and Manhattan, New York, was built between 1867 and 1883. It was designed and constructed by civil engineers John Augustus Roebling (1806–1869) and his eldest son, Washington Augustus Roebling (1837–1926). The Roeblings specialized in building suspension bridges and aqueducts.

Emily Roebling, Washington Roebling's wife, created the scrapbook in this collection. After her husband was confined to bed with "caisson disease" (the bends), Emily played an important role in the construction of the Brooklyn Bridge. She took over the correspondence; checked regularly on the work; delivered messages or requests to the engineers; kept records; and represented her husband at social functions.

Copy photoprints for this exhibition were made by OPPS.

Physical Description

There are 1,225 photographs, including silver gelatin photonegatives and photoprints. Other materials include bridge specifications, drawings, newspaper clippings, and Emily Roebling's scrapbook.

Subjects

The photographs document the construction of the Brooklyn Bridge and other structures built by John Augustus Roebling and his son, Washington Augustus Roebling. There are also portraits of the Roebling family.

Structures documented include the Boston Public Library; Brooklyn Bridge construction; the East River Bridge; the New York Public Library; the Niagara Falls Railroad Suspension Bridge; the Passaic Rolling Mill Company; Rensselaer Polytechnic Institute; Roebling chimney; the bridge over the Tehintchieu River in Bhutan; and the train bridge over the Potomac River.

Arranged: No.

Captioned: With subject information including location.

Finding Aid: No.

Restrictions: No.

EI·19

Brooklyn Edison Company Annual Reports Collection

Dates of Photographs: 1926–1935

Collection Origins

This collection of annual reports was assembled by an anonymous donor to document the Brooklyn Edison Company of New York. The collection was given to the division in 1976.

Physical Description

There are 60 silver gelatin photoprints mounted on fabric and bound into the two volumes of annual reports from 1926 to 1930 and from 1931 to 1935. Other materials include a book titled, *Generating Stations of the United Electric Light and Power Company, New York.*

Subjects

The photographs document electrical engineering projects of the Brooklyn Edison Company between 1926 and 1935, including installing and/or repairing air conditioners; boilers; generators; pumps; and turbines.

Arranged: In chronological order.

Captioned: With subject information, such as, location and type of machine.

Finding Aid: A list of this collection's materials exists in the division's Archives Inventory File.

Restrictions: No.

EI·20

F.P. Caruthers-Automatic Machine Controls Archival Collection

Dates of Photographs: 1960s

Collection Origins

This collection was assembled by F.P. "Phil" Caruthers to document an industrial machine controls convention in the 1960s.

Photographic studios represented include Actron Industries; Bendix Corporation; and Specialties, Inc., New York.

Physical Description

There are 120 photographs, including color dye coupler photoprints and silver gelatin photoprints. Other materials include correspondence, editorials, exhibit notes, operator manuals, parts manuals, presentations, publicity, and service manuals.

Subjects

The photographs document F.P. "Phil" Caruthers's industrial machine controls convention in the 1960s. There are photographs of exhibit booths, group photographs of an awards ceremony, guest speakers, machine parts, machinery, and tools.

Arranged: By convention exhibit.

Captioned: With subject information and then image number.

Finding Aid: No.

Restrictions: No.

EI·21

Cincinnati Milling Machine Company Collection

Dates of Photographs: 1966

Collection Origins

This collection was assembled by division staff to document the Cincinnati Milling Machine Company from the 1880s to the 1920s.

Physical Description

There are 85 photographs, including, color dye bleach photoprints (Cibachrome) and silver gelatin photoprints.

Subjects

The photographs document the physical plants and products of the Cincinnati Milling Machine Company from the 1880s to the 1920s, including grinder product displays, machine motors, milling machines, screw machines, and tap machines.

Arranged: No.

Captioned: Some with a number.

Finding Aid: No.

Restrictions: No.

EI·22

Connecticut River Bridge at Hartford Collection

Dates of Photographs: 1903–1905

Collection Origins

This collection was assembled by an unidentified individual to document the construction of the

Connecticut River Bridge at Hartford from 1903 to 1905. When it was dedicated in October 1908, the Connecticut River Bridge at Hartford was considered the largest stone arch bridge in the world.

This collection was purchased by the Smithsonian Institution in 1971.

Physical Description

There are 210 silver gelatin photoprints in a leather-bound album. Other materials include correspondence.

Subjects

The photographs document the construction of the Connecticut River Bridge at Hartford between 1903 and 1905. There is a group portrait of "Commissioners, Engineers, and Contractors at Laying Corner Stone, East Abutment, April 16, 1904."

There are also photographs of businesses, carriages, children playing, construction workers, houses, and street cars.

Arranged: Chronologically.

Captioned: On the album pages with location and date.

Finding Aid: No.

Restrictions: No.

EI·23

Cooper-Bessemer Collection

Dates of Photographs: 1910–1930

Collection Origins

This collection was assembled by division staff to document the Cooper-Bessemer Company of Mt. Vernon, Ohio, between 1910 and 1930.

Photographers and studios represented include Bells Studio, Casper, Wyoming; Connor Print, Grove City, Pennsylvania; Elvington Ardmore & Healton; Haynes Photo Co.; C.H. Ross, Shidler, Oklahoma; and Terry Engraving Co.

Physical Description

There are 6,000 photographs, including albumen photoprints; cyanotypes; silver gelatin dry plate lantern slides and photonegatives; and silver gelatin photonegatives (including one nitrate cirkut camera panorama) and photoprints (including eight panoramas). Some photoprints are mounted on linen. Other materials include cash books; company reports; motion picture film footage; and photomechanical reproductions.

Subjects

Most of the photographs are of train engines and other machinery made by Cooper-Bessemer shown in clients' production plants between 1910 and 1930. Clients whose facilities are shown include Lone Star Gas Company, Owens Bottle Company, and Sinclair.

There are also photographs of fishing boats; gas and oil production equipment; marine and stationary diesel engines; plant interiors; and power houses.

Arranged: By subject and type of material.

Captioned: Some; with subject and date.

Finding Aid: A 1953 finders' guide lists the photographs by negative number and gives the image sizes and subjects.

Restrictions: No.

EI·24

Coteau Bridge, Canada, Photograph Album Collection

Dates of Photographs: 1889 and 1911

Collection Origins

This collection came to the Smithsonian as part of the larger L.N. Edwards Collection which has been dispersed throughout the Institution.

Physical Description

There are 55 silver gelatin photoprints in an album.

Subjects

The photographs document the 1889 construction and the 1911 reconstruction of the Coteau Bridge in Canada, a multispan truss bridge.

Arranged: Chronologically.

Captioned: No.

Finding Aid: No.

Restrictions: No.

EI·25

Crown and Eagle Mill Collection

Dates of Photographs: Circa 1880–1975

Collection Origins

This collection was assembled by division staff to document a textile mill, the Crown and Eagle Mill, in North Uxbridge, Massachusetts, during the 1940s.

Photographers and studios represented include the Historic American Buildings Survey; Randolph Langenbach (photographer); and Thomas Paine, Weston, Massachusetts.

Physical Description

There are 115 photographs, including color dye coupler photoprints and silver gelatin photonegatives and photoprints. Other materials include bulletins; clippings; drawings; memoranda; newsletters; notes; schematics; and xerographic copies.

Subjects

The photographs document the Crown and Eagle Mill, a textile mill in North Uxbridge, Massachusetts, including exterior and interior shots of the

mill; the partial destruction of the mill by fire in 1975; and workers spinning and weaving cotton.

There are also photographs of Old Sturbridge Village and Whitin Mill in 1966.

Arranged: No.

Captioned: No.

Finding Aid: No.

Restrictions: No.

EI·26

Robert A. Cummings Collection

Dates of Photographs: 1892–1893, 1900–1939

Collection Origins

This collection was assembled by Robert A. Cummings (1866–1964), a civil engineer who worked in the field of reinforced concrete construction. Cummings began his career with the Norfolk & Western Railroad in 1890 as an assistant engineer. In 1903 he organized Cummings Structural Concrete Company and the Lehigh Valley Testing Laboratory. He worked primarily in Alabama; Washington, D.C. (Georgetown); New York; North Carolina; Ohio; Pennsylvania; and Virginia.

This collection was given to the Smithsonian in 1965.

Physical Description

There are 1,600 photographs, including silver gelatin dry plate photonegatives, silver gelatin photonegatives, and silver gelatin photoprints (900) mounted in 10 albums. Other materials include books, clippings, illustrations, and serial literature.

Subjects

The photographs document engineering projects, many of which were constructed of reinforced concrete, of Robert A. Cummings. There are photographs of barges; bridges; dams; drydocks; machinery; pilings; poles; project sites; ships; structural details of reinforced concrete construction; wharves; and workers in Alabama; New York; North Carolina; Ohio; Pennsylvania; Virginia; and Washington, D.C. (Georgetown).

Arranged: The albums are arranged chronologically by project.

Captioned: No.

Finding Aid: A list of materials in the division's Archives Inventory Files.

Restrictions: No.

EI·27

C.O. Dale Collection

Dates of Photographs: 1908–1920

Collection Origins

This collection was assembled by an anonymous donor to document the work of Chester O. Dale, a civil engineer. Dale was with the Braden Copper Company Hydraulic Power Development at Pangal, India, between 1908 and 1920.

Physical Description

There are 125 photographs, including cyanotypes and silver gelatin photoprints mounted in one album. Other materials include blueprints, correspondence, notes, and specifications.

Subjects

The photographs document the Braden Copper Company Hydraulic Power Development at Pangal, India, including diversion dams; exciters; main feeder excavations; penstocks; powerhouses; surge tanks; transformers; water turbines; and woodstave pipe lines.

Arranged: By subject, such as, type of equipment or facility shown.

Captioned: With location, date, and description.

Finding Aid: No.

Restrictions: No.

EI·28

De La Vergne Engine Company Collection

Dates of Photographs: 1926

Collection Origins

This collection was assembled by an anonymous donor to document the products of the De La Vergne Engine Company.

Physical Description

There are 30 silver gelatin photoprints mounted on linen. Other materials include blueprints and diagrams.

Subjects

All the photographs are of diesel engines built by the De La Vergne Engine Company around 1926.

Arranged: No.

Captioned: With engine type or model, location, and date.

Finding Aid: No.

Restrictions: No.

EI·29

William E. Dean Collection

Dates of Photographs: 1932–1950

Collection Origins

William E. Dean was a civil engineer involved in bridge construction in Florida from 1932 to 1950.

This collection was given to the Smithsonian Institution in 1967.

Physical Description

There are 40 photographs, including color dye coupler slides and silver gelatin photoprints. Other materials include articles, clippings, drawings, lecture notes, notes, pamphlets, specifications, and theses.

Subjects

The photographs document Florida bridge, causeway, and overpass civil engineering projects from 1932 to 1950, including the DuPont Bridge in Bay County; Mid-Bay-Grand Central Overpass in Tampa; Sebastian Inlet Bridge; Sunshine Skyway Bridge over Tampa Bay; and 36th Street Causeway to Miami Beach.

Arranged: No.

Captioned: With project dates and locations.

Finding Aid: A list of materials is in the division's Archives Inventory File.

Restrictions: No.

EI·30

Decorative Masonry Work Collection

Dates of Photographs: ND

Collection Origins

Unknown.

Physical Description

There are 400 cyanotypes mounted and assembled into 20 cyanotype collages. Each collage consists of up to 20 small cyanotype images.

Subjects

The photographs document architectural details and decorative masonry work, such as, cornices, pediments, and pilasters; English country homes; and Moorish and other Eastern influences in architecture. Many of the images are photographic reproductions of drawings.

Arranged: No.

Captioned: No.

Finding Aid: No.

Restrictions: No.

EI·31

Kalman J. DeJuhasz Papers

Dates of Photographs: Circa 1908–1959

Collection Origins

This collection was assembled by Kalman J. DeJuhasz (1893–1973), a mechanical engineer and professor of research engineering at Pennsylvania State University from 1928 to 1953.

Physical Description

There are 70 photographs, including silver gelatin dry plate photonegatives (20) and silver gelatin photoprints (50) mounted in a notebook. Other materials include books, catalogs, correspondence, notes, and publications.

Subjects

The photographs document engineering research machinery and unidentified people. The machinery includes a low-frequency surge filter; a multiple contractor; a Piezo-ray integrator; a recording analyzer for torsional vibrations; and a torsional vibration pickup.

Arranged: No.

Captioned: No.

Finding Aid: No.

Restrictions: No.

EI·32

Delaware Aqueduct Collection

Dates of Photographs: 1880–1970

Collection Origins

This collection was assembled by divisional staff and staff of the Historic Engineering Record. Photographers represented include David Plowden and Robert M. Vogel.

Physical Description

There are 155 photographs, including silver gelatin photonegatives and photoprints. Some are vintage originals, others are later photoprints made from historical photonegatives, and a few photoprints are from present day photonegatives. Other materials include drawings of the aqueduct and newspaper clippings.

Subjects

The photographs are of the Delaware Aqueduct (Lackawaxen, Pennsylvania) between 1847 and 1890 and of drawings of the aqueduct.

Arranged: No.

Captioned: With subject and date.

Finding Aid: No.

Restrictions: No.

EI·33

Delaware, Lackawanna, and Western Railroad Cyanotype Albums Collection

Dates of Photographs: 1906–1914

Collection Origins

This collection was assembled by George J. Ray, Chief Construction Engineer of the Delaware, Lackawanna, and Western Railroad. It was given to the Smithsonian in 1972. Photographers represented include William B. Barry.

Physical Description

There are 200 cyanotypes housed in eight albums. Other materials include two souvenir books.

Subjects

The photographs document facilities, such as, bridges, terminals, and yards of the Delaware, Lackawanna, and Western Railroad. There are photographs of the Hoboken freight terminal, passenger terminal ferryhouse, and transfer yard; Pier No. 1, Hoboken, New Jersey; the Susquehanna crossing improvement; and a transfer bridge.

Arranged: No.

Captioned: With subject and date.

Finding Aid: No.

Restrictions: No.

EI·34

Dodge Manufacturing Corporation Records Collection

Dates of Photographs: 1905–1924

Collection Origins

The Dodge Manufacturing Corporation of Mishawaka, Indiana, was founded in 1878 as a small wood specialties shop. It is now a division of Reliance Electric Company and produces mechanical power transmission equipment.

The collection was given to the Smithsonian Institution in 1970.

Physical Description

There are 3,400 photographs, including silver gelatin dry plate photonegatives and silver gelatin photoprints.

Subjects

The photographs document the facilities, products, and staff of the Dodge Manufacturing Company of Mishawaka, Indiana, between 1905 and 1924. There are exterior and interior views of the factory and images of anonymous people at work.

There are photographs of Dodge safety disc clutch parts; a Dodge-Timken counter shaft; double flange track wheels; a hydraulic speed gear unit for paper machinery; power transmission installations; pulleys; and rope drives.

Arranged: Two series. 1) Prints. 2) Photonegatives.

Captioned: The photonegatives, with the negative number and date. The prints, with subject information.

Finding Aid: No.

Restrictions: No.

EI·35

Beata Drake Covered Bridges Collection

Dates of Photographs: 1955–1966

Collection Origins

This collection was assembled by Beata Drake. Photographers and studios represented include Tom Bryan and the Delaware State Highway Department.

Physical Description

There are 2,100 photographs, including color dye coupler photoprints and silver gelatin photonegatives and photoprints. Other materials include annual reports; maps; photomechanical reproductions (postcards); publications; and reprints.

Subjects

The photographs document covered bridges in Connecticut; Delaware; Georgia; Massachusetts; New Hampshire; New Jersey; New York; Ohio; Rhode Island; Vermont; Virginia; and West Virginia.

Arranged: By geographical location.

Captioned: No.

Finding Aid: No.

Restrictions: No.

EI·36

Dredging Collection

Dates of Photographs: 1884–1970

Collection Origins

This collection was assembled by division staff from the 1884 *Osgood Dredge Catalog* and other sources.

Photographers and studios represented include W.R. Leland and OPPS.

Physical Description

There are 140 photographs, including albumen photoprints and silver gelatin photonegatives (some copies) and photoprints. Other materials include correspondence, newspaper clippings, notes, and xerographic copies.

Subjects

The photographs document the use of dredging machinery in canal construction in Boston and New York between 1884 and 1918. Photographs show cranes, derrick cars, ditching machines, hoisting machinery, patent boom dredges, and steam excavators.

Arranged: Into three series. 1) Osgood Dredge Catalog. 2) New York Engineering Company Dredges. 3) Ellicott Dredges.

Captioned: No.

Finding Aid: No.

Restrictions: No.

EI·37

Dudley Shuttles, Inc., Project Records Collection

Dates of Photographs: Circa 1880s–1966

Collection Origins

This collection was assembled by division staff from materials created by the Industrial Archeology Survey of 1966; and a separate accession of materials from Dudley Shuttles, Inc., also received in 1966. The survey studied the facilities of Dudley Shuttles, Inc., in 1966 as part of an ongoing industrial archeology project.

Dudley Shuttles, Inc., of Wilkinsonville, Massachusetts, was founded in 1842 by D.T. Dudley to manufacture power loom shuttles.

Photographers represented include Robert M. Vogel.

Physical Description

There are 550 photographs, including silver gelatin photonegatives and photoprints. Other materials include bills, blueprints, correspondence, historical data, invoices, orders, and patent information.

Subjects

The photographs document the Dudley Shuttles, Inc., facilities; and the manufacture of power loom shuttles by the company's staff between the 1880s and 1966.

The photographs include group portraits of unidentified workers (circa 1900); workers engaged in step-by-step production of power loom shuttles; and interior and exterior views of the factory from the 1880s to 1966 (when the survey was conducted).

Arranged: By subject.

Captioned: No.

Finding Aid: No.

Restrictions: No.

EI·38

Llewellyn N. Edwards Collection

Dates of Photographs: 1873–1952

Collection Origins

Llewellyn Nathaniel Edwards (1873–1952) was a civil engineer who specialized in the design of bridges and their history. Edwards studied bridge design practices of the prehistoric period to the 19th century, including the history and evolution of early American bridges. He also studied the bulking effect of moisture in sands; and the effect of mixing water on physical properties of mortars and concrete.

This collection was presented to the National

Museum by Edward's wife, Carolyn, between 1959 and 1970.

Photographers and studios represented include R.G. Bristol, Bellows Falls, Vermont; Bureau of Public Roads, Washington, D.C.; OPPS; the Salt River Project, Arizona; and Henry Tyrell.

Physical Description

There are 205 photographs, including albumen photoprints and silver gelatin photoprints. Other materials include blueprints, a cartoon, correspondence, newspaper clippings, notes, reprints, and xerographic copies.

Subjects

The photographs are primarily of dams in the United States, such as, Davis Dam on the Ohio River; Dundee Dam in Passaic, New Jersey; Theodore Roosevelt Dam; and Wood Dam in Blackstone, Massachusetts.

There are also photographs of the Bellows Falls Canal Company (1910); buggies; carriages; Post Road in McDowell City, North Carolina; and suspension foot bridges.

Arranged: No.

Captioned: With subjects, such as, geographical information.

Finding Aid: No.

Restrictions: No.

EI·39

Emery Testing Machine Collection

Dates of Photographs: ND

Collection Origins

This collection was assembled by an unknown donor to document the Emery Testing Machine, including its use in an arsenal.

Physical Description

There are 100 photographs, including silver gelatin photonegatives and photoprints. Other materials include engineering drawings.

Subjects

The photographs document the Emery Testing Machine, including unidentified materials shown before and after testing at the Watertown Arsenal in Watertown, Massachusetts.

Arranged: No.

Captioned: No.

Finding Aid: No.

Restrictions: No.

EI·40

Emmet Mercury Boiler Collection

Dates of Photographs: 1930–1935

Collection Origins

This collection was assembled by an unknown donor to document the history of Emmet Mercury Boilers between 1930 and 1935.

Physical Description

There are 115 photographs, including cyanotypes and silver gelatin photoprints mounted on linen. Other materials include blueprints, charts, correspondence, fact sheets, newspaper clippings, notes, operating instructions, reports, and a visitors' log.

Subjects

The photographs document Emmet mercury boilers and boiler installations between 1930 and 1935. There is also a signed portrait of Mr. Emmet. There are photographs of boilers; boiler tubes; furnace walls; furnaces; mercury boilers, including a Hartford Electric Light Company mercury boiler; a mercury turbine installation; and South Meadows Station turbines.

Arranged: By type of material.

Captioned: One autographed portrait of Mr. Emmet.

Finding Aid: No.

Restrictions: No.

EI·41

William J. Eney Collection *A.K.A.* Lehigh University Collection

Dates of Photographs: 1929–1956

Collection Origins

The collection was assembled by William J. Eney and the staff of Lehigh University to document engineering projects for research and teaching purposes.

Photographers and studios represented include G.R. Deits and Baumgartener Kleinschmidt.

Physical Description

There are 12 silver gelatin photoprints mounted in theses or reports. Other materials include correspondence, course outlines, model analyses, and model studies.

Subjects

The photographs document engineering models of bridges and structures; the Holston Bridge of the Tennessee Valley Authority; and studies of various unidentified arch ribs.

Arranged: No.

Captioned: With subjects and plate numbers.

Finding Aid: No.

Restrictions: No.

EI·42

Engineering and Industry Biography File

Dates of Photographs: 1950s–1980s

Collection Origins

This collection was assembled by division staff from diverse sources for research purposes.

Photographers, photographic distributors, manufacturers, and studios represented include Elliott & Fry, London; Envy-Pirou, Paris; Falk, New York; Pierre Selit, Paris; and Stereoscopic Company, London.

Physical Description

There are 600 photographs, including albumen cabinet cards; platinum photoprints; and silver gelatin photoprints. Other materials include biographical clippings; correspondence; a single engraving plate; reprints; and xerographic copies of obituaries.

Subjects

The photographs are portraits of engineers, innovators, and inventors from the 18th century to the present. Many of the images are photographic reproductions of graphics from books, magazines, newspapers, and other illustrated sources.

Individuals portrayed include Claude Bernard; Henry Bessemer; Jean Martin Charcot; Edward Cooper; George H. Corliss; A.J. Eyre; Abram S. Hewitt; Henry Lane; Pierre Charles L'Enfant; Gustave Lindenthal; Hiram Francis Mills; Samuel A. Montagne; William Mulholland; Alfred Nobel; Alexander Outerbridge; Timothy Palmer; Simeon Post; Bernard Romans; Amasa Stone; William Strickland; Andrew Talcott; John Wallace; George Waring; and William Weston.

Arranged: Alphabetically by last name.

Captioned: On the image with name of subject, and on the folder with full name and dates.

Finding Aid: No.

Restrictions: No.

EI·43

Engineering and Industry Collections Files

Dates of Photographs: Circa 1850s–1980s

Collection Origins

This collection was assembled by division staff. It is added to on an ongoing basis. It forms the major portion of the division working files, which are used as reference files for exhibits and research.

Photographers, studios, and distributors represented include E.J. Codd Company; H.G. Colver; Ellingwood Photo, Manchester, New Hampshire; Farr, Minneapolis, Minnesota; Galbraith Photo, Toronto; George Hall; Hartford Steam Boiler and Inspection Company; Keystone View Company; OPPS; Real Photo; William N. Rew; Science Museum, London; C.A.P. Strasbourg; University of Michigan Engineering Department; Underwood and Underwood; Robert M. Vogel; and Warner Photo Company.

Physical Description

There are 8,000 photographs, including albumen photoprints; color dye coupler photonegatives and photoprints; platinum photoprints; salted paper photoprints; and silver gelatin photonegatives and photoprints. Other materials include advertisements, articles, blueprints, catalogs, diagrams, drawings, engravings, specifications, technical literature, and trade literature.

Subjects

The photographs illustrate civil and mechanical engineering activities; equipment; facilities; products, including objects and structures; and museum exhibitions created by the division on these topics.

Objects illustrated include boilers, diesel engines, elevators, furnaces, ice making equipment, plumbing equipment, pumping equipment, refrigeration equipment, steam engines, and stokes.

Facilities illustrated include architectural structures, such as, Grand Central Station, canals, geothermal power stations, harbors, highways, hydroelectric power stations, iron works, ports, railroads, rapid transit, textile mills, tunnels, and viaducts.

Arranged: Into three series. 1) Engineering and industry files (30 subseries). 2) Oversize files (three subseries). 3) Overflow files (alphabetically by subject with subseries).

Captioned: With subject information.

Finding Aid: No.

Restrictions: No.

EI·44

Engineering and Industry Hydroelectric Collection

Dates of Photographs: 1912–1980s

Collection Origins

This collection was assembled by division staff from diverse sources.

Physical Description

There are 28 photographs, including albumen photoprints and silver gelatin photonegatives and photoprints. Other materials include clippings, notes, reprints, thermofax copies, and xerographic copies.

Subjects

The photographs document hydroelectric plants, both exterior and interior views. There are photographs of the General Electric plant at Normonberger Station, and the plant's Westinghouse generators.

Arranged: No.

Captioned: No.

Finding Aid: No.

Restrictions: No.

EI·45

Engineering and Industry Lantern Slide Collection

Dates of Photographs: 1886–1931

Collection Origins

This collection was assembled by division staff for research purposes.

Photographers and studios represented include L.C. Handy Photo, Washington, D.C.; W.H. Lawrence and B.S. Turpin; and the Massachusetts Institute of Technology Civil Engineering Department.

Physical Description

There are 5,000 silver gelatin dry plate lantern slides.

Subjects

The photographs document engineering activities, equipment, facilities, and projects. Activities documented include engineering inspection; moving an obelisk; rock drilling and riveting; tunneling; V drive ratio testing; and weighing. Objects illustrated include blueprints, boilers, bridges, canals, drawings, Egyptian temples, flywheel governors, and valves.

Corporate facilities and equipment illustrated include American Locomotive Company Diesel; Blooming Mills; a Fairbanks-Morse marine diesel generator set; a Hamilton diesel model; Ingersoll-Rand; and Nordberg marine diesel engine.

Arranged: By subject.

Captioned: Some with subject and date.

Finding Aid: No.

Restrictions: No.

EI·46

Engineering and Industry Negative Collection

Dates of Photographs: 1915–1980s

Collection Origins

This collection was assembled by division staff from photonegatives taken by the division and OPPS to document specimens in the National Museum of American History and in the field.

Photographers represented include Robert M. Vogel.

Physical Description

There are 9,725 silver gelatin photonegatives, of which 45 are on nitrate film.

Subjects

The photographs document civil and mechanical engineering activities, equipment, facilities, and projects. There are photographs of aqueducts, bridges, engines, factories, highway testing, hydroelectric stations, kilns, and mills.

Arranged: Two major series. 1) Safety negatives (arranged by negative number into eight subseries). 2) Nitrate negatives (unidentified and unarranged).

Captioned: With subject information, date, negative number, and photographer on the envelope.

Finding Aid: A card index to the safety negatives arranged alphabetically by subject and than by negative number.

Restrictions: No.

EI·47

Engineering and Industry Oversized Collection

Dates of Photographs: 1857–1967

Collection Origins

This collection was assembled by division staff from diverse sources.

Photographers and studios represented include Rell Clements; Bliss Bros.; S.A. Holmes, Photoviews, New York City; Ladd and Son, Muskegon, Michigan (1909–1910); E.E. Lashway; National Maritime Museum; National Portrait Gallery; C. Nettleton; OPPS; Marcus Ritger; N.L. Stebbens, Boston; H.E. Strout; Sun Oil Company; Talfor; University of Michigan, College of Engineering; and Underwood and Underwood.

Physical Description

There are 200 photographs, including albumen photoprints (some oversize); color dye coupler photoprints; a salted paper photoprint; and silver gelatin photoprints (some oversize cirkut camera images). Many photoprints are mounted or framed. Other materials include blueprints; drawings; engravings; glass photogravure plates; photomechanical prints; photostats; and prints.

Subjects

The photographs document engineering and industrial equipment, facilities, and projects, including Australian and American bridges; canals; heavy machinery; industrial plants and equipment; lighthouses; machine shops; railroad stations; railroad trestles; tunnels; and viaducts.

Facilities documented include the C.P. Bradway Machine Works (1965); the Clydesbank Shipyard (1901); and the Emerson and Stevens Ax Works (1967).

Projects documented include the Brooklyn Bridge; Chesapeake & Delaware Canal bridges; Eiffel Tower; Panama Canal; Roebling's Delaware and Hudson Canal aqueducts; St. Louis Exposition (1904); a water-turbine casing on boring mill; and the 1893 World's Columbian Exposition in Chicago (Manning, Maxwell & Moore Machine Shop exhibit).

Arranged: Some by type of material.

Captioned: With subject information, date, and some with OPPS negative number.

Finding Aid: No.

Restrictions: No.

EI·48

Engineering and Industry Photograph Collection

Dates of Photographs: 1870s–1980s

Collection Origins

This collection was assembled by division staff from diverse donations, exchanges, and purchases.

Photographers and studios represented include S.W. Ackerman, Cleveland; Anson, Broadway, New York; Edward Beyer; E.M. Bidwell; R.A. Bonine of Altoona, Pennsylvania; Daniel Brush; Canadian Photo Co., Vancouver, British Columbia; Centennial Photographic Company (W.I. Adams and L. Wilson); Conway Studios, New York; John Cornell; E.V. Crane; Davis and Sanford, New York City; Erickson, Worcester, Massachusetts; Gifford Brothers, Hudson, New York; Greif Bros; Cooperoyer, St. Paul; Ralph Greenhill; House of Photography, Inc., Boston; and E. Jessup, Middleton, New York.

Other photographers and studios represented include Leavitt of Newport, Rhode Island; Lenox Studios, New Jersey; McGrein; McKeown & Pfahler; Myers & Lesure, Middleton, New York; Nickerson and Collins; Warren J. Ogden, Jr.; George Perrin, New York; Philadelphia Museum of Art; David Plowden; Post & McLord, New York City; Runnels & Stateler; Tinkey Studio, Ohio; Quido Trapp's Photographic Atelier; Robert M. Vogel; Peter Vogt, Oakland, Maine; Fred Wittner, New York City; and Lawrence Wolfe, North Sutton, New Hampshire.

Other sources of photographs represented include Carnegie-Illinois Steel Corporation; Civil Engineering Division of the Bureau of Photography, Pittsburgh; 1876 Centennial Exposition; Frick Company, Pennsylvania; General Electric Company; Rundle Gilbert auction materials; Historic American Engineering Record; Johns Hopkins University;

MalGurian Association, New York City; National Park Service; OPPS; Cliff Peterson Collection; San Francisco Maritime Museum; Science Museum of London; Society of Industrial Archeology; and the Union Iron Works.

Physical Description

There are 14,500 photographs, including albumen paper photoprints; one ambrotype; color dye coupler photonegatives, photoprints, and phototransparencies; color dye diffusion transfer photoprints (Polaroid); cyanotypes; platinum photoprints; silver gelatin dry plate photonegatives; and silver gelatin photonegatives and photoprints. Many of the images are oversize or are panoramas which measure as large as 29″×41″. Other materials include advertisements; annual reports; articles; auction catalogs; blueprints; budgets; catalogs; clippings; conservation reports; correspondence; engravings; etchings; legal agreements; lithographs; loan reports and requests; newsletters; notes; object identification tags; pamphlets; patents; photograph albums; posters; press releases; price lists; railroad terminal location maps; reports; reprints; trade literature; and xerographic copies of articles.

Subjects

The photographs document civil engineering, heavy machinery, industrial archaeology, mechanisms, and production engineering primarily in North America.

The heavy machinery photographs document: 1) power machinery utilizing internal-combustion power (diesel engines, gas, gasoline engines, oil, and turbines), miscellaneous power equipment, muscle power, steam power (engines and turbines), tidal and wave power, water power (dams, pressure engines, turbines, and water wheels), and wind power; 2) air compressing, blowing, and pumping equipment; 3) refrigeration equipment for ice harvesting, mechanical cooling, and natural cooling; 4) construction machinery for earth moving, excavating, fastening, hoisting, materials handling, and mixing concrete.

The civil engineering photographs document: 1) construction machines, materials, and methods; 2) materials testing; 3) materials production; 4) building and structural mechanical equipment for air conditioning, elevators, escalators, heating, plumbing, and ventilating; 5) aqueducts, bridges, viaducts, and other spanning system construction and equipment; 6) structural engineering; 7) tunnels; 8) waterway engineering including canals, harbor, and river improvements; 9) dam construction and equipment; 10) highway and railroad construction and engineering; 11) water supply engineering and equipment; 12) materials handling and storage; and 13) construction and engineering of miscellaneous structures, such as, chimneys, tanks, and towers.

The production engineering photographs document: 1) machinery for precision linear measurement; 2) manufacturing machinery and processes for metal, wood, and other materials and for mass production; 3) related equipment and processes; 4) production-efficiency methods; and 5) other industrial processes.

The mechanisms photographs document: 1) automata; 2) office machines, methods, and systems exclusive of mathematical machines, such as, computers; 3) mechanical security devices, such as, locks, safes, and vaults; 4) mechanical sound recordings; and 5) timekeeping devices.

The industrial archaeology photographs document: 1) adaptive reuse documentation; 2) interpretation; 3) preservation; and 4) recording.

Arranged: Small portions of this collection are arranged chronologically, by subject, by geographic location, or by type of material.

Captioned: Most are captioned with subject information. Some also include photographer's name, accession number, negative number, and date.

Finding Aid: Indexes and accession cards serve as a preliminary finding aids to portions of this collection.

Restrictions: No.

EI·49

Engineering and Industry Production Engineering Slides

Dates of Photographs: 1970s–1985

Collection Origins

This collection was assembled by division staff from images created by OPPS and other sources between

1970 and 1985. It was assembled to document production machinery, such as, milling machines, mortisers, and punch presses.

Physical Description

There are 80 photographs, including color dye coupler slides (Kodachrome) and silver gelatin phototransparencies.

Subjects

The photographs document metal-working and wood production machinery, such as, "APM" punch presses; Ballard drills; band saws; Barnes molders; Barnes scroll saws; Barnes table saws; drill presses; Heim grinders; mortisers; pistol-grip lathes; Rogers tenoners; a rose engine lathe; shapers; Smith matchers; Smith mortisers; and universal mills.

Arranged: By subject heading.

Captioned: With the assigned OPPS negative number.

Finding Aid: A subject list for this collection is on the lid of the storage box.

Restrictions: No.

EI·50

Engineering and Industry Slide Collection

Dates of Photographs: 1908–1980s

Collection Origins

This collection was assembled by division staff from a variety of sources for public presentation purposes and research.

Physical Description

There are 1,760 photographs, including color dye coupler slides; a silver gelatin dry plate stereograph; and silver gelatin photonegatives and photoprints.

Other materials include reel-to-reel audio tape and microfilm.

Subjects

The photographs document engineering and industry primarily in the United States between 1908 and the 1980s, including Baltimore area textile mills; the Chicago World's Fair; dredges on the Erie Canal; Poole & Hunt Company; Rip Van Winkle Bridge; St. Johns Bridge; and various unidentified suspension bridges.

The collection also incorporates two slide shows: 1) *Bridges in History,* and 2) *5,000 Years of Civil Engineering.*

Arranged: No.

Captioned: No.

Finding Aid: No.

Restrictions: No.

EI·51

Erie Railway Collection

Dates of Photographs: 1906–1908, 1970s

Collection Origins

This collection was assembled by division staff from several outside donations, including gifts from the Erie-Lackawanna Railroad (Conrail) and Walter Olevsky of Carlstadt, New Jersey.

Photographers and studios represented include the Erie Railroad, Shohola, Pennsylvania; Fairchild Aerial Surveys, Inc.; OPPS; and Williams S. Young.

Physical Description

There are 650 photographs, including albumen photoprints; collodion wet plate photonegatives; cyanotypes; silver gelatin dry plate photonegatives; and silver gelatin photonegatives (some nitrate) and photoprints. Other materials include blueprints, correspondence, drawings, literature, maps, notes, newspaper clippings, and reports.

Subjects

The photographs document the Erie Railway between 1906 and 1908, including the Cascade (timber-arch) Bridge; Erie ferry boats; Erie Railway stations; hydraulic engineering construction activities; the Starrucca Viaduct and House; and the Susquehanna and Meadville shops.

Arranged: By type of material, and then by subject.

Captioned: With date and subject.

Finding Aid: No.

Restrictions: No.

EI·52

Fall River Mills Collection

Dates of Photographs: Circa 1870–1968

Collection Origins

This collection was assembled by division staff from materials created by the National Park Service, the New England Textile Mill Survey II (1968); and the Smithsonian. The collection was assembled to document the textile industry in Fall River, Massachusetts.

Photographers and studios represented include Kilburn Company, Littleton, New Hampshire; OPPS; and the Providence Journal Co.

Physical Description

There are 425 photographs, including silver gelatin photonegatives and photoprints. The photographs are both copy photoprints and vintage historical photoprints. Other materials include advertisements, correspondence, diagrams, plans, reports, and trade literature.

Subjects

The photographs document the textile mills in Fall River, Massachusetts, including contemporary exterior and interior shots. There are photographs of the buildings, facilities, production activities, and staff.

Mills documented include the American Linen Company; Barnard; Richard Borden Manufacturing Company; Charlton; Cornell; Davol; Durfee; Globe; Granite; Mechanics; Merchants; Metacomet; Osborne; Pocasset; Stafford; Troy Cotton and Woolen Manufactory; Union; Wamsutta Woolen; and Weetamoe.

Arranged: By subject.

Captioned: With subject information.

Finding Aid: An index giving the negative number, the image size, and a brief description of the image.

Restrictions: No.

EI·53

Richard Fisher Collection of Panama Canal Materials

Dates of Photographs: Circa 1911–1947

Collection Origins

This collection was assembled by Richard Fisher to document the construction of the Panama Canal. Fisher lived in the Panama Canal Zone during construction of the canal. The collection was given to the Smithsonian Institution in 1977.

Photographers or studios represented include J.A. Bruce, New York and Keystone View Co., New York.

Physical Description

There are 240 photographs, including albumen photoprints, cyanotypes, and silver gelatin photoprints. Other materials include books, collotypes, photolithographs, and photomechanical postcards.

Subjects

The photographs document the construction and operation of the Panama Canal between 1911 and 1947. There are photographs of the Canal Administration Building in Ancon; the Cathedral Plaza in Panama; construction sites and camps; Culebra

Cut; DeLessep's mansion in Colon; an emergency dam in Gatun; and ships moving through the canal.

Arranged: No.

Captioned: With date, location, and subject.

Finding Aid: A list of materials in the division's Archives Inventory File.

Restrictions: No.

Arranged: By subject.

Captioned: With subject information, such as, geographic locale or product name.

Finding Aid: A card file arranged by subject and type of material. One file folder labeled "Lincoln Tunnel *A.K.A.* Midtown Hudson Tunnel" has its own index.

Restrictions: No.

EI·54

James Forgie Collection

Dates of Photographs: 1905–1946

Collection Origins

James Forgie (1868–1958) was born in Scotland. He started his professional career as a civil engineer in London where he helped to build tunnels for the underground rapid transit system.

In 1902 the Pennsylvania Railroad brought Forgie to New York, where he worked on tunnels under the East and Hudson rivers. By 1914 he had worked on many tunnel projects in the United States and in Mexico. Forgie's last major project was Union Tunnel under the City of Baltimore.

Physical Description

There are 130 photographs, including silver gelatin dry plate photonegatives; a silver gelatin photonegative (oversize); and silver gelatin photoprints mounted on linen. Other materials include blueprints, correspondence, maps, notes, plans, and reports.

Subjects

The photographs document the tunnel engineering projects of James Forgie between 1905 and 1946. The photographs are of the Forgie grout machine; the Hudson & Manhattan Railroad; the Lincoln Tunnel (1937); the Midtown Tunnel (1936); the Pennsylvania Railroad Tunnel; the subway under the Flatbush Avenue Station; and the Toronto Harbor Works (1915).

EI·55

Foundation Company Collection

Dates of Photographs: 1913–1961

Collection Origins

This collection was assembled by an unknown creator to document the Foundation Company.

Photographers represented include Phillip Anderson; House of Photography, Inc., Boston, Massachusetts; A. Leigh Sanders, Baltimore, Maryland; Lenox Studios, Perth Amboy, New Jersey; and A.J. Schulte.

Physical Description

There are 3,100 photographs, including color dye coupler slides; and silver gelatin photonegatives, photoprints, and slides. Many prints are mounted on linen in 23 albums. Other materials include albums, blueprints, charts, diagrams, drawings, newspaper clippings, and patents.

Subjects

The photographs document the Boston Commons Garage; the Chase Manhattan Building; Hydraulic Dredge #216 in New Castle, Pennsylvania; the Idlewilde Plant; the Singer Building; the Scotia Dam; and the St. Lawrence River Bridge.

There are also images of an airplane assembling shop, cranes, a 500-foot chimney, and a power station.

Arranged: First by type of material, and then chronologically by job. The albums each represent a different project.

Captioned: With subject information.

Finding Aid: A card file compiled by Professor Charles Looney arranged chronologically by project which includes the date, location, name of project, and negative numbers.

Restrictions: No.

EI·56

Frick Company Collection

Dates of Photographs: 1872–1920

Collection Origins

This collection was assembled by the Frick Company of Waynesboro, Pennsylvania, a manufacturer of refrigeration and agricultural machinery, to document its products.

Photographic studios represented include the Hughes Company.

Physical Description

There are 500 silver gelatin photoprints (many mounted on linen or board). Other materials include catalogs, correspondence, letter books, maintenance booklets, price lists, refrigeration booklets, and repair lists.

Subjects

The photographs document the production facilties and refrigeration products of the Frick Company between 1872 and 1920. There are also numerous shots of these products installed in various client plants.

There are photographs of can dumpers; can hoists; cold rooms; evaporator coils; ice handling machinery; ice sculptures; refrigeration compressors (including large vertical compressors); the refrigerator ship *Aeolus;* and various unidentified World War I refrigerator ships with Frick cooling apparatus.

There are photographic reproductions of drawings of machinery.

Arranged: By subject into four series. 1) Ice making. 2) Refrigeration compressors. 3) Condenser and evaporator coils. 4) Marine work during World War I (1914–1918).

Captioned: With subject information.

Finding Aid: No.

Restrictions: No.

EI·57

Cass Gilbert Sketches Collection

Dates of Photographs: 1911–1936

Collection Origins

Architect Cass Gilbert (1859–1934) was known for his designs of the Minnesota State Capitol; the New York Life Insurance Building; the U.S. Customs House; the U.S. Supreme Court Building; and the Woolworth Building.

Photographers represented include B.G. Mitchell of Architecture Photography, New York City.

Physical Description

There are 70 photographs, including silver gelatin photonegatives and photoprints. Other materials include correspondence and newspaper clippings.

Subjects

The photographs are of buildings and monuments designed by architect Cass Gilbert, including the 1st Division Monument; U.S. Courthouse, New York City; U.S. Supreme Court Building; and the Woolworth Building during construction.

Arranged: No.

Captioned: With subject information.

Finding Aid: No.

Restrictions: No.

EI·58

Gilbreth Collection

Dates of Photographs: 1910–1980

Collection Origins

Frank Bunker Gilbreth (1868–1924) and Lillian Evelyn Moller Gilbreth (1878–1972), his wife, were construction engineers who pioneered industrial time-and-motion studies in the work place. The Gilbreths were also authors, teachers, and consultants to businesses and institutions in the areas of improvement of working conditions, industrial efficiency, and scientific management.

The Gilbreths invented the micro-motion and chronocyclegraph processes for determining fundamental units and methods of industrial education, as well as methods for training disabled soldiers for industrial life.

This collection was given to the division in 1982 by the Gilbreth family.

Photographic studios represented include Ohio State University; OPPS; and Purdue University.

Physical Description

There are 3,000 photographs, including albumen stereographs; a color dye coupler photoprint; color screen plate stereographs (Autochromes); silver gelatin dry plate stereographic phototransparencies; and silver gelatin photoprints. Other materials include the book *Cheaper by the Dozen* (written about the Gilbreth family); a cassette sound recording and a $\frac{1}{4}$″ sound tape titled "Inside Cheaper by the Dozen"; correspondence; patents; publications; and reports.

Subjects

The photographs document the personal lives and work of the Gilbreths from 1910 to 1924.

There are photographs of assembly boards; cyclegraphs; the Gilbreth clock; furniture; machinery; motion recording equipment; and the Taylor card filer.

Places illustrated include assembly lines; operating theaters; and the 1915 Panama-Pacific Exposition.

Studies documented include those of construction workers; factory workers and assembly lines; handicapped workers; medical workers and operating theaters; seated workers and chair studies; shoemakers; storage and stacking; time-and-motion studies; and workshops.

Family portraits include the Gilbreth children in Plainfield, New Jersey (1910–1912), Lillian M. Gilbreth with children (1911), and Martha Bunker Gilbreth (1912).

Arranged: By type of material and then by subject.

Captioned: Each slide is numbered, some are labeled with subject and date.

Finding Aid: An annotated index to the stereograph slide collection was written by David Shayt.

Restrictions: No.

EI·59

Gilman Manufacturing Company Collection

Dates of Photographs: ND

Collection Origins

Unknown.

Physical Description

There are 50 silver gelatin photoprints mounted on linen in one leather album titled "Gilman Manufacturing Co."

Subjects

The photographs document machines, machine parts, tools, and tool parts presumably manufactured by the Gilman Manufacturing Company.

Arranged: No.

Captioned: With name of the tool or tool part, size, and part number.

Finding Aid: No.

Restrictions: No.

EI·60

Grand Central Yard Improvements Progress Photographs Collection

Dates of Photographs: 1903–1924

Collection Origins

The New York Central Hudson River Railroad Company made improvements to the Grand Central Terminal and adjacent railroad and subway lines in New York City from 1903 to 1924. This collection documents those improvements.

This collection was given to the division in 1967 by Smithsonian Secretary S. Dillon Ripley, whose grandfather worked on this project.

Physical Description

There are 1,700 photographs, including cyanotypes and silver gelatin photoprints housed in 12 albums.

Subjects

The photographs document improvements made to the subway and railroad system of New York City from 1903 to 1924. There are also images of storefronts and subway stations.

There are photographs of construction, demolition, and excavations at sites, such as, Depew Place; Fordham Heights; 42nd to 56th Streets; Grand Central Terminal; Madison Avenue; Marble Hill; Morris Heights; Park Avenue; Port Morris; Vanderbilt Avenue; and Wall Street.

Arranged: Into 12 albums by location.

Captioned: With date, original negative number, and location.

Finding Aid: No.

Restrictions: No.

EI·61

Herbert S. Grassman Collection

Dates of Photographs: Circa 1920s

Collection Origins

This collection was assembled by Herbert S. Grassman, an engineer whose specialty was the design and stress testing of brick and concrete arches and piers.

Photographic studios represented include Manning Bros. of Detroit, Michigan.

Physical Description

There are 60 silver gelatin photoprints in a report entitled "Report on Test Arches & Piers, 1926." Other materials include blueprints, contracts, plans, photostats, and reports.

Subjects

The photographs document the design and testing of brick and concrete arches and piers. There are photographs of experimental arches and piers created for the Board of Water Commissioners in Detroit before and after stress tests.

Arranged: No.

Captioned: With subject information.

Finding Aid: A list of materials in the division's Archives Inventory File.

Restrictions: No.

EI·62

Hales Bar Lock and Dam Collection

Dates of Photographs: 1905–1944

Collection Origins

The Hales Bar Lock and Dam, located in Chattanooga, Tennessee, now is part of the Tennessee Valley Authority. It was the first multi-purpose dam built in the United States. This collection documents the construction, history, and the subsequent problems and repairs relating to this dam from 1905 to 1944.

Physical Description

There are 275 silver gelatin photoprints. One hundred of these photoprints are in a report titled, "Photographs of Hales Bar Lock & Dam, Chattanooga, Tennessee." Other materials include articles, blueprints, drawings, and reports.

Subjects

The photographs show the construction, repair, and general history of the Hales Bar Lock and Dam in Chattanooga, Tennessee, from 1905 to 1944. There are photographs of construction details; earth core samples; geological documentation before and after construction; limestone breccia; and models.

Arranged: By type of material and then in chronological order.

Captioned: With location, date, and number.

Finding Aid: A list of materials in the division's Archives Inventory File.

Restrictions: No.

EI·63

Hall Scripts Collection

Dates of Photographs: 1950s–1960s

Collection Origins

This collection was assembled by division staff as a record of exhibitions during the 1950s and 1960s. OPPS provided some of these photographs.

Physical Description

There are 55 silver gelatin photoprints. Other materials include content descriptions, correspondence, exhibit plans, scripts, and sketches.

Subjects

The photographs document the National Museum of American History exhibit halls managed by the Division of Engineering and Industry during the 1950s and 1960s. There are also photographs of exhibits in the Arts and Industries Building which predated the 1964 creation of the NMAH.

There are photographs of the Boyden Hydraulic Turbine; a compressed air drive; the Corliss engine; the Hall of Civil Engineering (1958–1964); the Hall of Power Machinery; steam engines; and steam turbines.

Arranged: By dates and exhibit name.

Captioned: With OPPS negative number.

Finding Aid: No.

Restrictions: No.

EI·64

Hamilton, Ohio, Machine Tool and Engine Builders Negative Collection

Dates of Photographs: 1890–1930s, 1960s

Collection Origins

This collection was assembled by an anonymous donor to document three companies in Hamilton, Ohio, that built machine tools and power machinery between 1890 and 1920: 1) Hooven, Owens, Rentschler Company (1882–1928); 2) Long and Allstatter (1871–1933); and 3) Niles, Bement, Pond Company (1899–1928).

All the photoprints in this collection are nonvintage duplicates made by OPPS from the original photonegatives. The photonegatives in the collection were donated to the division by the Ohio Historical Society around 1967.

Physical Description

There are 14,900 photographs, including silver gelatin dry plate photonegatives, and silver gelatin photonegatives and photoprints. Other materials include correspondence and xerographic copies of catalogs.

Subjects

The photographs document: 1) presses manufactured by Long and Allstatter (1871–1933); 2) steam engines, sugar machinery, and miscellaneous equipment manufactured or owned by Hooven, Owens, Rentschler Company (1882–1928); and 3) machine tools manufactured or owned by Niles, Bement, Pond Company (1899–1928) of Hamilton, Ohio.

There are also photographs of unidentified building exteriors; engine rooms; equipment; foundries; plants; processes; and tools.

Arranged: Into three series, by manufacturer's name and then by negative number. There are negatives missing in all three series.

Captioned: The glass negatives and OPPS prints are marked with negative numbers. The remainder of the collection is uncaptioned.

Finding Aid: A two-page collection summary.

Restrictions: No.

EI·65

Harpers Ferry Bridges Collection

Dates of Photographs: 1960s

Collection Origins

This collection was assembled by division staff to document the Potomac River bridges at Harpers Ferry.

Photographic studios represented include the Baltimore & Ohio Railroad Company.

Physical Description

There are 160 silver gelatin photoprints. Other materials include ephemera, maps, publications, reports, and reprints.

Subjects

The photographs document the construction of the Harpers Ferry Arsenal Span and the 1931 Harpers Ferry Railroad Bridge. There also photographs of blueprints and drawings of these bridges.

Arranged: By bridge and then chronologically in four series. 1) Harpers Ferry Railroad Bridge, 1834 to 1850. 2) Harpers Ferry Railroad Bridge, 1870 to 1893. 3) Harpers Ferry Railroad Bridge, 1894 to 1930. 4) Harpers Ferry Arsenal Span.

Captioned: No.

Finding Aid: No.

Restrictions: No.

EI·66

Hartford Steam Boiler Inspection and Insurance Company Records Collection

Dates of Photographs: 1935–1947

Collection Origins

This collection was assembled by the Hartford Steam Boiler Inspection and Insurance Company of Chicago, Illinois, to document steam boiler failures, such as, burned boilers, explosions, furnace collapse, and ruptures.

Photographers and studios represented include Associated Screen News, Ltd., Montreal, Canada; Bradley's of Tyler, Texas; Commonwealth Edison Photo; Croton Photo Services of New Westminister; Norman Edson, Burton, Washington; and Murray Studio, Omaha, Nebraska.

Physical Description

There are 150 photographs, including silver gelatin photonegatives and photoprints. Other materials include correspondence, newspaper clippings, publications, and reports.

Subjects

The photographs document steam boilers and boiler problems in Canada, England, and the United States.

Arranged: No.

Captioned: With location, date, description of type of boiler problem, and brand of boiler.

Finding Aid: No.

Restrictions: No.

EI·67

Hawthorne Works Collection

Dates of Photographs: June 1925

Collection Origins

Unknown.

Physical Description

There are 80 silver gelatin photoprints mounted in a leather-bound album entitled "Hawthorne Works, Western Electric Company, Inc., Bell System Educational Conference, Mechanical Engineers, Chicago, Illinois, June 22–27, 1925."

Subjects

The photographs document the Hawthorne Works, an electrical power plant, including the exterior and interior of the building, the lumber yard, machinery, and the water tower.

Arranged: No.

Captioned: With subject information, such as, building or machine name.

Finding Aid: No.

Restrictions: No.

EI·68

Julian Hinds Collection

Dates of Photographs: Circa 1908–1946

Collection Origins

Julian Hinds (1881–1977) received a B.S. degree in Civil Engineering from the State University at Austin in 1908. He worked on 52 projects during his career (1908–1946), most of which involved the construction of hydroelectric dams.

A full biography of Hind's life and career is included in the collection.

Photographers represented include Harold Laney of Wenatchee, Wisconsin.

Physical Description

There are 25 silver gelatin photoprints. Other materials include applications for license, blueprints, books, memoranda, publications, and reports.

Subjects

The photographs document dams constructed during the civil engineering career of Julian Hinds, as well as construction activities and dam sites. Projects illustrated include the Bull Run Dam #2 in Portland, Oregon; the California State Water Project; Cedar Springs Dam, California; the Elephant Butte Project in southwestern New Mexico; the Oroville Dam, California; the Piru Creek Project; and the Rocky Reach Hydroelectric Project of Public Utility District #1.

Arranged: By project name.

Captioned: With project name and description.

Finding Aid: An autobiographical report by Julian Hinds serves as a partial guide to this collection.

Restrictions: No.

EI·69

Hollingsworth and Whitney Paper Company Collection

Dates of Photographs: 1923

Collection Origins

Unknown.

Physical Description

There are 60 silver gelatin photoprints mounted in one paper-covered album. Other materials include correspondence and newspaper clippings.

Subjects

The photographs show dam and mill construction in Canada and the United States by firms, such as, the Canadian Cotton Company. Many images are of Maine.

Arranged: No.

Captioned: With subject and date information on the album page.

Finding Aid: No.

Restrictions: No.

EI·70

Hoopes, Bro. & Darlington Wheelworks Collection

Dates of Photographs: 1902–1969

Collection Origins

This collection was assembled by an unknown donor to document the machinery, plant (exterior and interior), products, and production activities of the Hoopes, Bro. & Darlington Wheelworks between 1902 and 1966. The company produced wheels for transportation vehicles.

Physical Description

There are 290 photographs, including a collodion gelatin wet plate lantern slide; color dye coupler phototransparencies; and silver gelatin photonegatives and photoprints. Other materials include correspondence, drafts, McBee cards, notes, questionnaires, reports, and research material.

Subjects

The photographs document wheelmaking for vehicles, such as, bicycles, carriages, cars, carts, and wagons. There are photographs of bicycle wheel production, cart wheel production, and final wheel inspection.

There also are photographs of a car accident: a

carriage with three people; a hickory mill in Perry, Florida; and a saw mill in Jackson, Mississippi (circa 1920).

Arranged: By type of material.

Captioned: Some, with the name of the company, SI negative number, date, and original negative number.

Finding Aid: No.

Restrictions: No.

EI·71

William Rich Hutton Papers

Dates of Photographs: 1850–1902

Collection Origins

William Rich Hutton (1826–1901) was a consulting civil engineer in New York City between 1868 and 1901.

Physical Description

There are 12 albumen photoprints. Other materials include contracts, correspondence, drawings, engineering designs, notebooks, and reports.

Subjects

The photographs are reproductions of drawings of the Hudson River Tunnel Railway Company tunnel and the proposed Nicaragua Canal.

Arranged: No.

Captioned: No.

Finding Aid: A card index arranged chronologically and then by subject.

Restrictions: No.

EI·72

Interborough Rapid Transit Subway Engine Photograph Collection

Dates of Photographs: Circa 1920–1960

Collection Origins

The collection was assembled by division staff for research purposes.

Physical Description

There are 125 silver gelatin photoprints. Other materials include diagrams, drawings, and photostats.

Subjects

The photographs are all of Interborough Rapid Transit engine-generators (built in 1903 and 1904 to power New York's first subway), and a NMAH model of one unit.

Arranged: No.

Captioned: With subject information.

Finding Aid: No.

Restrictions: No.

EI·73

International Bridge Collection

Dates of Photographs: 1870–1873, 1900–1901

Collection Origins

This photograph album was part of the L.N. Edwards Collection which was dispersed throughout the Smithsonian Institution. The album is titled "International Bridge, Canada, 1873 & 1901 Photographs of Reconstruction." It documents the original construction and the reconstruction of the International Bridge between New York and Ontario.

Photographic studios represented include the Simon SR Foto Studio.

Physical Description

There are 18 photographs, including albumen photoprints and silver gelatin photoprints in an album.

Subjects

The photographs document the original construction of the International Bridge between Buffalo, New York, and Ontario, Canada, from 1870 to 1873; and its reconstruction from 1900 to 1901.

Arranged: Chronologically.

Captioned: With subjects and dates.

Finding Aid: No.

Restrictions: No.

EI·74

J & W Jolly Company Collection

Dates of Photographs: 1880–1924

Collection Origins

The J & W Jolly Company of Holyoke, Massachusetts, manufactured papermaking machinery, power machinery, and water turbines.

Physical Description

There are 12 albumen photoprints. Other materials include drawings, reports, tracings, and turbine records.

Subjects

The photographs are of turbine assemblies and parts, and vertical water wheels manufactured by the J & W Jolly Company between 1880 and 1924.

Arranged: By type of material.

Captioned: No.

Finding Aid: An index to the drawings.

Restrictions: No.

EI·75

Kingsford Foundry and Machine Company Collection

Dates of Photographs: 1898–1926

Collection Origins

The Kingsford Foundry and Machine Company of Oswego, New York, was founded in 1864 to manufacture boilers and steam engines. The collection was given to the Smithsonian Institution in 1973.

Physical Description

There are 20 silver gelatin photoprints which are heavily retouched and mounted on cardboard for catalog illustrations. Other materials include blueprints, business records, catalogs, and sales information.

Subjects

The photographs document boilers; counterflow and unaflow steam engines; generators; and governors produced by the Kingsford Foundry and Machine Company of Oswego, New York, from 1898 to 1926.

Arranged: By subject.

Captioned: No.

Finding Aid: No.

Restrictions: No.

EI·76

Max Kronenberg Collection

Dates of Photographs: 1960s

Collection Origins

This collection was assembled by Max Kronenberg to document his work in the field of tool fatigue for research purposes.

Physical Description

There are 20 silver gelatin photoprints. Other materials include correspondence, lecture notes, publications, and reports.

Subjects

All the photographs are of fatigue and wear signs on metal-cutting tools.

Arranged: By subject.

Captioned: With subject information.

Finding Aid: No.

Restrictions: No.

EI·77

William Preston Lane Memorial Bridge Collection *A.K.A.* Chesapeake Bay Bridge Collection

Dates of Photographs: 1969–1974

Collection Origins

This collection was assembled by the consulting engineering firm of J.E. Greiner Company of Baltimore, designers of the William Preston Lane Memorial Bridge. The William Preston Lane Memorial Bridge spans the Chesapeake Bay between Sandy Point and Kent Island, Maryland.

Photographic studios represented include Stewart Brothers, Inc., of Rockville, Maryland.

Physical Description

There are 150 silver gelatin photoprints. Other materials include plans, proposals, reports, specifications, and a submission for a design competition.

Subjects

The photographs document the construction of the William Preston Lane Memorial Bridge over the Chesapeake Bay in Maryland. The photographs are of abutments; anchorages; cleaning, pointing, and patching concrete; excavation; general views of the bridge; girder spans; the hoisting of beams, cables, and other parts into position; pile driving; placing beams; setting concrete; and steel forms.

Arranged: No.

Captioned: With the date, camera position, or description.

Finding Aid: No.

Restrictions: No.

EI·78

Lawrence, Massachusetts, Textile Mills Collection

Dates of Photographs: Circa 1920s, 1967

Collection Origins

This collection was assembled by the New England Textile Mill Survey I from diverse sources. Photographers and studios represented include Randolph Langenbach; the New England Textile Mill Survey staff; and the Library of Congress.

Physical Description

There are 105 photographs, including silver gelatin photonegatives and photoprints. Other materials include notes, publications, reports, and reprints.

Subjects

The photographs document textile mills in Lawrence, Massachusetts, between 1848 and 1859. There are photographs of the Atlantic Mill (exteriors and interiors); the Lawrence machine shop; Pemberton Mill; and the Washington Mills gate house. There are also images of unidentified people working on looms.

Arranged: By name of firm or location.

Captioned: No.

Finding Aid: No.

Restrictions: No.

EI·79

Clyde C. Learned Collection

Dates of Photographs: 1919–1939, 1949

Collection Origins

Clyde C. Learned was a highway engineer, employed by the U.S. Department of Agriculture's Bureau of Public Roads in Denver, Colorado, from 1919 through 1949.

This collection documents Learned's career and includes annual reports for 1919 and 1920 on Berthoud Pass, Colorado, and Monarch Pass; and general reports on daily labor operations in Colorado, New Mexico, and Wyoming from 1927, 1931, 1932, 1934, 1939, and 1949. Note: This collection is being transferred to the Archives Center.

Physical Description

There are 350 silver gelatin photoprints in annual reports.

Subjects

The photographs document road construction and maintenance projects managed by the U.S. Department of Agriculture's Bureau of Public Roads in Colorado, New Mexico, and Wyoming, from 1919 to 1949.

There are photographs of bridges, ditches, drains, fences, natural drinking fountains, and road building at locations, such as, Berthoud Pass and Monarch Pass; and of snow plowing in the Rocky Mountains.

Arranged: Chronologically by project.

Captioned: No.

Finding Aid: A list of the reports in chronological order.

Restrictions: No.

EI·80

Leavitt Engine Collection

Dates of Photographs: Circa 1876–1900, 1960s

Collection Origins

This collection was assembled by division staff from diverse sources. The recent photographs were taken by John MacFarlane and division staff.

Erasmus Darwin Leavitt, Jr. (1836–1916) was a consulting mechanical engineer. He specialized in the design and construction of machinery for air compressing, for general power purposes, for hoisting, for ore stamping, and for pumping. Leavitt consulted on many projects, but was best known as the consulting and designing engineer of the Calumet and Hecla Mining Company (Boston and the Keewenaw Peninsula of Michigan). Leavitt was one of the founders of the American Society of Mechanical Engineers (1880) and a member of many professional organizations in Europe and the United States.

Physical Description

There are 210 photographs, including color dye coupler photoprints and silver gelatin photoprints. Other materials include data and drawings.

Subjects

The photographs primarily document Leavitt's machinery, principally at the Chestnut Hill (Boston) pumping engine, as well as at Calumet and Hecla.

The photographs are of machines including those for air compressing, hoisting, ore stamping, and pumping. There are also portraits of Leavitt.

Arranged: No.

Captioned: With subject information, such as, product name and geographical location.

Finding Aid: No.

Restrictions: No.

EI·81

James Leffel and Company Records Collection

Dates of Photographs: 1880s–1920s

Collection Origins

This collection was assembled by the James Leffel and Company, builders principally of hydraulic turbines.

Photographers and studios represented include Deluxe Studio Photo; John Hemmer, North Carolina; Merwin Studio, Wisconsin; and OPPS.

Physical Description

There are 950 photographs, including albumen panorama photoprints (some oversize); silver gelatin dry plate photonegatives; and silver gelatin photonegatives and photoprints. Other materials include advertising art, articles, catalogs, correspondence, newspaper clippings, patent office reports, patents, and test reports.

Subjects

The photographs document the facilities, installations, and products of the James Leffel and Company between the 1880s and the 1920s. There are photographs of boilers and stokers. There are also photographs of the construction, installation, and testing of boilers and turbines.

There are photographs which document the Caddyville Power Station; the Elephant Butte Project in New Mexico; and the Remmel Dam.

Arranged: Into two series by subject and assigned negative number.

Captioned: No.

Finding Aid: No.

Restrictions: No.

EI·82

Lombard Governor Corporation Collection

Dates of Photographs: 1901–1970s

Collection Origins

This collection was assembled by division staff from diverse sources to document the Lombard Governor Corporation of Ashland, Massachusetts.

Physical Description

There are 140 photographs, including silver gelatin dry plate photonegatives and silver gelatin photoprints. Other materials include blueprints, miscellaneous publications, price lists, and reports.

Subjects

The photographs document hydraulic-turbine governor production at the Lombard Governor Corporation. There are photographs of actuators, governors, plant interiors with machinery, pumps, safety devices, and turbines. Other firms documented include the Alabama RR Company.

Arranged: No.

Captioned: On their envelopes with subject, negative number, and date.

Finding Aid: No.

Restrictions: No.

EI·83

"Loose the Mighty Power: Impressions of the Steam Engine in America"

Dates of Photographs: 1979–1980

Collection Origins

This collection was assembled by division staff to document the exhibition of the same title. "Loose the Mighty Power: Impressions of the Steam Engine in America" was an exhibit designed by the division in 1979. OPPS provided many of the photographs in this collection.

Physical Description

There are 100 photographs, including silver gelatin photonegatives and photoprints. Other materials include correspondence, exhibit scripts, newspaper clippings, publications, and xerographic copies of items from the exhibit.

Subjects

The photographs document two portions of the National Museum of American History exhibit entitled "Loose the Mighty Power: Impressions of the Steam Engine in America" (1979): 1) The Steam Engine in American Life; and 2) The Steam Engine in the Landscape.

There are phototographs of locomotives, marine screw engines, mill engines, Otis's patent excavator, steam pumps, and sugar mill engines.

Arranged: By assigned negative number.

Captioned: No.

Finding Aid: No.

Restrictions: No.

EI·84

Lowell, Massachusetts Collection

Dates of Photographs: Circa 1922

Collection Origins

The collection was assembled by the proprietors of the Locks & Canals of Lowell, Massachusetts, who later gave the collection to the division.

Physical Description

There are 50 silver gelatin photoprints.

Subjects

The photographs document engineering projects in Lowell, Massachusetts, circa 1922. There are photographs of bridge, dam, and street construction; hydraulic power installations; and the Pawtucket Canal.

Arranged: No.

Captioned: With the photographer's original negative number, location, date, and time of day.

Finding Aid: No.

Restrictions: No.

EI·85

Charles T. Main Mill, Plant, and Factory Photograph Collection

Dates of Photographs: 1905–1935

Collection Origins

Charles T. Main (1856–1943) was a mechanical engineer. The collection documents Main's work on factories, hydroelectric plants, and textile mills in New England and at other locations.

Photographic studios represented include Poland Photo of Memphis, Tennessee.

Physical Description

There are 50 silver gelatin photoprints. Other materials include negative photostats.

Subjects

The photographs document exterior and interior views of factories, mills, and plants in New England designed by Charles T. Main. The factories, mills, and plants documented include the American Woolen Company storehouse; Bigelow Carpet Company; the Boston U.S. Army Supply Base; Clinton Wire Cloth Company storehouse #2; Dwight Manufacturing Company; Fulton Mills; Great Barrington Electric Light Company; and Ludlow storehouse.

Arranged: No.

Captioned: With subject information and location.

Finding Aid: No.

Restrictions: No.

EI·86

Mathew Mawhinney Industrial Furnace Collection

Dates of Photographs: Circa 1934–1955

Collection Origins

This collection was assembled by Mathew Mawhinney. Mawhinney received a master of science degree in engineering in 1925 from the Carnegie Institute of Technology. His specialty was furnace design. He held patents on billet-heating furnaces and soaking pits. Mawhinney was a test engineer for the Electric Furnace Company; Jones and Laughlin Steel Company; Tate Jones Furnace Company; and a consulting engineer in Salem, Ohio.

Photographers represented include J.W. Hughes, Detroit.

Physical Description

There are 150 silver gelatin photoprints. Other materials include blueprints, correspondence, reports, textbooks, and trade literature on furnace construction.

Subjects

The photographs are of furnaces, generators, and related equipment. Some of the furnaces shown are for heat treating, ingot heating, pipe normalizing, and plate heating.

Arranged: By type of material and then by assigned negative number.

Captioned: With a narrative subject description.

Finding Aid: The division's Archives Inventory File lists materials by type.

Restrictions: No.

EI·87

McIntosh and Seymour Engine Collection

Dates of Photographs: 1890s–1921

Collection Origins

The McIntosh and Seymour Corporation of Auburn, New York, was a builder of diesel and steam engines.

Physical Description

There are 15 silver gelatin photoprints. Other materials include contracts, drawings, orders, repair part orders, sketches, and specifications.

Subjects

The photographs document the unidentified engines and engine parts produced by the McIntosh and Seymour Corporation from 1900 to 1921.

Arranged: By type of material and then by assigned engine number.

Captioned: No.

Finding Aid: No.

Restrictions: No.

EI·88

Mechanisms Color Slide Collection

Dates of Photographs: 1930s–Present

Collection Origins

The Division of Mechanisms staff (now part of the Division of Engineering and Industry) created this collection to document the division's objects.

Physical Description

There are 1,000 color dye coupler phototransparenices.

Subjects

The photographs document artifacts in the Division of Engineering and Industry mechanisms collection.

There are photographs of 16th through 20th century light machinery, mechanisms, patent models, timekeeping devices, and related tools from Europe and the United States.

There are photographs of American clocks and watches (e.g., water clocks), automata, chronometers, European clocks and watches (e.g., L'epine watches), office machines, phonographs, and sundials.

There are photographs of two exhibits at NMAH: "Clockwork Universe" and the "Hall of Timekeeping."

Arranged: By subject, and then by subcategories.

Captioned: With the name of the object and its catalog number.

Finding Aid: No.

Restrictions: No.

EI·89

Mechanisms Information File *A.K.A.* Light Machinery Information File

Dates of Photographs: 1920s–Present

Collection Origins

This collection was assembled by division staff in the 1920s for exhibition, publication, and research purposes. Many photographs were taken by OPPS.

Physical Description

There are 900 silver gelatin photoprints.

Subjects

There are photographs of locks and keys; office equipment; patent drawings, machinery, time-keeping devices (such as clocks, sandglasses, sundials, and watches); tools and other equipment used to produce these objects; and typewriters.

Arranged: By subject.

Captioned: With subject descriptions.

Finding Aid: No.

Restrictions: No.

EI·90

Mechanisms Photograph Collection
A.K.A. Light Machinery Photograph Collection

Dates of Photographs: 1930s–Present

Collection Origins

The collection documents the Section of Mechanisms artifact collections. It is used for exhibition, publication, and research.

Physical Description

There are 2,300 silver gelatin photoprints.

Subjects

The photographs document automata; chronometers; clocks; horological tools; locks and keys; office equipment; phonographs; sandglasses; sundials; supplies; typewriters; and watches.

Arranged: By subject. 1) Clocks are arranged by country of origin and type of clock. 2) Watches are arranged by country of origin and maker (if known). 3) Locks and keys are arranged alphabetically by the maker's name. 4) Phonographs are arranged by manufacturer. 5) Automata are arranged by type.

Captioned: With catalog number and accession number.

Finding Aid: No.

Restrictions: No.

EI·91

Montgomery C. Meigs Collection

Dates of Photographs: 1853–1890

Collection Origins

This collection was assembled by division staff from diverse sources. A portion of this collection was given to the Smithsonian Institution in 1974.

Montgomery C. Meigs (1816–1892) served as an army engineer in Washington, D.C., from about 1853 to 1890. He created these papers during this period. Meigs also was an architect, diplomat, inventor, and scholar. He served as a regent of the Smithsonian Institution, and as the Quartermaster General of the U.S. Army during the Civil War.

Meigs is best known for his work as the design and construction engineer on the the Arts and Industries Building of the Smithsonian Institution (U.S. National Museum); General Post Office; Patent Office Building; Pension Building; U.S. Capitol (wings and dome); and the Washington Aqueduct.

Photographers represented include S.A. Holmes, New York; J.F. Jarvis; and possibly Meigs himself.

Physical Description

There are 725 photographs, including albumen photoprints; salted paper photoprints; and silver gelatin photoprints. These photographs are mounted in three albums and two portfolios. Other materials include drawings, etchings, maps, newspaper clippings, a photomechanical (collotype), and photostats.

Subjects

The photographs document Montgomery C. Meig's engineering projects in Washington, D.C., (circa 1853–1890) including the construction of the following: Cabin John Bridge; Capitol Machine Shop; F Street Elevation; General Post Office; Great Falls Dam; Hospital of the Insane; Patent Office Building; Pension Building; U.S. Capitol; WA Bridge #3 in Washington, D.C.; and Washington Aqueduct.

Other photographs are of architectural details; art work (including friezes); boats; Georgetown cityscapes; and machinery. There are also portraits of William R. Hutton and of Meigs, in uniform, holding a telescope.

Arranged: Into two series. 1) Scrapbooks with mounted images and clippings (chronologically and by construction project). 2) Photographs (in negative number order).

Captioned: With narrative description of the subject.

Finding Aid: An index for series 2 which lists the catalog number, a description, and the size of the photograph.

Restrictions: No.

EI·92

Mexican Power Station Collection

Dates of Photographs: 1907–1919

Collection Origins

This collection was assembled by members of the Electrical Engineering Department of Tufts College to document civil and mechanical engineering projects in Mexico from 1907 to 1919.

Physical Description

There are 40 silver gelatin photoprints.

Subjects

The photographs document mechanical and civil engineering projects in Chapultepec, La Noria, Necaxa, San Lorenzo, and Santa Cruz, Mexico.

There are photographs of boilers; dams; flumes;

penstocks; powerhouses; pumping stations; railroad construction; tunnel construction; and unidentified workers on payday.

Arranged: No.

Captioned: With subject information, such as, the name of equipment or structures shown.

Finding Aid: No.

Restrictions: No.

EI·93

Mills and Factories Collection

Dates of Photographs: 1920s–1980s

Collection Origins

This collection was assembled by division staff from diverse sources. Some of the materials were copied from original photographs in other divisions' collections. Segments of this collection came from the C. and G. Cooper Company; the Historic American Building Survey; the Library of Congress; the New England Textile Mills Survey; and Sach Boucher, Harrisville, New Hampshire.

Copy photographs came from the Merrimac Valley Textile Museum in North Andover, Massachusetts; the Boston Waterworks Collection of the Division of Engineering and Industry; and the Warshaw Collection of NMAH Archives Center.

Physical Description

There are 525 photographs, including silver gelatin photonegatives and photoprints. Other materials include advertisements, clippings, drawings, maps, notes, publications, and reports.

Subjects

The photographs document armories, factories, industry, and mill sites in New England, New Jersey, New York, and Pennsylvania.

There are photographs of Arctic Mill; Baltic Mill; Boston Belting Company; Busch; Campbell; Carolina Mill; Centerville Mill; China Mill; Chubb Company; Colt's Armory; Coventry Mill; Elizabeth Mill; Foot Joy; E.B. Frye & Sons Shop; Georgiaville Mill; Hamilton Mill; Harris Mill; Hillsboro Mill; Hope Mill; Lancaster Mills; Nashua Mill; Nonesuch Mill; Nonquit Spinning Wheel; Pepperill Manufacturing Company; C.S. Pierce Shoe Supplies; Whitter Mill; and Woonsocket Co. Mills.

Also included are photographs of drawings; layouts; maps; and plans of towns in Massachusetts, including Ballardsvale, Clinton, Dodgeville, Hebronville, Holyoke, New Bedford, and Southbridge.

Arranged: Alphabetically by state or county, then by corporate name (when known) or city and town.

Captioned: With the location; sometimes with the name of the corporation, and date.

Finding Aid: No.

Restrictions: No.

EI·94

Missouri River Improvement Project Collection

Dates of Photographs: 1895–1906

Collection Origins

This collection was assembled by the U.S. Army Corps of Engineers to document construction of dikes and piers along the Missouri River from 1895 to 1906.

Physical Description

There are 400 photographs, including cyanotypes and silver gelatin photoprints mounted in 17 albums. Some photographs unfold to form composite panoramas up to 15" long.

Subjects

The photographs document construction of piers and dikes along the Missouri River by the U.S. Army Corps of Engineers from 1895 to 1906.

Locations documented include Chamois Reach; Glasgow Reach; Howard's Reach; Huntsdale Reach; Jefferson City Reach; Little Blue Reach; Nebraska City Reach; Osage Point; Pelican Bend Reach; Portland Island; Randolf Bend; Rocheport Reach; Rulo Reach; and St. Joseph Reach.

Arranged: Chronologically.

Captioned: With location, date, and brief description of the image.

Finding Aid: No.

Restrictions: No.

EI·95

Nathan Morgan Collection

Dates of Photographs: 1911–1958

Collection Origins

This collection was assembled by Nathan Morgan (1911–   ) of Washington, D.C., a highway bridge engineer at the Bureau of Public Roads (now the Federal Highway Administration) between 1911 and 1945. Morgan specialized in welded bridges.

Photographic studios represented include Lollar's Studio of Birmingham, Alabama.

Physical Description

There are 1,400 silver gelatin photoprints mounted in binders, reports, scrapbooks, or loose. Other materials include blueprints, catalogs, clippings, reports, and trade literature.

Subjects

The photographs document bridge design and construction including bridges in Queenstown, Canada; Lewiston, New York; Providence, Rhode Island; Wheeling, West Virginia; and Belgrade, Yugoslavia.

There are photographs of the Concrete Bridge, Randolf Village, Vermont; Golden Gate Bridge, San Francisco, California; South Dakota Arch Bridge; State Bridge of Bridgeport, Vermont; and Watertown Bridge.

Arranged: No.

Captioned: With bridge name and location.

Finding Aid: The division's Archives Inventory File has a list of materials in this collection.

Restrictions: No.

EI·96

George S. Morison Collection

Dates of Photographs: Late 19th Century

Collection Origins

George Shattuck Morison was a civil engineer who specialized in the design of large bridges. He built ten bridges over the Missouri River, five over the Mississippi River, and one over the Ohio River. He also served as a member of the Panama Canal Commission from 1899 to 1903.

Morison designed bridges in New York and worked on the New York City waterfront. He also helped to locate a deep water harbor in southern California, and designed and built several viaducts.

Photographers and studios represented include Bailey & Neelands, Vancouver; Charles Besseler Co., New York; J.L. Brose, Chicago; J.A. Laird; Leavenworth Photographs; McIntosh Battery & Optical Co., Chicago; and J.C. Somerville, St. Louis.

Physical Description

There are 280 photographs, including albumen photoprints, cyanotypes (in an album), and silver gelatin dry plate lantern slides and photonegatives. Other materials include correspondence, leatherbound diaries, engravings, photogravures, and reports.

Subjects

The photographs document the career of George Shattuck Morison including his work on United States bridges and on the Panama Canal in the late 19th century.

There are photographs of the Bellefontaine Bridge, the Kansas City Bridge, the Memphis Bridge, and the Sioux City Bridge; and of Panama Canal construction.

Arranged: By type of material.

Captioned: Some glass negatives are captioned with location. Their envelopes show the negative number, name of subject, date, and remarks. Lantern slides have the date and subject etched into the emulsion.

Finding Aid: There is an online item-level index to the collection, and a separate 1903 index to the lantern slides. The collection is in the process of being cataloged.

Restrictions: No.

EI·97

New Croton Aqueduct Collection

Dates of Photographs: 1885–1887

Collection Origins

This collection was assembled and donated by the Massachusetts Institute of Technology in 1962.

Physical Description

There are 17 cyanotypes mounted on board.

Subjects

The photographs document the site of the Massachusetts Quaker Bridge Dam and Reservoir (around 1885–1887). There are also photographs of the Aqueduct of New Croton; the Sleepy Hollow highway bridge; and the surrounding landscape. Some construction activity is shown.

Arranged: No.

Captioned: With subject information, such as, location and project name.

Finding Aid: No.

Restrictions: No.

EI·98

New England Textile Mill Survey I

Dates of Photographs: 1967

Collection Origins

This collection was assembled in 1967 by division staff for a report on early New England mills.

Photographers represented include Jack E. Boucher and Randolph Langenbach.

Physical Description

There are 200 photographs, including color dye coupler transparencies, and silver gelatin photonegatives and photoprints. Other materials include clippings, correspondence, funding information, memoranda, press releases, and reports.

Subjects

The photographs document textile mills in New Hampshire and Massachusetts as they appeared in 1967. There are photographs of architectural details, floor plans, machinery in plant interiors, and mill exteriors. Mills documented include Amoskeag Manufacturing Company; Amoskeag Paper Mills; Lawrence Machine Shop in Lawrence, Massachusetts; river dye house and bleach house; and Stark Mills and other mills in Manchester, New Hampshire.

Arranged: By type of material.

Captioned: No.

Finding Aid: No.

Restrictions: No.

EI·99

New York State Barge Canal Collection

Dates of Photographs: 1911–1912

Collection Origins

This collection was assembled by an anonymous donor to document the reconstruction of New York State's Erie Canal, which was renamed the New York State Barge Canal. It was given to the Smithsonian Institution in 1969.

Physical Description

There are 250 silver gelatin photoprints.

Subjects

These photographs document the reconstruction (1911–1912) of the Erie Canal, which was later renamed the New York State Barge Canal. There are photographs of unidentified construction sites along the canal system which includes 525 miles of waterways from Lake Erie to the Hudson River, with extensions to Cayuga Lake, Lake Champlain, Lake Ontario, and Seneca Lake.

Arranged: No.

Captioned: No.

Finding Aid: No.

Restrictions: No.

EI·100

Niagara Falls Power Company Collection

Dates of Photographs: 1900–1917

Collection Origins

This collection was assembled by the division to document the construction of the Niagara Falls Power Company's hydroelectric plants and allied structures from 1900 to 1917.

It was donated by the Niagara Mohawk Company.

Physical Description

There are 1,750 silver gelatin photoprints. About 1,450 of these photoprints are mounted in albums.

Subjects

The photographs document the construction of the Niagara Falls Power Company hydroelectric plants from 1900 to 1917. There are photographs of canals; generators; governors; plant interiors; river views; transmission lines; turbines; and unidentified people. There are also images of the Erie Canal (New York State Barge Canal).

Arranged: Into two series. 1) Loose photographs (arranged by subject). 2) Albums of photographs (arranged chronologically).

Captioned: Loose photographs are captioned with subject and date information.

Finding Aid: Each album has an item-level index which lists image dates, titles, and brief descriptions.

Restrictions: No.

EI·101

Niagara Railroad Collection

Dates of Photographs: Circa 1880s–1920

Collection Origins

Unknown.

Physical Description

There are 140 silver gelatin dry plate photo-negatives.

Subjects

The photographs document the Niagara Railroad and its architectural structures, such as, terminals, between the 1880s and the 1920s, predominantly in New York state.

Arranged: In chronological order by date of creation.

Captioned: With date.

Finding Aid: No.

Restrictions: No.

EI·102

Nicaragua Canal Collection

Dates of Photographs: Circa 1898

Collection Origins

This collection was assembled by George W. Brown, a New York City engineer, who worked on the Nicaragua Canal project in 1898.

Physical Description

There are 40 silver gelatin photoprints tipped into a small album. Other materials include correspondence and a logbook.

Subjects

The photographs in this collection document George W. Brown's work on the construction of the Nicaragua Canal Bridge in 1898.

There are photographs of sites along the Nicaragua Canal, such as, Blewfields and Greytown; a breakwater; dredges; and railroad sites of the Nicaragua Canal Company.

There also are portraits of 'Beastie'; George W. Brown; Davis; S.S. Evans; E.P. Humphrey; Hatch; Mrs. M. Irving; 'J.S.'; Montgomery Meigs; Moorman; Park; Schurig; and Dr. Williams.

Arranged: No.

Captioned: Many prints have a narrative description and a date.

Finding Aid: No.

Restrictions: No.

EI·103

Nickerson & Collins Refrigeration Collection

Dates of Photographs: 1910–1912

Collection Origins

The Nickerson & Collins Company was the publisher of *Ice and Refrigeration* between 1910 and 1912. The collection was given to the museum in 1963.

Physical Description

There are 450 silver gelatin photoprints. Many of the photographs are mounted on board or linen and have been retouched. Other materials include blueprints and publications.

Subjects

The photographs document Nickerson & Collins's clients, facilities, and products between 1910 and 1912.

There are photographs of cold storage facilities; food markets; ice handling apparatus; the National Poultry and Egg Company; refrigeration equipment; plants; skating rinks; and tank rooms.

Arranged: No.

Captioned: With a narrative subject description.

Finding Aid: No.

Restrictions: No.

EI·104

Nordberg Manufacturing Company Collection

Dates of Photographs: Circa 1905–1980s

Collection Origins

The Nordberg Manufacturing Company built heavy power and mining machinery between 1905 and the present. The collection was donated to the division by the company.

Photographers represented include Brown Studio, Los Angeles; Jos. Brown & Son, Photographer; Hallenbech, Chicago; Hankwitz Photographers, Wisconsin; Moyer Photos, New Jersey; and Runder-Markham Photo Co., Inc., Missouri.

Physical Description

There are 14,500 photographs, including color dye coupler slides; silver gelatin dry plate lantern slides and photonegatives; and silver gelatin photonegatives and photoprints. The prints are tipped into one bound report and one bound album. Other materials include blueprints, catalogs, a construction report, linen tracings, notebooks, order books, reprints, test results, time records, and trade literature.

Subjects

The photographs document the equipment, facilities, and products of the Nordberg Manufacturing Company between 1905 and the 1980s. There are photographs of engines (diesel and steam), mine hoists, and vessels powered by Nordberg engines.

There are also images of the exterior and interior views of Marcy Mill; the Nordberg Plant; the Oklahoma Iron Works Plant; and the St. Louis Boat Company.

Arranged: Some glass and film photonegatives are arranged by negative number and some prints are arranged by contract number.

Captioned: Many glass negatives are in envelopes labeled with the accession number; negative number; job number; catalog number; and subject. Print captions include subject and negative number.

Finding Aid: No.

Restrictions: No.

EI·105

Northern Pacific Railway Collection

Dates of Photographs: 1880s–1945

Collection Origins

This collection was assembled by the staff of the Northern Pacific Railway between 1880 and 1945.

Physical Description

There are 215 silver gelatin photoprints.

Subjects

The photographs document the construction of the Northern Pacific Railway (1885–1890), including its Tacoma shops (1890). It also documents construction of bridges and coalbunkers.

Arranged: By subject.

Captioned: With subject and date.

Finding Aid: No.

Restrictions: No.

EI·106

Norton Grinding Company Collection

Dates of Photographs: ND

Collection Origins

This collection was assembled by the Norton Grinding Company staff to document their products and staff. It was later donated to the division.

Physical Description

There are 65 silver gelatin photoprints. Thirty are mounted on board.

Subjects

The subjects of the collection are the equipment, machinery, and products of the Norton Grinding Company. There are photographs of grinding machines; grinding shops; grindstones; ground work pieces; lab experiments; plant interiors; and portable grinders.

Arranged: By subject heading, such as, object name or type.

Captioned: With object name or type.

Finding Aid: No.

Restrictions: No.

EI·107

Robert F. Olds Collection

Dates of Photographs: Circa 1930s–1940s

Collection Origins

Robert F. Olds was a civil engineer for the Tennessee Valley Authority based in Knoxville. The collection documents the construction of dams and reservoirs in Tennessee.

It was donated to the Smithsonian Institution by a private donor in the early 1970s.

Physical Description

There are 50 silver gelatin photoprints, both loose and in project reports. Other materials include blueprints, contracts, and supply catalogs.

Subjects

The photographs document civil engineering projects conducted by the Tennessee Valley Authority from the 1930s to the 1940s, such as, the Pick Wick Landing Dam, Ross Dam, and Sacandaga Reservoir.

Arranged: No.

Captioned: No.

Finding Aid: No.

Restrictions: No.

EI·108

PCC and St L RR Collection A.K.A. Penn Central Railroad Collection

Dates of Photographs: 1925–1927

Collection Origins

This collection was assembled by an anonymous donor to document the construction of a second PCC and St L line (full name unknown) between Pierron and Collinsville, Illinois, from 1925 to 1927. The company later was absorbed by the Pennsylvania Railroad. This collection was given to the Smithsonian Institution in 1977 by a private donor.

Photographic studios represented include Blythe Studio, Illinois, and Voegele Studio, Illinois.

Physical Description

There are 210 silver gelatin photoprints.

Subjects

The photographs document the construction of two sections of a railroad line: from Pierron to St. Jacobs, and from St. Jacobs to Collinsville, Illinois, between 1925 and 1927.

There are photographs of bridges, stations, tracks, and unidentified workers.

Arranged: Two subject divisions. 1) Pierron to St. Jacobs, Illinois (1925–1926). 2) St. Jacobs to Collinsville, Illinois (1926–1927).

Captioned: With subjects, such as, object name or location.

Finding Aid: The division's Archives Inventory File includes a brief description of this collection.

Restrictions: No.

EI·109

Panama Canal Commission Collection

Dates of Photographs: 1904–1935

Collection Origins

This collection was created by the Panama Canal Commisssion.

Physical Description

There are 1,250 silver gelatin dry plate photonegatives.

Subjects

The photographs are panoramas of the Panama Canal showing equipment; locks with "mule locomotives"; ships; shops; towns; and windmills.

There are photographs of machinery, including cement mixers, cranes, dredges, hand and machine drills, hoists, pavers, portable compressors, steam shovels, tractors, and turbines.

Arranged: By subject into sixteen series. 1) Canal construction. 2) Locks. 3) Slides and removal. 4) Dredges. 5) Canal panoramas. 6) Construction machinery. 7) Power plant construction. 8) Piers and marine terminals. 9) Bridges. 10) Construction scenes and blasting. 11) Government structures. 12) Towers, cranes, and hoisting. 13) Dam construction. 14) Panama railroad trestles. 15) Water towers and gas holders. 16) Engineering.

Captioned: With a narrative subject description and dates.

Finding Aid: A two-page finding aid titled *Index to Panama Canal Commission Negatives* includes a brief description of the types of negatives in each subject heading.

Restrictions: No.

EI·110

Parsons, Brinckerhoff, Quade and Douglas Records Collection

Dates of Photographs: 1905–1918

Collection Origins

William Barclay Parsons (1859–1932) founded the engineering firm of Parsons, Brinckerhoff, Quade and Douglas in New York City in 1885. The collection was created by the firm, which is still active.

The collection was given to the division in 1967.

Physical Description

There are 150 silver gelatin photoprints bound within project reports.

Subjects

The photographs document the engineering projects of Parsons, Brinckerhoff, Quade and Douglas of New York City between 1905 and 1918.

The photographs are of hydroelectric plants, power plants, and railroad tunnels, in Alabama; California; Cuba; Georgia; New York; and Pennsylvania. Specific projects documented include the Compania del Puerto, Havana, Cuba; the Georgia Railway and Power Company, Atlanta, Georgia; the Niagara, Lockport, and Ontario Power Company; the North Georgia Electric Company hydroelectric developments and transmission system; the Schuylkill County Properties near Shenandoah, Pennsylvania; the tunnel of the New York and Long Island Railroad; and the Tuskegee, Alabama Water Supply System.

Arranged: No.

Captioned: No.

Finding Aid: The division's Archives Inventory File has a list of collection reports, listed alphabetically by title, which includes the name of the client and date of the project.

Restrictions: No.

EI·111

F.R. Patch Manufacturing Company Collection

Dates of Photographs: 1905–1918

Collection Origins

The F.R. Patch Manufacturing Company of Rutland, Vermont, produced stone working machinery between 1905 and 1918.

Photographic studios represented include the Andres Stone and Manufacturing Company.

Physical Description

There are of 55 photographs, including albumen photoprints, silver gelatin dry plate photonegatives, and silver gelatin photoprints.

Subjects

The photographs document the physical plant, processes, and products of the F.R. Patch Manufacturing Company of Rutland, Vermont, between 1905 and 1918. There are photographs of carborundum machinery; engines; grinders; plant interiors; polishers; and stone cutting machinery.

Arranged: No.

Captioned: No.

Finding Aid: No.

Restrictions: No.

EI·112

Paul Steam-Heating System Company Collection

Dates of Photographs: 1900–1915

Collection Origins

The Paul Steam-Heating System Company issued licenses for the use of their patents. They worked with Chauncey Matlock, New York City, a designer; the James P. Marsh Co., Chicago, Illinois, which made air valves; the T.B. Cryer Co., Newark, New Jersey, which made exhausters; and the Hancock Inspirater Co., which made ejecters.

This collection was given to the division in 1957 by T.B. Cryer.

Photographers and studios represented include Salgers Studios, Kentucky, and Frank M. Wallenlech, Chicago.

Physical Description

There are 155 photographs, including an albumen photoprint and silver gelatin photoprints. Other materials include blueprints, correspondence, licenses, lists of installations, patents, reports, and testimonials.

Subjects

The photographs document the licenses, patents, and products of the Paul Steam-Heating System Company between 1900 and 1915.

There are photographs of air valves, ejectors, exhausters, and plans and diagrams of heating systems. There are also images of the Dubuque City Water Works.

Arranged: No.

Captioned: With subject information.

Finding Aid: No.

Restrictions: No.

EI·113

Pelton Water Turbine Collection

Dates of Photographs: 1907–1908, 1919–1923

Collection Origins

This collection forms part of the Pelton Company archive. It was given to the Smithsonian by a successor firm.

Physical Description

There are 30 silver gelatin dry plate photonegatives.

Subjects

The photographs document the production of Pelton turbines (1907–1908 and 1919–1923).

Arranged: By assigned number.

Captioned: With the date of production and negative number.

Finding Aid: No.

Restrictions: No.

EI·114

Pennsylvania Railroad, New York City Improvement Project Collection

Dates of Photographs: Circa 1909

Collection Origins

This collection was assembled by division staff from various sources. The stereographs were purchased in 1979 from a dealer.

Physical Description

There are 45 photographs, including albumen stereographs, silver gelatin dry plate photonegatives, and silver gelatin photoprints.

Subjects

The photographs document the Pennsylvania Railroad's work in New York City, including the Pennsylvania Station foundations and the East and Hudson river tunnels.

Arranged: No.

Captioned: No.

Finding Aid: No.

Restrictions: No.

EI·115

Phelps-Dodge Collection

Dates of Photographs: Circa 1916–1925

Collection Origins

Unknown.

Physical Description

There are 90 photographs, including silver gelatin dry plate photonegatives and silver gelatin photoprints.

Subjects

The photographs document the Phelps-Dodge Company's construction of bombs and explosive shells during World War I.

There are photographs of grinders; hydraulic lathes; lathes; plant interiors; heavy thread-milling machines; and a Warren hydraulic change gear (1916).

Arranged: Into two series. 1) World War I hydraulic bomb lathes. 2) Phelps-Dodge Company plant interiors, products, and machinery.

Captioned: With subject information.

Finding Aid: No.

Restrictions: No.

EI·116

David Plowden Bridge Collection *A.K.A. Bridges: The Spans of North America* Collection

Dates of Photographs: 1970–1976

Collection Origins

David Plowden is an author and photographer. This collection contains many of the views from his book, *Bridges: The Spans of North America.* New York City: Viking Press for Studio Books, 1974. Some photographs also were used in an exhibition to publicize the book.

Physical Description

There are 17 silver gelatin photoprints.

Subjects

The photographs document bridges of North America, including covered, suspension, and truss bridges.

There are also photographs of details of bridges, such as, arches and pylons; and bridge silhouettes.

Arranged: No.

Captioned: No.

Finding Aid: No.

Restrictions: No.

EI·117

Charles Richardson Pratt Collection

Dates of Photographs: 1881–1930

Collection Origins

This collection was assembled by C.R. Pratt (1860–1935), a mechanical engineer of Montclair, New Jersey. In 1890, Pratt and Frank J. Sprague developed the Sprague-Pratt Elevator, the first electric elevator capable of heavy-duty, high-rise service. This collection was purchased in 1973 from Pratt's daughter.

Photographers and studios represented include Charles A. Dunlap; A.H. Folsom Photo, Massachusetts; L. Kuhn, Commercial Photo, New Jersey; William Patterson, New Jersey; and Washington Souvenir Co.

Physical Description

There are 85 photographs, including albumen photoprints, platinum photoprints, and silver gelatin photoprints. A few images are toned or tinted. Other materials include blueprints, correspondence, letterbooks, line drawings, reports, and trade literature.

Subjects

The photographs document elevators and elevator components of the Sprague-Pratt Company between 1881 and 1930. There are photographs of automobile transmissions; elevator assemblies; miscellaneous elevator parts; Otis Elevators; the Sprague-Pratt Elevator; a steam elevator by Whittier Machine Company; a variable stoke pump elevator; and the Watson Elevator. There is also a photograph of the Campbell, Whittier & Company Works in Boston.

There are also portraits of C.R. Pratt and his family; and of the 39th Meeting of the American Society of Mechanical Engineers at the State, War, and Navy Building in Washington, D.C., which includes Pratt and Mary Ladd Pratt, his wife.

Arranged: By type of material and subject.

Captioned: With subject information.

Finding Aid: The division's Archives Inventory File has a box list of the materials in this collection.

Restrictions: No.

EI·118

Providence Engineering Works Records Collection

Dates of Photographs: 1881–1933

Collection Origins

The Providence (Rhode Island) Engineering Works was successor to the Rice and Sargent Company and the Providence Steam Engine Company. This collection documents the activities of the company under all three names. It was given to the Smithsonian Institution in 1965.

Photographers and photographic studios represented include the Dodge Motor Co. Photograph Collection; OPPS; and the Sipp Machine Co., New Jersey.

Physical Description

There are 900 photographs, including silver gelatin photoprints (some mounted on linen); silver gelatin photonegatives (on diacetate, nitrate, and triacetate); and silver gelatin dry plate photonegatives. Other materials include advertisements; blueprints; cost records; a drawing book; notes; order books; parts and pattern listings; publications; a shipping book; and standard and special engine details.

Subjects

The photographs document the Rice and Sargent steam engines, a major product line of the Providence Engineering Works. There are photographs of centrifugal pumps; generators; governors; machine tools; marine engines; and interior shop views.

Arranged: No.

Captioned: With narrative subject descriptions.

Finding Aid: The division's Archives Inventory File has a partial collection list which gives the size, negative number, and a brief description.

Restrictions: No.

EI·119

Puerto Rico Road Building Album Collection

Dates of Photographs: 1900–1945

Collection Origins

This collection was assembled by the Bureau of Engineering during the administration of Charles H. Allen, the first Civil Governor of Puerto Rico.

This collection was given to the Smithsonian in 1970 by a private donor.

Physical Description

There are 135 silver gelatin photoprints mounted in a leather album. Some prints are tinted.

Subjects

The photographs document road-building in Puerto Rico between 1900 and 1945. There are pho-

tographs of abutments; bridges; concrete pipes; culverts; excavations; retaining walls; and stone quarrying. There are photographs of the following finished roads: Arecibo to Ponce, Cagugas to Humacao, from Comercio northward, Guayama to Arroyo, Mayaguez to Las Marias, and Moca to San Sebastian.

Arranged: Chronologically by project.

Captioned: With a narrative subject descriptions on album page.

Finding Aid: No.

Restrictions: No.

EI·120

Pullman Works Manufacturing Collection

Dates of Photographs: 1880s–1940s

Collection Origins

The Pullman Car Works were producers of railroad cars between the 1880s and the 1940s. Pullman Car Works staff created the collection to document production activities, facilities, and machinery.

Note: This collection was separated from a larger collection of car photographs in the Division of Transportation.

Physical Description

There are 325 photographs, including silver gelatin dry plate photonegatives, and silver gelatin photonegatives and photoprints. Other materials include a publication.

Subjects

The photographs document the equipment (for metal and wood working), the facilities, and the production techniques of the Pullman Car Works from the 1880s to 1940s.

There are photographs of production scenes

showing air drilling; bending machines; grinding; hydraulic presses; plate drilling; punching line work; radial sawing; riveting; turning; and woodplaning.

There are also photographs of interior plant scenes and inspection operators at work.

Arranged: In two series. 1) Original photonegatives. 2) Copy photonegatives and photoprints. Within the two series materials are arranged by original negative number.

Captioned: With subject, date, and negative number.

Finding Aid: No.

Restrictions: No.

EI·121

Quebec Bridge Collection

Dates of Photographs: 1916, 1970s

Collection Origins

This collection was created by the Quebec Bridge Company and was later donated to the division for research use.

Photographic studios represented include the Chesterfield & McLaren Studio.

Physical Description

There are 260 silver gelatin photoprints mounted on loose sheets of black album paper.

Subjects

The photographs document the construction of the Quebec cantilever railroad bridge in Quebec, Canada, in 1916. There are photographs of construction; the fabricating plant's equipment; interiors; men at work; and steel parts being loaded on trains for shipment to the site.

Arranged: No.

Captioned: No.

Finding Aid: No.

Restrictions: Some for reference only. No duplication allowed.

EI·122

Railroad Station Historical Society Archives Collection

Dates of Photographs: Circa 1900–1980s

Collection Origins

This collection consists of the archives of the Railroad Station Historical Society, which is headquartered in Crete, Nebraska. The Society gathers data, maintains records, and publishes information regarding railroad stations through a semi-annual newsletter. The Division of Engineering and Industry is the repository for the society's archival materials.

Photographers represented include S.R. Burgess; J.R. Carl; T.W. Dixon, Jr.; and G.E. Ford, Jr.

Physical Description

There are 1,200 photographs, including color dye coupler photonegatives, photoprints, and slides; and silver gelatin photonegatives and photoprints. Other materials include correspondence and newsletters.

Subjects

The photographs document historical railroad stations, dating from 1900 through the 1980s, throughout Canada, Denmark, England, and the United States.

Arranged: By negative number.

Captioned: With subject and date.

Finding Aid: An index listing image number; railroad name; location; date of construction; date of the original photograph; whether the image is a print or a negative; and content remarks.

Restrictions: No.

EI·123

Samuel E. Reed Covered Bridge Collection

Dates of Photographs: 1947–1964

Collection Origins

This collection was assembled by Samuel Edward Reed (1872–1964) and Grace Fillmore Reed (1885–   ) of Bradford, Illinois, between January 1947 and March 1964, from a variety of sources.

Two of the photographs were taken by the Reeds; all others were purchased during their travels. Grace Reed arranged the material into albums by geographic area.

Physical Description

There are 1,440 photographs, including albumen photoprints (two are stereographs); color dye coupler slides; color dye diffusion photoprints (Polaroid); and silver gelatin photoprints.

Subjects

The photographs document covered bridges in Canada and the United States and were taken between 1947 and 1964. There are photographs of bridges from: Wood Date, Delaware; Haw Creek, Illinois; Geneva, Indiana; Old Town, Maine; Forest Lake and Harurch, Massachusetts; Bold Hill, Oregon; Troy, Vermont; Erwin, West Virginia; and Madison, Wisconsin. There are also photographs which show buggies or cars entering covered bridges.

Arranged: Into three series. 1) Eleven scrapbooks arranged alphabetically by state or province and then by bridge name. 2) Eight scrapbooks and a three-ring binder index arranged by country, and then by state, name of bridge, name of the river it spans, name of nearby town, and date. 3) Loose slides organized by country, and state or province.

Captioned: With subjects, such as, country, state, bridge, river, and date.

Finding Aid: An index to the second series lists the images by country; state; bridge name; river name; town name; and gives the appropriate notebook and page number.

Restrictions: No.

EI·124

Robert B. Rice Collection

Dates of Photographs: Prior to 1940

Collection Origins

This collection was created by engineer Robert B. Rice.

Physical Description

There are 215 photographs, including collodion wet plate lantern slides and silver gelatin photoprints. Other materials include correspondence; fuel-burning reports; manuscripts; pamphlets; and a survey of internal combustion engines.

Subjects

The photographs document diesel engines made by Atlas Imperial; Buda; Cooper-Bessemer; Fairbanks-Morse; General Motors; Hamilton; and International Harvester.

Arranged: By company name.

Captioned: Folders are labeled with company names.

Finding Aid: An item-level index to large format photoprints.

Restrictions: No.

EI·125

Rip Van Winkle Bridge Collection

Dates of Photographs: 1933–1934

Collection Origins

The State of New York, Department of Public Works, Division of Engineering, created this collection to document construction of the Rip Van Winkle Bridge over the Hudson River at Catskill, New York, between 1933 and 1934.

State of New York photographers represented include A.C. Dario, F.J. Hart, and A. McMahon.

Physical Description

There are 90 silver gelatin photoprints.

Subjects

The photographs document the construction of the Rip Van Winkle Bridge in Catskill, New York, between 1933 and 1934. There are photographs of the bridge during various construction stages, construction crews at work, and pier interiors.

Arranged: By State of New York assigned photograph number.

Captioned: With the State of New York photograph number; subject; camera location or point of view; date; and remarks.

Finding Aid: No.

Restrictions: No.

EI·126

John A. Roebling's Sons Company Collection *A.K.A.* Blair Birdsall Collection

Dates of Photographs: 1928–1956

Collection Origins

This collection was assembled by the staff of the John A. Roebling's Sons Company. The company was created by the sons of John Augustus Roebling (1806–1869), the designer of the Brooklyn Bridge, to document the firm's bridge construction projects.

The company was operated by Washington Augustus Roebling (1837–1926), president; Ferdinand W. Roebling (ND), treasurer and general manager; and Charles Gustavus Roebling (1849–   ).

The collection was donated to the division by Blair Birdsall, the firm's former chief engineer.

Physical Description

There are 5,000 silver gelatin photoprints. Most images are mounted in leather albums. Other materials include blueprints, clippings, handwritten notes, publications, reprints, sketches, and specifications.

Subjects

The photographs document aerial tramway and bridge projects of the John A. Roebling's Sons Company, between 1928 and 1950, in Mexico and the United States.

There are photographs of the Amparo Mining Company Tramway, Etzalan, Jalisco, Mexico; A. T. & T. Company; Chain Bridge, Washington, D.C.; Crown Point Spar Company Tramway, Crown Point, New York; Gillespie Company Tramway, High Falls, New York; Homeopathic State Hospital for the Insane, Allentown, Pennsylvania (tramway); Hudson River Bridge; Mt. Hood Tramway, Oregon; Potomac River Highway Bridge; Rappahannock River Bridge; and the West Virginia Pulp and Paper Company Conveyor Bridge.

There are also photographs of bridges constructed by other firms which used Roebling cable or manufacturing specifications, such as, the High Falls, New York bridge.

Arranged: By project, and then chronologically.

Captioned: With subject, such as, location, and date.

Finding Aid: A partial list.

Restrictions: No.

EI·127

William J. Savage Company Records Collection

Dates of Photographs: 1917–1939

Collection Origins

The William J. Savage Company of Knoxville, Tennessee, manufactured crushing, milling, and pulverizing equipment used in cotton, feed, and flour mills from 1917 to 1939.

Physical Description

There are six photographs, including cyanotypes and silver gelatin photoprints. Other materials include blueprints, correspondence, and office files.

Subjects

The photographs document products produced by the William J. Savage Co. from 1917 to 1939, such as, counter shaft drive and cross shaft drive batch mixers; crushing, milling, and pulverizing equipment; and turbines used in cotton, feed, and flour mills. Also included is a 1919 group portrait of department heads of the C. and G. Cooper Company.

Arranged: No.

Captioned: No.

Finding Aid: No.

Restrictions: No.

EI·128

63rd Street (NYC) Tunnel Collection

Dates of Photographs: Circa 1969

Collection Origins

This collection was assembled by division staff from material created by the New York City Transit Authority to record the construction of the 63rd Street Tunnel under the East River, a project to improve and extend the city's subway system during the 1960s.

Physical Description

There are 50 silver gelatin photoprints. Other materials include correspondence, cost estimates, memoranda, newspaper clippings, press releases, and proposals.

Subjects

The photographs document the construction of the 63rd Street Tunnel in New York City, including photographic reproductions of drawings, models, and plans of the tunnel.

There is one group portrait of the signing of the tunnel contract with project executives George W. Benisch; Alfred C. Maevis; Frank P. Robertson; William J. Ronan; Daniel T. Scannell; and Walter L. Schlager.

Arranged: No.

Captioned: The group photograph is captioned.

Finding Aid: No.

Restrictions: No.

EI·129

Skinner Engine Company Collection

Dates of Photographs: Circa 1920s

Collection Origins

The Skinner Engine Company of Erie, Pennsylvania, manufactured steam engines during the 1920s. Company staff created the collection to document their line of steam engines.

Photographers represented include Bert G. Covell of Alabama.

Physical Description

There are 800 silver gelatin photoprints mounted on linen.

Subjects

The photographs document the plant and products of the Skinner Engine Company during the 1920s, including engine parts and details; the factory exterior and interior; and slide-valve and universal uniflow engines.

Arranged: By subject.

Captioned: No.

Finding Aid: No.

Restrictions: No.

EI·130

Lawrence Talma Smith Collection

Dates of Photographs: Circa 1927–1940, 1951–1957

Collection Origins

This collection was assembled by Lawrence Talma Smith (1899–   ), a Chicago structural engineer.

Smith documented projects for the Chicago Park District; Florence Lake Tunnel in California; and the Holland Tunnel in New York City.

This collection was given to the Smithsonian in 1974 by Smith's daughter.

Physical Description

There are 400 photographs, including silver gelatin photoprints and 24 uncut rolls of tightly curled silver gelatin photonegatives on nitrate. Due to its preservation state, the roll film was unavailable for surveying. Other materials include drawings, reports, specifications, and a thesis.

Subjects

The photographs document structural engineering projects with which Lawrence Talma Smith was involved between 1927 and 1940 and from 1951 to 1957.

There are photographs of the following projects: the Chicago Park District; Florence Lake Tunnel in California; and Holland Tunnel in New York City.

Chicago Park District work that was documented includes Bridge #3; Calumet Park Pier; Chicago River Bridge; Edens Spur–Tri-State Utility survey; Garfield Park Chimney; Illinois State Turnpike; Jackson Park; Leif Erikson and 47th Street Foot Bridge; Monroe Street Viaduct; the 63rd Street Foot Bridge; Soldier Field and Pistol Range; South Bridge; the 39th Street Viaduct; and the Wilson and Lake Lawrence Avenue Bridge.

There are also photographs of asphalt laying, concrete curing, and ornamental concrete work.

Arranged: No.

Captioned: With subject and date.

Finding Aid: A partial list in the division's Archives Inventory File.

Restrictions: No.

EI·131

S. Morgan Smith Company Collection

Dates of Photographs: 1890–1914

Collection Origins

The S. Morgan Smith Company was founded by inventor and entrepreneur S. Morgan Smith. The company, now the hydraulic turbine division of the Allis-Chalmers Company, York, Pennsylvania, manufactures water turbines. The collection was given to the division in 1968.

Physical Description

There are 2,100 photographs, including silver gelatin dry plate photonegatives and silver gelatin photoprints. Other materials include advertising art work and catalogs.

Subjects

The photographs document the equipment, facilities, personnel, and products of the S. Morgan Smith (Allis-Chalmers) Company from 1890 to 1914.

There are photographs of engines; fire pumps; generators; paper machinery; power-transmission machinery; Smith-Vaile and Stilwell-Bierce turbines; and turbines for the Sao Paulo Tramway Light and Power Company.

There are photographs of the construction of a dam and hydroelectric station by the Atlanta Water and Electric Power Company. There are also images of the construction of the Mathis Dam near Atlanta, with high-tension wires, and railroad-bridge and substation construction.

Arranged: In albums by subject.

Captioned: With subject information.

Finding Aid: 1) The division's Archives Inventory File includes a collection inventory. 2) There is also an index of negatives which has the job title, technical data, date, and description.

Restrictions: No.

EI·132

Snake River Irrigation Project Album

Dates of Photographs: Circa 1912

Collection Origins

Unknown.

Physical Description

There are 60 silver gelatin photoprints mounted in a single album.

Subjects

The photographs document the Snake River Project in Arizona, circa 1912. There are photographs of desert landscapes with wagons; irrigation canals; men at camps; men building pump stations; and pump stations.

Arranged: In chronological order.

Captioned: No.

Finding Aid: No.

Restrictions: No

EI·133

Society for Industrial Archeology Collection

Dates of Photographs: 1968–Present

Collection Origins

The Society for Industrial Archeology was based in the Smithsonian's Division of Engineering and Industry. Some photographs predate the Society's founding in 1972.

Photographers represented include John Cory, Ottawa; F. Lee Eiseman, Boston; and Randolph Langenbach, Boston.

Physical Description

There are 615 photographs, including color dye coupler photoprints and silver gelatin photoprints. Other materials include correspondence; fliers; meeting agendas; membership information; newsletters; and pamphlets.

Subjects

The photographs document 19th century industrial sites and structures visited during the Society's conferences and tours in the 1970s.

There are photographs of the circular gasometer enclosure in Troy, New York; cotton mills in Richmond, North Carolina (circa 1869); Day Basket Works in Maryland; Lippitt Mill in Rhode Island (circa 1810); Principio Furnace in Maryland (circa 1836); Stewartstown in Pennsylvania; stone-cutting building in Seneca, Maryland (circa 1840); and a water wheel built by Henry Burden (1851).

There are also images of the Industrial Archeology Conferences of 1968, 1972, and 1973, which toured Cooper-Union, New York City; the industrial sites of Troy, New York; the Irdaen Canal Bridge; Quinebaug, Massachusetts; and Watson's Mill, Paterson, New Jersey.

Arranged: No.

Captioned: With subject, date, and negative numbers.

Finding Aid: No.

Restrictions: No.

EI·134

Southwark Foundry and Machine Company Collection

Dates of Photographs: ND

Collection Origins

The Southwark Foundry and Machine Company, Philadelphia, Pennsylvania, was a manufacturer of heavy power and manufacturing machinery.

The company staff created this collection to document its products and facilities.

Physical Description

There are 30 silver gelatin photoprints.

Subjects

The photographs document the machinery; physical plant; production processes; and products of the Southwark Foundry and Machine Company in Philadelphia, Pennsylvania.

There are photographs of baling presses; high and low pressure hydraulic accumulators; hydraulic pumps; plate planers and profiling machines in the Navy Yard, Philadelphia; and pulp presses.

Arranged: No.

Captioned: No.

Finding Aid: No.

Restrictions: No.

EI·135

David Taylor Model Basin Collection

Dates of Photographs: 1940s–1950s

Collection Origins

This collection consists of a report by Mills Dean III, entitled "Frontier Days of Electronic Measurements of the Taylor Model Basin." The report contains photographs of the model basin and diagrams of its construction. It was donated by an anonymous individual.

Physical Description

There are 70 photographs, including a silver gelatin photonegative and photoprints. Other materials include clippings, notes, patents, records, reprints, and stock certificates.

Subjects

The photographs document the equipment, facilities, staff, and testing activities of the David Taylor Model Basin in the 1940s. Photographs are of cathode ray tube recording channels; circuits; diagrams; a dynamometer; sections of ships at sea; and a static and dynamic ship analog computor.

There are also photographs of the David Taylor Model Basin (exterior and interior shots); the electronics laboratory (1945); Model Basin staff; and the 24th Annual Meeting of the Eastern Section of the Seismological Society of America (June 1952, Buffalo, New York).

Arranged: The photoprints are within the Dean report. The rest of the collection is unarranged.

Captioned: With dates.

Finding Aid: No.

Restrictions: No.

EI·136

Treloar Railroad Station Collection

Dates of Photographs: 1970s

Collection Origins

The photographs were taken by Elmer Treloar of Highland Park, Detroit, Michigan.

Physical Description

There are 600 silver gelatin photonegatives.

Subjects

The photographs document railroad stations in Canada and the United States in the 1970s.

There are photographs of the Ann Arbor Railroad car passenger office, Elberta, Michigan; Ann Arbor Railroad car passenger office, Howell, Michigan; Baltimore & Ohio Station in Deshler, Ohio; Baltimore & Ohio Station in Tiffin, Ohio; and Canadian National Station in Beaverton, Ontario.

Arranged: By railroad name and location of the structure.

Captioned: With subject; date; film type; location; and name of station.

Finding Aid: No.

Restrictions: No.

EI·137

Turner Machine Company Collection

Dates of Photographs: ND

Collection Origins

The Turner Machine Company of Danbury, Connecticut, built hat machinery. The collection was donated by the firm in 1970.

Physical Description

There are 40 photographs, including silver gelatin dry plate photonegatives; and silver gelatin photoprints and a photonegative. Other materials are advertisements and correspondence.

Subjects

This collection documents hat making machinery manufactured by the Turner Machine Company.

Arranged: By subject.

Captioned: No.

Finding Aid: No.

Restrictions: No.

EI·138

Verrazano Narrows Bridge Collection

Dates of Photographs: 1959–1964

Collection Origins

This collection was assembled by a private donor to document the construction of the Verrazano Narrows Bridge from 1959 to 1964 by the Triborough Bridge and Tunnel Authority. The bridge stands between Staten Island and Brooklyn, New York.

Physical Description

There are 100 photographs, including silver gelatin photonegatives and photoprints. Other materials include a notebook and publications.

Subjects

The photographs document construction of the Verrazano Narrows Bridge between Brooklyn and Staten Island, New York, from 1959 to 1964. There are also photographs of the completed bridge.

Arranged: A portion of the prints are mounted in a notebook entitled "Triborough Bridge and Tunnel Authority Narrows Bridge Perspective Views & Construction Photographs." The rest of the collection is unarranged.

Captioned: With narrative subject information.

Finding Aid: The division's Archives Inventory File has a list of materials in this collection.

Restrictions: No.

EI·139

Washington, D.C., Bridges Collection

Dates of Photographs: Circa 1890–1910, 1970s

Collection Origins

This collection was assembled by John Meigs, a Washington, D.C., civil engineer. It was given to the Smithsonian in 1965 by the City of Washington, D.C.

Physical Description

There are 125 photographs, including cyanotypes and silver gelatin photonegatives and photoprints. Other materials include a letterbook and notebooks.

Subjects

The photographs document bridges and bridge construction in the Washington, D.C., area between 1890 and 1910. There are photographs of bridge foundations; and concrete, steel, and stone bridges. Specific bridges documented include the Potomac Highway (14th Street) Bridge; the Washington Aqueduct Bridge; and the Washington Channel Bridge.

Arranged: No.

Captioned: With subject and dates.

Finding Aid: No.

Restrictions: No.

EI·140

Washington Water Supply Aqueduct Collection

Dates of Photographs: 1960s–1970s

Collection Origins

This collection was assembled by division staff to document the construction of the Washington (Potomac) Aqueduct.

Physical Description

There are 90 photographs, including silver gelatin photonegatives and photoprints (including a stereograph). Other materials include xerographic copies of correspondence; and a xerographic copy of a report entitled "History of Washington Aqueduct" by Washington District Corps of Engineers, 1953.

Subjects

The photographs document the history of the Washington (Potomac) Aqueduct. There are photographs of the aqueduct construction; decoration and ornamentation (between 1853 and 1881); and pipes and conduits.

Arranged: No.

Captioned: No.

Finding Aid: No.

Restrictions: No.

EI·141

Robert Lee Weide Collection

Dates of Photographs: Circa 1930s

Collection Origins

Robert Lee Weide was a construction engineer with the James Baird Company of Washington, D.C. This collection was given to the Smithsonian Institution by Weide's heirs in 1980.

Photographic studios represented include Leet Bros., Inc.; and the Potomac Electric Power Company, Bennings Plant, Washington, D.C.

Physical Description

There are 200 silver gelatin photoprints (some oversized panoramas). Half of the photographs are mounted in three photograph albums.

Subjects

The photographs illustrate engineering projects including bridges, dams, power plants and schools, worked on by Robert Lee Weide in the 1930s.

There are photographs of Boulder Dam, Colorado; Coleman Falls, Virginia; Coosawattee River, Georgia; Folger Library, Washington, D.C.; Madeira School for Girls; Normal High School; and the Potomac Electric Power Company, Bennings Plant, Washington, D.C.

Arranged: By subject.

Captioned: With date and location.

Finding Aid: No.

Restrictions: No.

EI·142

West Point Foundry Collection

Dates of Photographs: 1898–1979

Collection Origins

This collection was assembled by division staff from diverse sources to document the history of the West Point Foundry, Cold Spring, New York.

Physical Description

There are 170 photographs, including copy color dye coupler photoprints and copy silver gelatin photoprints. Other materials include maps and a report on the foundry.

Subjects

These copy photographs document American foundries and foundry sites including those of Cold Spring, Nelsonville, and West Point. Note: Many images were originally taken in the 1860s.

Towns documented include Cold Spring and Nelsonville, New York. Other areas illustrated include the West Point foundry site; and the Hudson River gorge near the foundry.

Activities and products shown include manufacturing of Parrot guns for the Union Army; and marine and stationary steam engines. The color images are of a painting by John Ferguson Weir (1841–1926) called *The Gun Foundry.*

Arranged: By subject into four series. 1) Details of Weir's painting. 2) Hudson River and Cold Spring foundry site. 3) Maps. 4) A foundry site in Nelsonville, New York.

Captioned: No.

Finding Aid: No.

Restrictions: No.

EI·143

Westinghouse Electric and Manufacturing Company Collection

Dates of Photographs: 1881–1920

Collection Origins

This collection consists of the customer order and photographic records of the Westinghouse Electric and Manufacturing Company, East Pittsburgh, Pennsylvania (moved in 1920s to Lester [Philadelphia], Pennsylvania). It was given to the Smithsonian in 1965 by the Company.

Physical Description

There are 6,000 photographs, including cyanotypes and silver gelatin photoprints. Other materials include bulletins, business records, catalogs, and instruction books.

Subjects

The photographs document the equipment, facilities, installations, products, and staff of Westinghouse Electric and Manufacturing Company of Pennsylvania from 1881 to 1920.

There are photographs of automobile engines; blowing engines; generating engines; horizontal and vertical Corliss engines; horizontal and vertical gas engine-generators; Ribbet exhaust heaters; and Westinghouse engines (compound, junior, and standard).

There are also photographs of factories, mills, power plants, and steelworks including the Mankato Gas and Electric Company station (construction and plant views); and the Trafford City foundry.

Arranged: Into two series. 1) Photographs. (Arranged by type of product or subject heading into 12 series). 2) Records.

Captioned: With subject information.

Finding Aid: The division's Archives Inventory File has a list of photographs with the negative number, subject, and location.

Restrictions: No.

EI·144

Westinghouse Philippine Power-Mission Collection

Dates of Photographs: May 28–July 8, 1947

Collection Origins

This collection was assembled by Ray Quick, an employee of Westinghouse Power. Quick explored the power potential of the Philippine Islands between May 28th and July 8th of 1947.

The collection is in the form of a travelog. It was donated by Quick's heirs.

Physical Description

There are 150 silver gelatin photoprints mounted in a leather-bound album.

Subjects

The photographs document Quick's acquaintances and his travels to the Philippines. Most of the images are group portraits or scenic landscapes. Places shown include Corregidor; Guam; Itogon Trail; La Guardia Airport; and Manila Bay.

There are photographs of fish weirs, graves of Americans, rivers, scenic landscapes, and sunken ships. There are also photographs of the Philippines National Power Company in Luzon.

Arranged: No.

Captioned: With subject information.

Finding Aid: No.

Restrictions: No.

EI·145

Wheeling & Lake Erie Railway Collection

Dates of Photographs: 1905–1942

Collection Origins

This collection was created by the Wheeling & Lake Erie Railway. It consists of official company photographs documenting the history and growth of the company from 1905 to 1942.

Physical Description

There are 950 photographs, including silver gelatin dry plate photonegatives and silver gelatin photoprints.

Subjects

The photographs document the equipment, staff, and structures of the Wheeling & Lake Erie Railway Company (between 1905 and 1942).

There are photographs of bridges, cars, crossings, docks, lights, locomotives, ore unloaders, outbuildings, passenger and freight stations, roads, rolling stock, rotary car dumpers, signals, tanks and water towers, tracks, tunnels, and yards.

People illustrated include concert bands and veteran employees at conventions. There are also photographs of Chagrin Falls.

Arranged: Into two series. 1) Photonegatives. 2) Photoprints, subdivided by location.

Captioned: With OPPS negative number.

Finding Aid: A guide listing negative number; name of railway division; county and state; date; view direction; and a description.

Restrictions: No.

EI·146

Joseph Whitworth Collection

Dates of Photographs: 1981–1983

Collection Origins

This collection was assembled by division staff as research and documentation materials for an 1984 exhibition titled "Joseph Whitworth: Toolmaker: 1803–1887."

Joseph Whitworth (1803–1887) was a mechanical engineer from Manchester, England, who established new standards for machine tool production in the 19th century. Some of his early machinery and tools are illustrated in this collection.

Photographers represented include Hervey Green of the Science Museum of London, England, and Eric Long of OPPS.

Physical Description

There are 130 photographs, including color dye coupler photoprints; dye diffusion transfer photoprints (Polaroid); and silver gelatin photoprints. Other materials include an accession memorandum, advertisements, correspondence, drawings, and notes.

Subjects

The photographs document the machinery and tools produced by Joseph Whitworth, such as, cutting tools; drill and reamer bits; etching tools; lathes; plug and ring gauge sets; tap and die sets; and thread chasing tools.

Arranged: By type of material and subject.

Captioned: No.

Finding Aid: No.

Restrictions: No.

EI·147

Willys-Overland Company Collection

Dates of Photographs: 1914–1917

Collection Origins

This collection was assembled by staff of the Willys-Overland Company between 1914 and 1917. It documents the steps involved in the making of ordnance shells.

Physical Description

There are 105 photographs, including silver gelatin photonegatives on nitrate and photoprints.

Subjects

This collection documents World War I ordnance shell production at the Willys-Overland Company.

Arranged: No.

Captioned: With narrative subject information.

Finding Aid: No.

Restrictions: No

EI·148

Raymond E. Wilson Covered Bridge Collection

Dates of Photographs: 1962–1967

Collection Origins

This collection was assembled by Raymond E. Wilson to document covered bridges throughout the United States.

Physical Description

There are 1,500 photographs, including color dye coupler slides (Ektachrome and Kodachrome) and silver gelatin photoprints. Other materials include books and pamphlets.

Subjects

The photographs document American covered bridges from 1962 to 1967 in Alabama; California; Connecticut; Georgia; Illinois; Indiana; Massachusetts; Missouri; New York; North Carolina; South Carolina; and Virginia.

Arranged: By type of material, then by region and state.

Captioned: With location; date; orientation; bridge name; and waterway.

Finding Aid: No.

Restrictions: No.

EI·149

"With Edison at Schenectady" Collection

Dates of Photographs: 1892

Collection Origins

This collection was assembled by William H. Butler for publication in 1892 as a guide to the new Edison General Electric Works in Schenectady, New York.

Photographers and studios represented include American Aristotype Co., Jamestown, New York; Falk of 949 Broadway, New York City; and Talbot of Schenectady.

Physical Description

There are 24 silver gelatin photoprints (POP chloride) mounted in a leather-bound album. Many of the prints are composites, made from collodion wet plate photonegatives, and printed on Aristo paper.

Subjects

The photographs document the Edison General Electric Works in Schenectady, New York, during Thomas Edison's tenure there in 1892.

There are photographs of the correspondence department; the foundry; foremen and other staff; and the power station. There is also a view from the crane in No. 9 shop.

Arranged: Unarranged in an album.

Captioned: With subject information on album pages.

Finding Aid: No.

Restrictions: No.

EI·150

Wolverine Gasoline and Diesel Engines Collection

Dates of Photographs: 1950–1973

Collection Origins

This collection was assembled by Albert W. Hagan, a Florida engineer. Hagan used this collection as source material for his history (unpublished) of the Sintz-Wolverine Company. This collection was given to the Smithsonian Institution in 1978 by Hagan.

Physical Description

There are 100 silver gelatin photoprints. Other materials include blueprints, catalogs, clippings, correspondence, and handbooks.

Subjects

The photographs document the equipment, facilities, and products of the Sintz-Wolverine Company.

There are photographs of air compressors, boats, an electroplating company, engine rooms, pumps, shop views, sub-chaser engines, and Wolverine diesel and gasoline engines.

Arranged: Chronologically.

Captioned: With subject (often product identification) and date.

Finding Aid: An index includes type and title of documents, dates, sizes, and subjects.

Restrictions: No.

EI·151

Silas H. Woodard Collection

Dates of Photographs: Circa 1899–1914, 1926, 1930–1932

Collection Origins

This collection was assembled by Silas H. Woodard, a civil engineer who specialized in dams, foundation work, power development, and tunnels.

Woodward served as engineer for the Isthmian Canal Commission (1899–1902); the Pennsylvania Railroad (1902–1909); the East River Tunnel from South Ferry, Manhattan, to Joralemon Street in Brooklyn (1908–1909); and the Engineering Board of the St. Lawrence River Power Development Commission (1930s). This collection was given to the division in 1968.

Photographic studios represented include the Pullis Photo Studio.

Physical Description

There are 30 silver gelatin photoprints mounted in one leather-bound album. Other materials include blueprints, an Isthmian Canal Commission Report (1899–1901), publications, and specifications.

Subjects

The photographs document the construction of the East River Tunnel and the St. Lawrence River Power project. Most of the images are of construction workers on the job; or of the projects' progress.

Arranged: By subject.

Captioned: With narrative subject information.

Finding Aid: The division's Archives Inventory File has an inventory which lists negative numbers, dates, and subjects.

Restrictions: No.

EI·152

World War II Bomb-Damage Collection

Dates of Photographs: ND, 1945

Collection Origins

This collection was assembled by an anonymous donor to document the aftermath of the atom bomb attack on Nagasaki, Japan, and bomb attacks on Manila, in the Philippines, during World War II. It was given to the Smithsonian in the mid-1960s.

Physical Description

There are 360 photographs, including collodion wet plate lantern slides; a color dye coupler phototransparency; and silver gelatin photonegatives, photoprints, and phototransparencies.

Subjects

The photographs document atomic bomb damage to the cities and populations of Nagasaki, Japan, and conventional bomb damage in Manila, in the Philippines, during World War II. There are also a few earlier images of both places.

There are photographs of street scenes showing destroyed buildings, and people injured or killed by bombs.

Arranged: Into two series. 1) Bombing of Japan. 2) Bombing of the Philippines.

Captioned: No.

Finding Aid: No.

Restrictions: No.

EI·153

Henry R. Worthington Corporation Collection

Dates of Photographs: 1910–1952

Collection Origins

Henry R. Worthington (1817–1880) was a hydraulic engineer who designed and built pumping machinery. His Brooklyn works was the largest supplier of this machinery in the world.

Worthington was also president of the Nason Manufacturing Company in New York City and founder of the American Society of Mechanical Engineers.

Physical Description

There are 930 photographs, including albumen photoprints, platinum photoprints, and silver gelatin photonegatives and photoprints. The majority are silver gelatin photoprints mounted in five albums. Other materials include blueprints, correspondence, and miscellaneous trade literature.

Subjects

The photographs document the Henry R. Worthington Corporation's equipment, facilities, products, staff, and staff activities. Over 50 percent of the collection shows vertical compressor installations.

Facilities illustrated include the administration building, the chemical laboratory, the emergency hospital, installations, machine shops, and plant interiors. Products illustrated include centrifugal pumps, compressors, engines, and hydraulic equipment.

Staff illustrated include international students; interns; salesmen in Brooklyn, New York, and Seattle; and student engineers. Staff activities illustrated include banquets, educational activities, and manufacturing and production.

Arranged: Roughly, by subject.

Captioned: With subject and location information.

Finding Aid: No.

Restrictions: No.

EI·154

Worthington-Simpson Collection

Dates of Photographs: 1914–1920s

Collection Origins

This collection was created by the Worthington-Simpson, Ltd., Corporation (of England) to document the firm's products and plant. It was donated to the Smithsonian Institution in January 1975.

Photographers represented include Michael Fedison.

Physical Description

There are 550 silver gelatin photoprints, 75 of which are mounted in an album.

Subjects

The photographs document the physical plant and products of the Worthington-Simpson, Ltd., Corporation from 1914 to 1929.

The photographs of the plant include the brass foundry; drawing room and offices; gas blowing-engine shop; laboratory and test room; machine shop; plant exterior (Lowfield Works); power house; smith shop; and testing house.

Products shown include air compressors and blowers; compound, duplex, and single pumps; feedwater heaters; fly-wheel pumps; marine pumps; rotative dry vacuum pumps; and water-power pumps.

Also shown are Worthington-Simpson installations in clients' factories, such as, the Springfield Metallic Casket Co., of Ohio, in 1925.

Arranged: By subject.

Captioned: With size of the print and subject.

Finding Aid: An index, organized by assigned numbers, with subject description.

Restrictions: No.

GA

Division of Graphic Arts

Division of Graphic Arts
National Museum of American History
Smithsonian Institution
Washington, D.C. 20560
Curator
(202) 357-2877
Hours: Monday–Friday, 10 a.m.–4 p.m.

Scope of the Collections

There are three photographic collections with approximately 9,000 images in the Division of Graphic Arts.

Focus of the Collections

These photographs are used primarily as reference materials to study the technological and social history of commercial and fine arts printing and printmaking in the United States and Europe from the 14th century to the present.

This division's holdings document artists; bank note engraving; bookbinding tools and techniques; map printing; papermaking tools and techniques; printing for the blind; printing presses; printmaking and photomechanical tools and techniques; and type founding.

Photographic Processes and Formats Represented

In addition to standard 20th century slide, photoprint, and photonegative processes held as reference material, there are approximately 5,000 accessioned specimens of early photomechanical processes. Included are commercial processes, such as, collotypes, photogravures, photolithographs, and Woodburytypes; experimental works; and patent submissions representing modern pictorial printing from the period of 1845 to 1890.

Other Materials Represented

This division collects art prints in many processes, including chromolithography, engraving, etching, lithography, monotype, and woodcut. It also collects bookbinding and papermaking tools; cartoon drawings; embossed printing for the blind; etched and engraved plates; etching and engraving tools; illustrated books; posters; printing presses; printing type and matrices; typefounding equipment; and many commercial printing examples.

Access and Usage Policies

The division is open to the public by appointment only. There is a division-wide finding aid for accessioned materials. Certain materials are restricted due to their copyright status. Xerographic and photographic copies may be made of unrestricted images. There is a charge for photographic copies which is dependent on the prevailing rates of OPPS.

Publication Policies

In addition to obtaining permission from the Smithsonian Institution to reproduce a photograph, researchers may have to obtain permission from the copyright holder. The Smithsonian Institution is not necessarily the copyright holder. The credit line is: "Courtesy of the Smithsonian Institution, National Museum of American History, Division of Graphic Arts."

GA·1

Graphic Arts Photograph File

Dates of Photographs: 1920s–Present

Collection Origins

This collection was assembled by division staff to document the history of printing and printmaking. Most photoprints were made from negatives on file with OPPS. Others were duplicated from outside sources or received as donations. Note: Most photographs were created since the 1930s.

Physical Description

There are 6,370 silver gelatin photoprints. Most are copy images.

Subjects

The photographs document printing and printmaking activities, applications, equipment, personnel, and processes in Asia, Europe, and the United States, between the 15th century and the present.

Among the activities shown are commercial and photomechanical processes; demonstrations of printing equipment; fine arts processes; Japanese drawing, engraving, and printing; news reporting; trades allied to the graphic arts; typography; and writing. Division exhibitions are also illustrated.

Equipment illustrated includes bookbinding equipment; composing sticks; distributing, setting, and type casting machines (including the Linotype, Monotype, and Simplex machines); electrotyping equipment; engraving machines; papermaking equipment (including moulds, presses, and watermarks); paper marbling equipment; paper ruling machines; printing presses (including copperplate, lithographic, and type presses); printing rollers; stereotyping equipment; type cases and frames; and type, type moulds, plows, and pump pots. Also illustrated are equipment for artists' and commercial printing processes, patent office scale models of equipment, and tools.

Processes illustrated include aquatint; calligraphy; cartoon production; chromolithography; collotype; compound plate printing; copper engraving; drawing; drypoint; engraving; etching; grinding; halftone; hand printmaking; inkmaking; letter-press; line cut; lithography; machine engraving; medal engraving; mezzotint; miniature painting; monotype; nature printing; offset; oil painting; paper marbling; photogravure; photolithography; pochoir; rotogravure; rubbings; siderography; silkscreen; stencil; three-color scanning; typesetting; watercolor; woodburytype; and woodcut.

Individuals and artists shown include Eleanor Acker; Josef Albers; James Allen; Irving Amen; Alexander Anderson; Andrea Andreani; Vera Andrus; John Taylor Arms; Jules Arnoult; N. Arnoult; Irene Aronson; Robert Blum; Louis Daguerre; Hippolyte Fizeau; Deborah Goldsmith; Joseph Henry; Dard Hunter; F.E. Ives; John Baptist Jackson; Jacob Kainen; Karl Klic; J. Kraemer; Thomas Moran; John H. Murphy; Joseph Nicephore Niepce; J.B. Obernetter; G. Ortlieb; Paul Pretsch; S. Dillon Ripley; John Sloan; Bartholomeus Spranger; Thomas Sully; William Henry Fox Talbot; John Trumbull; and Frederick Von Egloffstein. There are also photographs of unidentified newsboys and newspaper men and printers.

Arranged: In self-indexing notebooks by subject topic.

Captioned: No.

Finding Aid: No.

Restrictions: Some are for reference only. No duplication allowed.

GA·2

Graphic Arts Slide Collection

Dates of Photographs: 1970s–Present

Collection Origins

This collection was assembled by division staff from diverse sources for use in lectures and presentations.

The collection serves as a staff reference collection on the history of the graphic arts. The collection documents the history of maps, printmaking tools and techniques, as well as prints included in the division's collections and exhibitions. Some images were duplicated from outside sources or received as donations.

Physical Description

There are 2,520 photographs, including color dye coupler (Ektachrome and Kodachrome) and silver gelatin slides (10%).

Subjects

The photographs document the history of graphic arts equipment, machinery, and processes; graphic arts products (such as, embossers for the blind, fine art prints, maps, and medals); and trades allied to the graphic arts (such as, inkmaking and papermaking). Most images deal with graphic art in the United States. A few images are of European or Oriental items and processes.

Among the types of equipment, machinery, and tools included in this collection are binding machinery and tools; commercial print shops; copper plates for medal engraving; electrotyping machinery; embossing equipment; hand and machine type casting tools; inkmaking tools and equipment; lever presses; papermaking tools and equipment; printing tools and equipment; ruling machines; stereotyping machinery; type casting and composing shops; type specimens; and wooden presses.

Occupations shown include advertising copy production; book binders; commercial artists; commercial printers; embossers for the blind; fine artists; hand type casters; illustrators; journalists; and map producers.

Arranged: Into 18 series by subject. 1) Printing. 2) Type. 3) Allied trades. 4) Prints by identified artists. 5) Prints by unidentified artists. 6) Lithography and chromolithography. 7) Photomechanical relief, intaglio, and miscellaneous processes. 8) Commercial prints. 9) NMAH exhibit "Embossing for the Blind." 10) NMAH exhibit "What's in a Map." 11) NMAH exhibit "The Naming of America." 12) NMAH exhibit "Story of a News Story." 13) NMAH Hall of News Reporting. 14) Special exhibits. 15) Presses and tools. 16) Maps. 17) Medal engraving. 18) Duplicate slides.

Captioned: Some provide the source of the illustration, date of the object shown, catalog number of the item shown, and occasionally an artist's or creator's name.

Finding Aid: No.

Restrictions: Some are for reference only. No duplication allowed.

GA·3

Graphic Arts Subject File

Dates of Photographs: 1920s–Present

Collection Origins

This collection was assembled by the division in the 1920s as a reference file. It traces the history of graphic arts in Asia, Europe, and the United States from the 14th century to the present. The collection focuses on the tools and technology of printing and printmaking.

Physical Description

There are 100 silver gelatin copy photoprints. Other materials include accession records; announcements and checklists; biographical notes; catalogs; correspondence; exhibition notes; invoices; newspaper clippings; press releases; reprints; and service contracts.

Subjects

The photographs trace the history of the graphic arts in Asia, Europe, and the United States from the 14th century to the present. They document specific artists; art works; graphic art processes; and techniques.

There are also photographs of special exhibits managed or created by the division staff from the 1920s to the present. Some of the exhibits documented are "The Mechanical Artist" (1981); "Elizabeth Keith" (1929); and "American Etching 1850 to 1950."

Arranged: Into two series. 1) General reference file. 2) Special exhibits file. Each is arranged alphabetically by subject or topic.

Captioned: The storage envelopes are labeled with subject information.

Finding Aid: An index to series 2, the Special exhibits file, is available.

Restrictions: No.

MA

Division of Mathematics

Division of Mathematics
Note: This division is now a section
in the new Division of Computers,
Information, and Society
National Museum of American History
Smithsonian Institution
Washington, D.C. 20560
Dr. Peggy Kidwell, Museum Specialist
(202) 357-2392
Hours: Monday–Friday, 8 a.m.–4:30 p.m.

Scope of the Collections

There are five photographic collections with approximately 12,800 images in the Division of Mathematics.

Focus of the Collections

These photographs are used primarily as research material to document objects which illustrate the history and technology of mathematics, such as, astrolabes; calculators; calendrical computer systems; cash registers; computing devices; electronic circuits; geometric models; gnomonic instruments; harmonic and differential analyzers; integrators; mathematical scales; planimeters; ruling and dividing engines; slide rules; and tabulators.

Photographic Processes and Formats Represented

Collections contain standard 20th century slide, photoprint, and photonegative processes, primarily color dye coupler slides and silver gelatin photoprints.

Other Materials Represented

This division also collects artifacts; catalogs; clippings; instruction sheets; lists; original and photocopied manuals; notes; publications; and reprints.

Access and Usage Policies

The collections are open by appointment to all scholarly researchers. Please write for an appointment at least one week in advance of the desired visit. There are partial finding aids to some collections. Photographic copies of many images are available from OPPS.

Publication Policies

In addition to obtaining permission from the Smithsonian Institution to reproduce a photograph, researchers may have to obtain permission from the copyright holder. The Smithsonian Institution is not necessarily the copyright holder. The preferred credit line for photographs is: "Courtesy of the National Museum of American History, Smithsonian Institution."

MA·1

Mathematical Devices History Collection

Dates of Photographs: Circa 1920–Present

Collection Origins

The collection was assembled by the division staff from outside donations to document mathematical devices, primarily those in outside artifact collections.

Photographic studios represented include Auto Digital Electrical Company, Ceac, Control Data Corporation, IBM, Maddida, and Nadan.

Physical Description

There are 4,500 photographs, including color dye coupler slides (Ektachrome and Kodachrome) and silver gelatin photoprints. Other materials include catalogs, clippings, instruction sheets, lists, manuals, publications, and reprints.

Subjects

The photographs document mathematical devices, such as, analog equation solvers; analog integrators (including harmonic and differential analyzers and synthesizers); astrolabes; computers; difference engines; digital devices; divination tools; geometric devices (including drawing instruments and space measurement devices); slide rules/sectors; and time measurement devices (including gnomonic devices).

Arranged: By subject heading.

Captioned: With simple descriptive statements; the date; the person, event, or object portrayed; and the negative number and catalog number of the object.

Finding Aid: 1) Two-page topical guides, such as, "Abacus," "Highlights of Digital Computing," "Astrolabes," "Differential Analyzers," and "Microcomputers." Each guide includes a brief history of the topic; a brief annotated bibliography; a listing of up to ten selected photographs (along with their catalog numbers, negative numbers, type of object, and location); and the address of the division. 2) A computerized master file arranged by catalog number. The file lists the object catalog number; OPPS negative number; object name; type of view; photograph date; and the location of the negative.

Restrictions: No.

MA·2

Mathematics Catalog Card Collection

Dates of Photographs: 1960s–Present

Collection Origins

The division staff created this card catalog to document the accessioned objects in their artifactual collections. It was begun in the 1960s and was discontinued in the 1970s. Some of the photographs in this collection were taken by OPPS.

Physical Description

There are 1,000 silver gelatin photographs which are dry mounted onto catalog cards (4″ × 6″).

Subjects

The photographs document the accessioned computational and measuring objects in the division's holdings. There are photographs of adding machines, analog devices, astrolabes, calculating machines, calculators, calendar discs, compometers, difference engines, differential analyzers, drawing instruments, facing and dividing engines, harmonic analyzers, length measurers, mathematical devices, microprocessors, plantimeters, punched card computers, and scales.

Arranged: By the catalog number of the object illustrated in the photograph.

Captioned: The cards contain information on the artifacts shown, including the object name and description; the object accession and catalog numbers; the date acquired; the donor's name; and the division name.

Finding Aid: No.

Restrictions: No.

MA·3

Mathematics Division Accessioned Objects Collection

Dates of Photographs: 1950s–Present

Collection Origins

This collection was assembled by the division staff to document accessioned objects in their collections. Many of the photographs were taken by OPPS.

Physical Description

The collection has 3,800 photographs, including color dye coupler slides (Ektachrome and Kodachrome) and silver gelatin photoprints.

Subjects

The photographs document mathematical objects within the division's collections. There are photographs of adding machines; analog devices; astrolabes; calculating machines; calculators (hand held); calendar discs; compometers; compendia; dials; stepped drum calculating machines; difference engines; differential analyzers; direct multiplication calculating machines; drawing instruments; exhibits; facing and dividing engines; harmonic analyzers; length measurers; microprocessors; pinwheel calculating machines; plantimeters; punched card computers; scales; torquetums; and teaching devices.

Arranged: Alphabetically by major subject heading, and then by specific type of object shown.

Captioned: Some, with narrative subject descriptions; the date; the person, event, or object portrayed; and the negative number and catalog number of the object.

Finding Aid: Two page topical guides to certain subjects, such as, "Abacus," "Astrolabes," "Differential Analyzers," "Highlights of Digital Computing," and "Microcomputers." Each guide includes a brief history; a brief annotated bibliography; a listing of up to ten selected photographs (along with their catalog numbers, negative numbers, type of object, and location); and the address of the division.

Restrictions: No.

MA·4

Mathematics History Photograph Collection

Dates of Photographs: 1920s–Present

Collection Origins

This collection was assembled by the division staff to document other respositories' collections on the history of computing and mathematics.

Physical Description

There are 2,450 photographs, including color dye coupler slides (Ektachrome and Kodachrome) and silver gelatin photoprints.

Subjects

The photographs document computational and measuring objects within other museums (non-Smithsonian) and in private collections; and the events, people, and places which relate to the history of computing and mathematics.

There are photographs of analog devices; analytical engines; card and tape processors; difference engines; digital, electronic, and mechanical devices; dividing and ruling engines; geometric models; museum exhibits (including non-Smithsonian Institution exhibits); and slide rules.

Activities illustrated include divination; mathematics education; and presentations on computer science and mathematics. There are also portraits of computer scientists, mathematicians, and scientists in related fields.

Arranged: By subject heading.

Captioned: With subject heading; the date; the person, event, or object portrayed; and the negative number and catalog number of the object.

Finding Aid: 1) Two-page topical guides that include a brief history of the topic; a brief annotated bibliography; a listing of up to ten selected photographs (along with their catalog numbers, negative numbers, type of object, and location); and the address of the division. 2) A computerized master file arranged by catalog number. The file lists the catalog number of the object shown; OPPS negative number; name of the object; type of view; date the photograph was taken; and the location of the negative.

Restrictions: No.

MA·5

Psychology Reference File

Dates of Photographs: 1890–Present

Collection Origins

This collection was assembled by division staff from diverse sources to document the history of psychology. The collection documents associations, individuals, institutions, and objects relating to this field.

Physical Description

There are 450 photographs, primarily silver gelatin photoprints, housed in 14 albums. Other materials include articles, biographies, and reprints on associations and institutions.

Subjects

The photographs document the history of psychology, including images of early research laboratories, portraits of pioneers of psychology, and of psychology staff at institutions, such as, Clark, Cornell, and Harvard universities. There are photographs of experimental psychological techniques and tools used between 1890 and 1930.

There are also a number of images of the 1893 World's Columbian Exposition.

Arranged: Into three series. 1) Biographical files. 2) Institution files. 3) Photographs.

Captioned: With the date of photograph, the location, and the person or institution shown.

Finding Aid: No.

Restrictions: No.

MS

Division of Medical Sciences

Division of Medical Sciences
National Museum of American History
Smithsonian Institution
Washington, D.C. 20560
Michael Harris, Museum Specialist
(202) 357-2413
Hours: Monday–Friday, 10 a.m.–4 p.m.

Scope of the Collections

There are 20 photographic collections with approximately 20,200 images in the Division of Medical Sciences.

Focus of the Collections

These photographs document the fields of dentistry, medicine, pharmacology, and public health, primarily in the United States. Images include dental equipment; diagnostic equipment; drug manufacturing apparatus; eyeglasses; hearing aids; hospital interiors and exteriors; manufacture of medical instruments; medical instrumentation; orthotics; portraits of notable medical doctors; and prosthetics.

Photographic Processes and Formats Represented

Photographs include standard 20th century color dye coupler photonegatives, photoprints, and slides; and silver gelatin photonegatives, photoprints, and slides. Early photographic processes include albumen photoprints and collodion wet plate lantern slides and photonegatives.

Other Materials Represented

This division also collects account books; advertisements for patent medicine; anatomical charts; blueprints; business records; certificates; correspondence; clippings; dental equipment; drawings; drug manufacturing apparatus; journals; laboratory equipment; microfilm; microscopes; motion picture film footage; pharmaceutical manufacturing information; physicians' diplomas; prescription forms; public health posters; quack medical devices; radiology apparatus; reprints; scrapbooks; surgical instruments; uniforms; and xerographic copies of EKGs.

Access and Usage Policies

The collections are open to scholarly researchers by appointment. Interested researchers should include their research topic, the type of material which they would like to view, and their research aim in a cover letter.

Publication Policies

In addition to obtaining permission from the Smithsonian Institution to reproduce a photograph, researchers may have to obtain permission from the copyright holder. The Smithsonian Institution is not necessarily the copyright holder. The preferred credit line is: "Courtesy of the National Museum of American History, Smithsonian Institution."

MS·1

American Hospital Photograph Collection

Dates of Photographs: 1880s–1950s

Collection Origins

This collection was assembled by division staff from diverse sources. Portions of the collection are from the Belleview Hospital, Lennox Hill Hospital, Massachusetts General Hospital, and the National Institutes of Health.

Physical Description

There are 450 photographs, including albumen photoprints, collodion wet plate lantern slides, and silver gelatin photoprints.

Subjects

The photographs document United States hospital facilities and hospital life. They show hospital buildings, grounds, kitchens, laboratories, lounges, medical offices, and staff. Among the hospitals illustrated are Belleview Hospital, Lennox Hill Hospital, Massachusetts General Hospital, and the National Institutes of Health.

Arranged: By the type of hospital (psychiatric or clinical research hospital); then alphabetically by the name of the specific hospital.

Captioned: With OPPS negative number.

Finding Aid: An item-level list called "Photographic List—Medicine," which includes the negative number, the title, the number of copies of the original which are available in divisional files, and, on occasion, if the prints are in color or black-and-white.

Restrictions: Some for reference only. No duplication allowed.

MS·2

American Soda Fountain Photograph Collection

Dates of Photographs: Circa 1890s–1950s

Collection Origins

This collection was assembled by the Division of Medical Sciences primarily from the collection of the magazine *Drug Topics*, which is currently housed at the American Institute for the History of Pharmacy at the University of Wisconsin. The original *Drug Topics* collection is estimated to contain 20,000 photographs.

Physical Description

There are 80 silver gelatin photoprints.

Subjects

The photographs document American soda fountains from the 1890s through the 1950s. The images also document the interiors of drug stores during this period. There are photographs of beverage, cosmetic, and drug advertising; commercial interior design; cultural history (such as costume); and soda fountain equipment.

Arranged: Partially organized by OPPS negative number.

Captioned: With OPPS negative number.

Finding Aid: There is a list available that includes the negative number, and a brief description which includes the store name, the type of soda fountain, and its location.

Restrictions: All collection users should credit the *Drug Topics* Photograph Collection at the American Institute for the History of Pharmacy, Madison, Wisconsin.

MS·3

Green Vardiman Black Collection

Dates of Photographs: Circa 1867–1926

Collection Origins

Green Vardiman Black was born in Illinois in 1836. He was a self-educated dentist and physician who served in the Union Army's dental corps. In 1864 Black established his own practice. He did research in pathology and reconstructive dentistry from 1870 until his death in 1914. He invented dental instruments and procedures and held many academic posts. From 1890 until 1915, Black served as Dean of Northwestern University's School of Dentistry.

Physical Description

There are 35 silver gelatin photoprints. Other materials include microfilm (two reels), reprints, and scrapbooks.

Subjects

The photographs document dentistry, including dental processes, techniques, and tools, in the United States from 1867 through 1926.

Arranged: No.

Captioned: No.

Finding Aid: There is a list of microfilmed material in the collection.

Restrictions: No.

MS·4

Boericke and Tafel Homeopathic Pharmacy Photograph Collection

Dates of Photographs: 1880s–1970s

Collection Origins

The collection was assembled by division staff from diverse sources, including original records created by the Boericke and Tafel Homeopathic Pharmacy.

A portion of the collection was created by the Smithsonian Institution for a movie that documents the Boericke and Tafel Homeopathic Pharmacy's field expeditions and manufacturing processes.

Physical Description

There are 4,500 photographs, including color dye coupler photoprints and silver gelatin photoprints.

Subjects

The photographs document the Boericke and Tafel Company of Philadelphia, a homeopathic pharmacy and manufacturing facility. There are photographs of Boericke and Tafel field expeditions to gather specimens; manufacturing processes; the physical plant (manufacturing plant); and staff of the company. The manufacturing and processing scenes were taken primarily in the Philadelphia area.

Note: About 15% of the collection consists of motion picture stills from a 30-minute movie produced by the Smithsonian on pharmacy and medicine.

Arranged: Roughly by size and type of process.

Captioned: No.

Finding Aid: An item-level inventory.

Restrictions: No.

MS·5

Christmas Seal League of Pittsburgh Photograph Collection

Dates of Photographs: Circa 1910–1970

Collection Origins

The Christmas Seal League of Pittsburgh and its predecessor, the Tuberculosis League of Pittsburgh, were non-profit organizations dedicated to the fight against communicable disease. The photographs were used by these organizations for public relations purposes.

Studios represented include the Lou Farris Studio of Pittsburgh.

Physical Description

There are 750 photographs, including silver gelatin dry plate photonegatives and silver gelatin photoprints (mounted on board).

Subjects

The majority of the photographs document fund raising and public relations activities of the Tuberculosis League of Pittsburgh and its heir, the Christmas Seal League of Pittsburgh. There are photographs of dances; exhibitions; luncheons; and Pittsburgh Pirate fund raisers. The photographs also document clean air lobbying organizations and fresh air camps.

Arranged: In two series. 1) Numerically by assigned number. 2) Chronologically.

Captioned: No.

Finding Aid: An item-level index to "Public Health" images arranged by negative number. It tells whether the image is in black-and-white or color, the number of copies available, and a brief subject description.

Restrictions: Researchers should credit the Christmas Seal League of Pittsburgh.

MS·6

Department of Health of the City of New York Collection

Dates of Photographs: 1870s–1930s

Collection Origins

This collection was assembled by New York City's Department of Health between the 1870s and the 1930s. It was used in early campaigns for legislation to clean the streets, for care of tubercular patients, and for fresh air therapy in the schools.

Some of the photographs were later published in the book *American Public Health*.

Physical Description

The 675 photographs include collodion wet plate lantern slides (some of which are tinted), silver gelatin dry plate photonegatives, and silver gelatin photoprints. Other materials include drawings and graphic prints.

Subjects

The photographs document the activities of New York City's Department of Health during the late 19th and early 20th centuries. The images document doctors; interiors of hospitals; medical operations; and patients (including those with physical abnormalities).

There are also photographs of public health activities and facilities including blood banks; diphtheria toxin horse farms; laboratories; the posting of quarantine notices; tubercular patient care; and visiting nurse services.

Arranged: The lantern slides are arranged alphabetically by subject heading.

Captioned: The lantern slides are labeled with the name of the medical procedure being undertaken, the diagnosis, the location of the operation, and an explanation of what is being shown.

Finding Aid: 1) A "Photographic List—Public Health" has the title, negative number, number of image copies available, and if the item is tinted. 2) A division card catalog which lists subject headings; catalog number; accession number; negative number; title of the photograph; and name of the photographer or the source of the photograph.

Restrictions: No.

MS·7

Freemont Free Public Library in Philadelphia 1876 Centennial Collection

Dates of Photographs: 20th Century

Collection Origins

This collection was assembled by division staff from copy images of original photographs of the 1876 Centennial Exposition in the Freemont Free Public Library in Philadelphia, Pennsylvania. The copy material was used for the "1876 Centennial Exhibit" in the Arts and Industries Building of the Smithsonian.

Physical Description

There are 825 photographs, including photonegatives (125) and silver gelatin photoprints (700). The photonegatives are housed at OPPS. Most of the images are copies.

Subjects

The photographs document the 1876 Centennial Exposition in Philadelphia. There are photographs of exposition buildings, exhibits, fountains, and statuary.

Arranged: By negative number.

Captioned: With the negative number, accession number, description of the object, location, and installation shown. Many also have assigned numbers from the original photographer.

Finding Aid: A card file is being developed for this collection. It will index the photographs by subject,

such as, the building shown; the corporation; the state or country; and the artist or title of the statuary or fountain.

Restrictions: For research only. No duplication allowed.

Researchers should credit the Freemont Free Public Library, Philadelphia.

MS·8

Bruno Z. Kisch Collection

Dates of Photographs: 1944–1970

Collection Origins

Bruno Z. Kisch (1890–1966) was a Czechoslovakian cardiologist who lived in Germany until the rise of fascism. He was known for his use of the scanning electron microscope to study cardiac tissue. Kisch was Medical Director of Yeshiva University (1938–1962). He helped establish the American College of Cardiology (1949), and served as its president (1951–1953). This collection is part of Kisch's professional papers.

Physical Description

There are 50 silver gelatin photoprints (SEMs). Other materials include clippings; correspondence; journals; notes; 15 notebooks (with xerographic copies of EKG graphs); and reprints.

Subjects

The photographs are scanning electron microscope (SEM) images of cardiac (heart) tissue.

Arranged: By type of material.

Captioned: No.

Finding Aid: No.

Restrictions: No.

MS·9

Eli Lilly and Company Collection

Dates of Photographs: 20th Century

Collection Origins

This collection was assembled by Eli Lilly and Company staff to document the physical plant, products, and staff of the company.

Physical Description

There are 200 silver gelatin photoprints.

Subjects

The photographs document the Eli Lilly and Company pharmaceutical company, including the laboratory; manufacturing plant; medical products (such as, pills and syrups); and staff.

Arranged: No.

Captioned: Some with subject information.

Finding Aid: A "Photographic List—Pharmacy" gives negative numbers, image dates, descriptions, and often the number of duplicate images.

Restrictions: No.

MS·10

M*A*S*H Photograph Collection

Dates of Photographs: ND

Collection Origins

This collection was assembled by Michael Harris, a museum specialist in the Division of Medical Sciences, from diverse sources, including color slides from the 20th Century Fox movie *M*A*S*H;* photographs of the "M*A*S*H" exhibition (1980s) at NMAH taken by OPPS; photographs of MASH units from the U.S. Department of Defense; and photographs from Korean Conflict veterans (including 19 photographs from a McLean, Virginia, nurse).

Physical Description

There are 1,500 photographs, including color dye coupler slides and silver gelatin photoprints.

Subjects

The photographs document the Mobile Army Surgical Hospitals (MASH units) in Korea during the Korean Conflict and the later dramatization of this topic in the movie and on television. Medical patients are shown arriving, departing, and during treatment. Military medical staff are shown both at work and off duty (including at meals and during recreation).

Arranged: Into four series by source of image. 1) Color slides from the 20th Century Fox movie, *M*A*S*H.* 2) Photographs of MASH units from the U.S. Department of Defense. 3) Photographs from a former MASH nurse. 4) Photographs of the NMAH "M*A*S*H" exhibit.

Captioned: With names of people shown.

Finding Aid: No.

Restrictions: The color slides are for reference only. No duplication allowed.

MS·11

Medical Diorama Photograph Collection

Dates of Photographs: Circa 1934

Collection Origins

This collection was assembled by the UpJohn Company of Kalamazoo, Michigan, to document 37 dioramas which comprised the 1934 exhibit "The Manufacture of Medicines."

The collection was donated to the division in 1934.

Physical Description

There are 55 silver gelatin photoprints housed in one notebook.

Subjects

The photographs document 37 dioramas in a 1934 Division of Medical History exhibit titled "The Manufacture of Medicines." The dioramas illustrated the creation of liniments, pills, poultices, and other manufactured medications and health aids.

Arranged: The notebook of photographs is arranged in the same order as the 37 dioramas in the 1934 exhibit, "The Manufacture of Medicines." The miscellaneous unlabeled prints of the exhibit are unarranged.

Captioned: Most include the narrative exhibit labels from the dioramas.

Finding Aid: No.

Restrictions: No.

MS·12

Medical History Collection

Dates of Photographs: 20th Century

Collection Origins

This collection was assembled by the staff of the Division of Medical Sciences from a variety of donors and sources for research purposes.

The collection is part of the division's subject reference files documenting medical topics, such as, dentistry, hospitals, pharmacy, and physicians.

Physical Description

There are 600 silver gelatin photoprints. Other materials include account books, anatomical charts, clippings, materia medica, patent medicine advertisements, pharmaceutical manufacturing information, physicians' certificates, physicians' diplomas, prescription forms, prints, public health posters, and reprints.

Subjects

The photographs document medical and pharmaceutical topics, including antibiotics, baldness, beauty, dentistry, drugs, enzymes, hospitals, medical equipment, medical processes, pharmaceutical manufacturing, and public health.

Among the people illustrated are Black Americans in the medical sciences, dentists, medical personnel, and physicians.

Arranged: Alphabetically by subject heading.

Captioned: No.

Finding Aid: No.

Restrictions: No.

MS·13

Medical History Photographic Reference Notebook Collection

Dates of Photographs: ND

Collection Origins

This collection was assembled by the Division of Medical Sciences staff to reflect their research interests.

The photographs came from diverse sources, including images copied out of books and publications. The photographs document materials within division collections, as well as materials from collections outside of the Smithsonian Institution.

Note: This collection also serves as a topical finding aid to the Medical Sciences Photograph Collection.

Physical Description

There are 2,000 photographs within 129 albums, including color dye coupler photoprints and slides, and silver gelatin photoprints.

Subjects

The photographs document anatomy, bloodletting, dentistry, Egyptian medicine, electrotherapy, obstetrics, rehabilitative medicine, and static electrical medical techniques.

Equipment and tools documented include diagnostic implements, ear instruments, endoscopes, general medical instruments, kidney machines, medicine cases, microscope photographs, orthotics, prosthetics, respirators, spectacles, surgical instruments, surgical tables, and thermometers.

Places documented include the Battle Creek Sanitarium in Michigan (exterior, interior, and staff); Chevalier Jackson Library; Codman & Shurtleff store (of Boston); miscellaneous hospitals (from the Grace Goldin Annual Report); Smithsonian Medical Exhibits; and the Moody Medical Library (University of Texas at Galveston).

There are portraits of Helen Keller (including group portraits with Agnes De Mille and with George Bernard Shaw). There are also photographs of the Medical Centennial and medical illustrations.

Arranged: Alphabetically by subject.

Captioned: With the negative number, the image source (in most cases), whether a copy image is available, and the subject matter.

Finding Aid: No.

Restrictions: No.

MS·14

Medical Sciences Photograph Collection

Dates of Photographs: 20th Century

Collection Origins

This collection was assembled by the Division of Medical Sciences staff from diverse sources to document the history of medicine and dentistry from the 12th century to the present.

Physical Description

There are 4,000 photographs, including albumen photoprints; color dye coupler photoprints, phototransparenies, and slides; and silver gelatin photoprints (original and copy). Most are silver gelatin photoprints.

Subjects

These photographs document dentistry and medicine including: anatomy; anesthesia; child care; hospitals (exteriors and interiors); medical implements (such as calipers); medical schools; medical societies; military medicine; portraits of American medical personnel (including quacks and quackery); rehabilitative equipment; and therapy and treatment.

Arranged: There are four series in this collection. 1) Images of accessioned objects in the Division of Medical Sciences. 2) A master reference file of photographs arranged by negative number. 3) A browsing copy photoprint file arranged by topic. 4) A photoprint index arranged topically by assigned subject heading.

Captioned: All photographs are labeled with the negative number, most also have an object accession number and a narrative description.

Finding Aid: 1) A listing which identifies the negative number, accession/catalog number, subject contents, and date for series number one. 2) The Medical History Photographic Reference Notebook Collection serves as finding aid to this collection.

Restrictions: Some for reference only. No duplication allowed.

MS·15

Naito Museum of Japan Collection

Dates of Photographs: Circa 1970s

Collection Origins

This collection was assembled by the Division of Medical Sciences to document graphics and objects loaned by the Naito Museum of Japan for a special exhibit on the medical and pharmaceutical history of Japan in the 19th and 20th centuries.

Physical Description

There are 130 photographs, including color dye coupler phototransparencies and slides.

Subjects

These photographs reproduce 19th and 20th century Japanese medical and pharmaceutical graphics from the Naito Museum of Japan. There are also reproductions of an unidentified 18th century scroll and a statue.

Arranged: No.

Captioned: No.

Finding Aid: An item-level list of the photographs which tells the name of the object, dates, and process or medical technique covered.

Restrictions: No.

MS·16

Norwich Eaton Pharmaceutical Collection

Dates of Photographs: 1940s

Collection Origins

This collection was created by the Norwich Eaton Pharmaceutical Company of Norwich, New York, to document their production of poison gas diagnostic kits.

Physical Description

There are 50 silver gelatin photoprints.

Subjects

The photographs document the Norwich Eaton Pharmaceutical Company's business offices, delivery trucks, and manufacturing plant.

There are also photographs of Norwich Eaton's World War II production of poison gas diagnostic kits.

Arranged: No.

Captioned: No.

Finding Aid: No.

Restrictions: No.

MS·17

Parke-Davis Company Collection

Dates of Photographs: ND

Collection Origins

This collection was assembled by the Parke-Davis Company of Detroit, Michigan, to document their pharmaceutical plant, production activities, and products.

Physical Description

There are 100 silver gelatin photoprints. Other materials include blueprints, clippings, correspondence, drawings, and reprints.

Subjects

The photographs document the manufacturing and production of pharmaceuticals in the Detroit plant of the Parke-Davis Company. Activities shown include inspection of medications; manufacturing; plant interiors during cleanup activities; plant repair; and production.

Arranged: No.

Captioned: No.

Finding Aid: "Photographic List—Medicine" gives the image title, negative number, and the number of copies available within the division.

Restrictions: No.

MS·18

Science and Information Service Collection

Dates of Photographs: 1940s–1970s

Collection Origins

This collection was assembled by the Science and Information Service for their editorial photograph collection. The collection was created as a public information service. The collection was donated to the Smithsonian Institution when the Science and Information Service was dismantled in the late 1970s.

Physical Description

There are 4,000 silver gelatin photoprints. Other materials include clippings; editorial material (on public health and pharmaceutical care); reprints; and xerographic copies.

Subjects

The photographs document dental care, medical treatments, pharmacies, and public health.

Arranged: Into two sections. 1) Public health and pharmacy. 2) Medical and dental. The file is further divided into 33 subject headings.

Captioned: Some with subject information.

Finding Aid: 1) Subject lists, such as, "Photographic List—Pharmacy" and "Photographic List—Public Health." The lists enumerate negative number, title, number of copies available, the dates, and if the image is in color. 2) An item-level inventory with brief descriptions of each image.

Restrictions: No.

MS·19

Smallpox Eradication Campaign Photograph Collection

Dates of Photographs: ND

Collection Origins

This collection was assembled by the Smallpox Eradication Campaign Headquarters staff. The photographs show smallpox victims. These images were carried by field workers as an aid to identification of other cases of infectious smallpox in an area. The field worker would show the pictures to residents and ask if they had seen anyone nearby with similar symptoms.

Physical Description

There are 30 color dye coupler photoprints (including original prints).

Subjects

This photographs are of human smallpox victims, with emphasis on physical symptoms.

Arranged: No.

Captioned: No.

Finding Aid: A list with the negative number, the name of the victim, the type of symptoms, and the date.

Restrictions: No.

MS·20

Veterans Administration Prosthetics and Orthotics Collection

Dates of Photographs: 1920s, 1940s–1960s

Collection Origins

This collection was assembled by the Veterans Administration's New York office to document their activities in fitting U.S. military veterans with prosthetic and orthotic devices, such as, limbs.

Physical Description

There are 300 photographs, including silver gelatin photonegatives (some diacetate and nitrate) and photoprints.

Subjects

Most of the photographs show the fitting of World War I, World War II, and Korean Conflict veterans with prosthetic and orthotic devices, including artificial arms and legs.

There are photographic reproductions of drawings of prosthetic and orthotic devices. There are also photographs of the manufacture of prosthetic and orthotic devices in a California aircraft manufacturing plant.

Arranged: By negative number.

Captioned: Storage envelopes are labeled with the negative number, project number, type of original (for example, line drawings), and type of device being fitted. Some are also labeled with the date.

Finding Aid: No.

Restrictions: No.

MI

Division of Musical Instruments

Division of Musical Instruments
National Museum of American History
Smithsonian Institution
Washington, D.C. 20560
Cynthia Hoover and John Fesperman, Curators
(202) 357-1707
Hours: Monday–Friday, 10 a.m.–5 p.m.

Scope of the Collections

There are ten photographic collections with approximately 50,800 images in the Division of Musical Instruments.

Focus of the Collections

These photographs document the history and technology of music, as well as musical performances using keyboard, mechanical, percussion, string, and wind instruments in the western world. The division also maintains iconographic files documenting the role of musical instruments and music in art. These photographs document division object collections as well as objects in other institutions. Several collections include images of 19th century American bands.

Photographic Processes and Formats Represented

The collections include standard 20th century slide, photoprint, and photonegative processes, such as, color dye coupler photoprints, slides, and photonegatives; and silver gelatin photoprints and photonegatives.

Other Materials Represented

The division collects musical instruments from the United States and Western Europe including automata; clavichords; harpsichords; organs; percussion; pianos; strings; and winds.

Access and Usage Policies

Researchers should write or call 48 hours in advance for an appointment to use the collection. Photographic copies can be purchased from OPPS at the prevailing rate.

Publication Policies

In addition to obtaining permission from the Smithsonian Institution to reproduce a photograph, researchers may have to obtain permission from the copyright holder. The Smithsonian Institution is not necessarily the copyright holder. The preferred credit line is: "Courtesy of the Smithsonian Institution, National Museum of American History, Division of Musical Instruments, [Collection Name]."

MI·1

Accessioned Object File of the Division of Musical Instruments

Dates of Photographs: ND

Collection Origins

This collection was assembled by division staff from photographs taken by OPPS to document the accessioned musical instrument collection. Eventually all accessioned objects within the division will be reproduced in this collection. Note: This collection's photonegatives are housed at OPPS.

Physical Description

There are 5,000 silver gelatin photoprints.

Subjects

The photographs document musical instruments including: 1) Banjos; 2) Bowed strings; 3) Brass; 4) Clavichords; 5) Dulcimers—plucked and hammered; 6) Guitars; 7) Harpsichords; 8) Organs; 9) Percussion; 10) Pianos; 11) Plucked instruments; 12) Woodwinds; and 13) *Violin Treasures* (a publication utilizing divisional holdings).

Arranged: By type of instrument, then chronologically by catalog number.

Captioned: With the catalog number, negative number, title of the instrument or type of instrument, source and location of the instrument, the maker and period of the instrument, and full provenance of the instrument.

Finding Aid: No.

Restrictions: No.

MI·2

Division of Musical Instruments Exhibit Files

Dates of Photographs: 1960s–Present

Collection Origins

This collection was assembled by the division staff to document their exhibits. Note: Most of the materials date from the mid-1960s through the early 1970s.

Physical Description

There are 5,100 photographs, including color dye coupler slides and silver gelatin photoprints. Other materials include correspondence; drawings; exhibit catalogs; exhibit scripts; invitations; and notes.

Subjects

The photographs document exhibits created by the NMAH Division of Musical Instruments since the 1960s, including "Fiddles and Bass Viols in America," "Hall of Musical Instruments," "Museum of Music," "Music Machines," "Music Making," and "Tuning Up." There are also photographs of the Smithsonian's Arts and Industries Building "1876 Exhibit" and others from the Natural History Museum's Department of Ethnology exhibits.

Arranged: Into three series by type of material and exhibit. 1) Two notebooks of slides of the "Special Exhibition on Instruments," 1961. 2) Five notebooks documenting the NMAH exhibit "Tuning Up." 3) Division exhibit files.

Captioned: No.

Finding Aid: A catalog to objects (not photographs) used in division exhibits which lists object accession numbers, subject headings, negative numbers, notes, and correspondence.

Restrictions: For reference only. No duplication allowed.

MI·3

Division of Musical Instruments Slide Collection

Dates of Photographs: ND

Collection Origins

This collection was assembled by the division staff to document the division's activities, events, exhibits, objects, and reference materials.

Physical Description

There are 3,000 photographs, including color dye coupler slides and a few silver gelatin slides.

Subjects

The photographs document musical instruments (such as, keyboard instruments, organs, percussion, stringed, and woodwind instruments); as well as concerts; exhibits; and publicity utilizing these instruments. Most of the instruments illustrated appear to be from the division's collections.

Arranged: First by subject heading, then by catalog number, or on occasion, by negative number.

Captioned: No.

Finding Aid: No.

Restrictions: For reference only. No duplication allowed.

MI·4

Iconography of Bands in America Photograph Collection

Dates of Photographs: ND

Collection Origins

This collection was assembled by division staff from two major sources. A portion of this collection was gathered by the Smithsonian Institution Traveling Exhibition Service (SITES) for the "Bands in America" exhibit. Many of these images appear to have been copied from the periodical *Leslie's Illustrated Weekly Newspaper,* which dates from the Civil War. Margaret and Robert Hazen, of Washington, D.C., donated a large portion of memorabilia to this collection.

Physical Description

There are 800 photographs, including silver gelatin photonegatives and photoprints. All are photographic reproductions of art works.

Subjects

The photographs reproduce art works (including drawings, illustrations, paintings, pastels, and other formats), which depict American and European bands and band instruments (in America) from the 18th century to the present.

There are photographic reproductions of work by the following artists: N. Currier; E. Forbes; Gavarni; W. Huddy; D. Kelly; McKillop; and Motley.

Arranged: Part is arranged alphabetically by the last name of the artist who originally created the work.

Captioned: Each print is labeled with the artist's full name and life dates; instruments shown in the illustration; publication source of the illustration; source of the acquisition; and on occasion, the medium of the original illustration.

Finding Aid: No.

Restrictions: No.

MI·5

Iconography of Musical Instruments

Dates of Photographs: ND

Collection Origins

This collection was assembled by the Division of Musical Instruments to document the role of music and musical instruments in art.

The art work reproduced in the collection was created by various Western artists of the 16th through the 19th centuries.

Physical Description

There are 30,000 silver gelatin photoprints. Other materials include an accompanying card file.

Subjects

The photographs reproduce art works which show musical instruments. The pictures include several peripheral portraits of individuals, including Thomas Jefferson, at concerts or with instruments.

Arranged: Alphabetically by the last name of the artist who produced the original image.

Captioned: No.

Finding Aid: There is a two-part card index to this collection. 1) The first card index section is cross-referenced by instrument, subject, and museum, gallery, or collection origin. The index also lists the last name of the artist who created the illustration. 2) The next section of the card index is arranged alphabetically by the artist's last name. These cards list the artist's full name; dates; country of origin; title of the artist's work reproduced; medium of the work; name of the collection in which the work is housed; a bibliography of the work; the subjects of

the work; the instruments shown in the reproduction; and an assigned number.

Restrictions: Available to qualifed researchers by appointment.

MI·6

Latin American Organ Information Files

Dates of Photographs: ND

Collection Origins

This collection was assembled by the staff of the Smithsonian Institution Mexican Organ Project which was coordinated by J. Scott Odell and John Fesperman with the collaboration of photographer David Hinshaw.

The project resulted in John Fesperman's book, *Organs in Mexico*. Raleigh, N.C.: Sunbury Press, 1979.

Physical Description

There are 2,200 photographs, including color dye coupler photonegatives, photoprints, and slides; and silver gelatin photonegatives and photoprints. Other materials include clippings; correspondence; data sheets; drawings; notes; and reprints.

Subjects

The photographs document organs discovered in Latin America. The countries visited include Ecuador, Mexico, and Peru. Most images are of Mexican church pipe organs.

Arranged: Into two series by type of material. 1) The photoprints are arranged by country, geographic region, and city. The files are then subdivided by the owner of the organ—usually a church. 2) The slides are arranged by negative number.

Captioned: The slides are labeled with the negative number; photographer's name; date; location and name of the church in which the organ is housed; name or type of instrument; and type of view of the organ.

Finding Aid: 1) The slides are partially cross-referenced (in attached notes) by location. 2) The photographs are described in accompanying data sheets which indicate the building, location, and condition of specific pipe organs.

Restrictions: Available to qualified researchers by appointment.

MI·7

Theron McClure Viola Da Gamba Photograph Collection

Dates of Photographs: ND

Collection Origins

This collection was assembled by donor Theron McClure from a variety of publications and historical sources. Some of the original photographs were taken by McClure.

Physical Description

There are 800 silver gelatin photoprints. Other materials include clippings of illustrations of instruments, graphic prints, reprints, and xerographic copies.

Subjects

The photographs document European stringed instruments, primarily the viola da gamba, from the 16th to the 19th centuries. There are also some images of celli, ethnic instruments, the iconography of the viol, and instruments believed to be precursors to the viola da gamba.

Arranged: In 13 notebooks, first by subject, then chronologically.

Captioned: With the name of the instrument; source and date of the original print or graphic; the artist's country of origin; size of the original art work; the museum housing the original art work; and a bibliographic citation on the publication in which the original reproduction was found.

Finding Aid: The collection has a card index arranged alphabetically by the last name of the artist who created the original print or painting. The index lists the artist's full name, life dates, the century to which the artist has been assigned, and the country of origin of the artist.

Restrictions: No.

MI·8

Musical Instruments in Other Institutions Photograph Collection

Dates of Photographs: ND

Collection Origins

This collection was assembled by division staff to document the musical instrument holdings of other institutions.

Many of the photographs were copied, purchased, or traded from other institutions. Some images were copied directly from books.

Physical Description

There are 1,200 silver gelatin photoprints. Other materials include correspondence and notes concerning the instruments.

Subjects

The photographs document musical instruments, including keyboard instruments (such as, clavichords, pianos, spinets, and virginals); reed instruments (such as, bassoons, clarinets, oboes, and saxophones); and woodwinds (such as, flutes and piccolos). The photographs illustrate the major characteristics of each instrument.

Some of the images are photographic reproductions of book illustrations.

Arranged: By type of instrument.

Finding Aid: An alphabetical card index to the collection, cross-referenced by 1) instrument name; 2) instrument dealer or maker; 3) chronology or provenance; and 4) the name of the individual associated with the instrument.

The catalog cards list the object number; name of the instrument; maker of the instrument; place and date of manufacture; collection in which the instrument resides; type of illustration in the file; correspondence concerning the instrument; and in some cases, the names of the previous owners or dealers.

Captioned: No.

Restrictions: For reference only. No duplication allowed.

MI·9

Musical Instruments Organ Design Information Files

Dates of Photographs: 1960s–1970s

Collection Origins

This collection was assembled by John Fesperman, Curator of the Division of Musical Instruments, during his research on North American pipe organ design.

Physical Description

There are 700 photographs, including color dye coupler slides (1%) and silver gelatin photoprints (99%). Other materials include correspondence and notes.

Subjects

The photographs document North American pipe organs, primarily church organs, between the 1960s and 1970s.

Arranged: First by type of material, then alphabetically by location.

Captioned: No.

Finding Aid: No.

Restrictions: No.

MI·10

Hugo Worch Photographic Collection of Keyboard Instruments

Dates of Photographs: Circa 1930s

Collection Origins

Hugo Worch (1855–1938) was an American collector and dealer in keyboard instruments. He ran a family store in Washington, D.C., that sold gramophones, gramophone records, keyboard instruments, radios, and sheet music. The business was started by his father in 1863. Hugo Worch had over 200 instruments and over 2,000 instrument photographs at the time of his death.

This collection was created to document the development of the American piano industry from the 1790s until the 1850s. The collection was later expanded to include European clavichords, harpsichords, and pianos.

Physical Description

There are 2,000 silver gelatin photoprints.

Subjects

The photographs document highly decorated American keyboard instruments dating from the 1790s to the 1850s. They also document European clavichords, harpsichords, organs, and pianos from the same period. There are many photographs which show details of keyboard construction.

There are also images of exhibitions of such instruments; the manufacture of these instruments; the sale and advertisement of keyboard instruments; and sheet music from the same era.

Arranged: By assigned number.

Captioned: With the location and the name of the keyboard instrument manufacturer, as well as an assigned number.

Finding Aid: There is a two-part card catalog to this collection. Section 1 is arranged in numerical order by assigned number and serves as an inventory of the collection. Section 2 is arranged by subject headings. The catalog card includes the maker's name, an assigned number, assigned subject headings, and cross-references. The card may also list the source and the dates of the original illustration or reproduction.

Restrictions: No.

PH

Division of Photographic History

Division of Photographic History
National Museum of American History
Smithsonian Institution
Washington, D.C. 20560
Eugene Ostroff, Curator
(202) 357-2059
Hours: Monday–Friday, 10 a.m.–4 p.m.

Scope of the Collections

There are 58 photographic collections with approximately 155,000 images in the Division of Photographic History.

Focus of the Collections

This division documents the historical and technological development of photography and its predecessors from the 1700s to the present. The collection includes exhibition documentation; photographic equipment; photographs of and by well-known photographers; process examples; and technological information.

Photographic Processes and Formats Represented

Early photographic processes and formats represented include albumen photoprints and photonegatives; ambrotypes; calotype photonegatives; carbon photoprints; carbon transfer photoprints; carbro photoprints; cartes-de-visite; collodion wet plate lantern slides and photonegatives; color screen plate phototransparencies (Autochromes and Joly); culinary process photoprints (including: glycerin-albumen-gelatin photoprints, beer-albumen-gelatin photoprints, honey-albumen-gelatin photoprints, and milk-albumen-gelatin photoprints); cyanotypes; daguerreotypes; diazo photoprints; French tissue stereographs; glue photoprints; gum bichromate photoprints; "hillotypes"; and Ippertypes.

Other processes and formats include palladium photoprints; pannotypes; photographic jewelry (stanhopes); platinum photoprints; salted paper photoprints; silver gelatin dry plate photonegatives; silver gelatin photoprints (bromoil); stereographs; theodolites; tintypes; and tinted zoetrope strips.

Contemporary processes represented include color dye coupler photoprints, color dye diffusion transfer prints; color dye transfer separation photoprints, photonegatives, and slides; radiographs; and silver gelatin photonegatives on both nitrate and safety base film and photoprints.

Other Materials Represented

This division collects books and book illustrations of early cameras; ceramics bearing photographic images; copper engravings; correspondence by photographic inventors; exhibition announcements; exhibition reviews; fantascope discs; furniture from photo laboratories and studios; graphic prints (including woodcuts, wood engravings, and lithographs); motion picture footage; patent drawings of photographic equipment; photograph albums; photocopies of photographic related items; and photographers' biographical information.

The division also collects photographic equipment, such as cameras; photographic jewelry and souvenirs; photographic projection and viewing equipment; photomechanicals (including autotypes, collotypes, lithoprints, tinted phenakistiscopes, photogravures, and woodburytypes); physiognotraces; portraits of photographers; posters; press releases; scenes of photographers at work; and technical and trade literature. The division has a technical subject file.

Access and Usage Policies

The collections are open to the public by prior appointment only. There is a division-wide finding aid to these collections which is an item-level card catalog accession file. Certain materials within the collections are restricted and may not be photographically or xerographically copied.

Publication Policies

In addition to obtaining permission from the Smithsonian Institution to reproduce a photograph, researchers may have to obtain permission from the copyright holder. The Smithsonian Institution is not necessarily the copyright holder. The preferred credit line is: "Courtesy of the National Museum of American History, Smithsonian Institution."

PH·1

Aldebaran and Capella Collection

Dates of Photographs: 1906, 1907

Collection Origins

A man named Aldebaran and a woman named Capella were young early 20th century photographers (forenames unknown).

While on a trip to the Netherlands they created three albums in the form of a journal written to an absent friend. Capella appears to have been the primary author, although they both served as photographers.

The albums describe their travels on land and sea. The handwritten text is heavily illustrated with platinum photoprints, illustrating both the places they visited and the people they met.

Two albums are titled "By Waterways: Being Unmailed Letters Containing An Entirely Veracious But Fortunately Not Entirely Complete Record of A Summer Vacation Punctuated By Many Holland Schnapps Taken at Random by the Authors" (1906); and "Letters From Below Sea Level: Being the Account of a Watery Pilgramage as Recorded by 2 Cameras yet Left Undelivered Until Today by the Culprits" (1907). The third album was unavailable.

The three albums were purchased by the division from a commercial vendor.

Physical Description

There are 550 platinum photoprints housed in two albums with handwritten text. (Note: The third album was not available for viewing.)

Subjects

The photographs are architectural studies; cityscapes; landscapes; portraits of the Dutch; and seascapes of the Netherlands taken in 1906 and 1907.

Cities documented include Amsterdam; Haarlem; Middleburg; Rotterdam; St. Maarten; and Volendam. The photographs show beaches (some with bathing machines and changing tents); canals; carriages; docks; harbors; markets; ships; and St. Laurence Kerk.

Among the individuals illustrated are Dutch bicyclists; Dutch street vendors; Dutch townspeople (some in traditional costume); and traveling companions.

Arranged: Chronologically.

Captioned: Surrounding essays provide narrative subject information.

Finding Aid: No.

Restrictions: No.

PH·2

Ambrotype Collection

Dates of Photographs: 1850s–1870s

Collection Origins

This collection was assembled by division staff from a variety of sources.

Physical Description

There are 1,000 ambrotypes. Several of the ambrotypes are on dark violet or ruby-black glass. This collection includes an 8″ × 10″ ambrotype and a stereographic ambrotype.

Subjects

Most of the photographs are studio portraits of individual American children, men, and women, dating from the 1850s to the 1860s. There are a few studio group portraits of American Indians and sports teams.

There are also several exteriors of American farms, houses, and landscapes.

Arranged: In division catalog number order.

Captioned: No.

Finding Aid: A browsing notebook serves as a visual finding aid for 135 of the ambrotypes. It consists of xerographic copies of ambrotypes in catalog number order. The catalog number, drawer number, and the date are marked on the xerographic copy.

Restrictions: No.

PH·3

Autochromes Collection

Dates of Photographs: 1904—1922

Collection Origins

This collection was assembled by division staff from diverse sources.

Autochromes were the first practical single-plate method of color photography. The process was patented by the Lumiere brothers in France in 1904. The plates were commercially manufactured from 1907 to the early 1930s.

Photographers and studios represented include Stanley Artiurs Studio, Wilmington, Delaware; Auguste Lumiere; and Thomas A. Smillie.

Physical Description

There are 400 color screen plate phototransparencies (Autochrome).

Subjects

The photographs document cityscapes; figure studies; garden studies; landscapes; portraits; scenic views in Europe and the United States; and still lifes.

There are many pictorialist figure studies of women posing on the beach, by a pool, in the woods, with flowers, or in studios.

There are still lifes of flowers and fruit; landscapes of wooded areas; and studies of formal gardens (including those of Mrs. Alufers Dupont Rencourt at Winterthur, Delaware). Flowers shown include azaleas, dahlias, golden gloves, irises, and poppies.

There are landscapes of the eastern United States including Castle Island, Hamilton, Monticello, and Williamsburg, Virginia; Pink Beach; Quarry Garden; and Whale Island.

Many images are scenic views taken in Europe, such as, Durham Cathedral; Hyde Park in London; the Jungfrau, Matterhorn, and Monch mountains; and Stalheim.

Arranged: By geographic area or subject.

Captioned: With subject information, such as, flower names, tree names, or location.

Finding Aid: No.

Restrictions: No.

PH·4

Richard Avedon Collection

Dates of Photographs: 1945—1967

Collection Origins

Richard Avedon (1923—) studied with Alexey Brodovitch (art director of *Harper's Bazaar* from 1934—1958) at the Design Laboratory of the New School for Social Research in New York.

Avedon was a staff photographer for both *Harper's Bazaar* and for *Junior Bazaar*. In 1966 Avedon became staff photographer for *Vogue*. His work includes advertising, dance, fashion, portrait, and theatre photography.

This collection was donated to the Smithsonian Institution by the photographer between November 16, 1962 and December 1966.

Physical Description

There are 1,080 photographs, including color dye coupler photoprints, and silver gelatin photonegatives and photoprints (some contact prints or oversize). Most of the photographs are silver gelatin photoprints, some of which are signed. Other materials include color proofs from *Harper's Bazaar*; copper plate engravings used in full color reproductions; engraver's proof prints; and magazine layouts with prints (including *Harper's Bazaar* covers).

Subjects

The photographs are primarily portraits of famous Americans or visitors to America, including actors; architects; artists; astronauts; authors; ballet dancers; composers; conductors; curators; designers; entertainers; filmmakers; hostesses; models; musicians; news reporters; poets; politicians; and royalty. There are also a few images of Italy and of New York City Hall weddings.

Among those portrayed are Louis Armstrong; Leonard Bernstein; Rudolf Bing; Julian Bond;

Truman Capote; Charlie Chaplin; T.S. Eliot; Judy Garland; Allen Ginsberg; John Glenn; Katharine Hepburn; Aldous Huxley; Martin Luther King III; Wanda Landowska; Eric Leinsdorf; Carson McCullers; Krishna Menon; Arthur Miller; Marilyn Monroe; Rudolf Nureyev; Pablo Picasso; Ezra Pound; Robert Rauschenberg; Jean Renoir; Bertrand Russell; Norman Thomas; and Frank Lloyd Wright.

There are individual and group portraits (187) of the John F. Kennedy family taken before the Presidential inauguration, including a formal studio portrait series of Caroline Kennedy, Jacqueline Kennedy (in her inaugural dress), John F. Kennedy, and John F. Kennedy, Jr.

Arranged: By division catalog number, and then by subject.

Captioned: Some with names. Some are signed by Avedon.

Finding Aid: An item-level index lists catalog number, size, and description or title.

Restrictions: For research purposes. No duplication allowed.

PH·5

Donald Beattie Collection *A.K.A.* Barr and Wright Studio Collection

Dates of Photographs: Late 1860s–1870s

Collection Origins

The Barr and Wright Studio was a photographic portrait studio in Houston, Texas, active during the late 1860s and 1870s.

Donald Beattie donated the collection to the division. Beattie also donated approximately 2,000 Barr and Wright negatives to the Hams County Heritage Society in Houston, Texas.

Physical Description

There are 1,850 collodion wet plate photonegatives. Contact prints are being produced of these images.

Subjects

Most of the photographs are studio portraits of individual Texas children, men, and women, particularly citizens of the Houston area during the 1860s and 1870s. There are also some group portraits of families and sports teams.

Arranged: By assigned division catalog number.

Captioned: No.

Finding Aid: Reference file of contact prints arranged by catalog number.

Restrictions: No.

PH·6

Freda Berla Collection

Dates of Photographs: 1950s

Collection Origins

Mrs. Freda Berla of Washington, D.C., assembled these photographs to document a vacation trip. She later gave the collection to the division.

Note: Because the collection was unavailable for viewing, this description is based upon division records.

Physical Description

There are 140 "stereo realistic" color phototransparencies which measure 1⅝″ × 4″.

Subjects

These photographs document a cruise and vacation trip taken by Mrs. Freda Berla. She visited Antigua; New Orleans, Louisiana; and the Yucatan Peninsula during the 1950s.

Arranged: In chronological order.

Captioned: With subject information.

Finding Aid: No.

Restrictions: No.

PH·7

Albert Boni Collection

Dates of Photographs: 1842–1971

Collection Origins

This collection was assembled by Albert Boni from materials received from Susanna Grece, Johann Heinrich Schulze, and others. The collection was assembled to document the history of photography. It was donated to the division by Boni in 1971.

Note: Most of these images have been removed and are housed either under the name of the photographer or under the type of process in other division image collections.

Photographers and studios represented include George Barker; Beard; the Mathew Brady Studio; William Constable; Detroit Publishing Company; W. & D. Downey; Roger Fenton; Franck; Keystone View Company; Leck & Whitfield; William Notman; Napoleon Sarony; Underwood and Underwood; Brett Weston; and Edward Weston. Note: A portion of this collection consists of daguerreotypes from the William Constable Photographic Archives.

Physical Description

There are 6,200 photographs, including albumen cabinet cards, cartes-de-visite, photoprints, promenade cards, and stereographs (1,423). There are also ambrotypes (12); daguerreotypes (144); platinum photoprints; a salted paper photoprint; silver gelatin lantern slides (538) and photoprints; stanhope trinkets (25); and tintypes. Four thousand photographs are in 81 albums dating from the 19th century.

Other materials include a book of essays on photochemistry by Johann Heinrich Schulze dating from 1727; cameras (28); photographic apparatus (such as, celluloid photographic cases); postcards; and a wood engraving from a daguerreotype.

The 144 daguerreotypes include whole plates, half plates, quarter plates, sixth plates, and ninth plates. The 12 ambrotypes include whole plates and half plates, and smaller images. Six images are portraits in Union cases, one is a double case.

The stanhopes are small ivory trinkets, such as, letter openers, which have miniature inset photoprints with a cover which incorporates a magnifying glass. There are seven complete stanhopes and 18 fragments. Of the fragments, 11 contain a photoprint sample and lens.

Subjects

The majority of the ambrotypes and daguerreotypes in the collection are portraits of unidentified people. There are also three ambrotypes of horse-drawn transportation (a carriage, a cart, and a hearse); and two daguerreotypes of Horseshoe Falls at Niagara Falls.

The lantern slides are largely cityscapes; genre scenes (often idealized or posed); landscapes; magic lantern and vaudeville program headers and trailers (announcements); and news events of the 19th century.

The stereographs illustrate architecture; cityscapes; curiosities; natural wonders; occupational studies; portrait shots of famous people; and world-wide travel photography.

The paper photoprints document events; genre scenes; landmarks; landscapes; portraits of royalty, social figures, and world leaders; and still lifes. There is a composite photograph of the 1876 Ecole Polytechnique class; a portrait of Prince Napoleon (by the Mathew Brady Studio); a series based on a song; and a study of various occupations, including street vendors.

The cartes-de-visite are portraits of American intelligentsia, European nobility, and the socially prominent.

Arranged: The collection has been dispersed. It is housed by type of material and arranged by catalog number.

Captioned: No.

Finding Aid: No.

Restrictions: No.

PH·8

Mathew B. Brady Collection

Dates of Photographs: 1850s–1880s

Collection Origins

This collection was assembled by division staff from diverse sources.

In December 1920, the National Museum of History and Technology Photographic Section received 108 Brady items from the U.S. War Department Chief Signal Officer in Washington, D.C. This accession is believed to have been from images sold to the United States government.

An additional 119 images came from other sources, including the GAF Corporation.

Mathew B. Brady (1823–1896) came from an impoverished Irish farming family in upstate New York. After arriving in New York City, Brady studied daguerreotype production, possibly under Samuel F.B. Morse, and John W. Draper. In 1844 Brady opened a photography studio in New York City, where he became know for his portraits of celebrities. In 1858 he opened a gallery in Washington, D.C., and in 1860 he opened a second gallery in New York City.

Brady was a businessman who had a large volume operation employing many other well-known photographers and a small army of processing and finishing staff. Brady's studios made albumen photoprints, collodion wet plate photonegatives, and daguerreotypes. Many of the images were tinted.

In addition to his portrait photography, Brady and his staff documented the Civil War, at Brady's own expense, in over 7,000 photonegatives. To save himself from bankruptcy, Brady sold his set of Civil War negatives to the firm of E. and H.T. Anthony Company. Another set of 5,000 negatives was bought by the government in order to pay the storage charges.

Photographers represented include James Brown, George Cook, Alexander Gardner, and Timothy O'Sullivan.

Physical Description

There are 225 photographs, including albumen photoprints (cartes-de-visite and several stereographs) and collodion wet plate photonegatives.

Subjects

The photographs document battle scenes, group camp scenes, and portraits of American politicians and soldiers during the American Civil War.

There are portrait photographs taken during President Grant's administration, including members of Grant's family, officials, and politicians. Other portraits are of ambassadors, celebrities, foreign royalty, and other notables; and many unidentified soldiers.

Among the individuals shown are Madame Catacazy; General George Armstrong Custer; Jefferson Davis; Hamilton Fish; General Ulysses S. Grant; General Winfield Scott Hancock; General Sam Houston; President Abraham Lincoln; and General Philip Sheridan.

Among the locales and scenes shown are a camp near Belle Plain, Virginia; Camp 67th, New York Infantry; a convalescent camp near Alexandria, Virginia; Falls Church, Fredericksburg, and Richmond, Virginia; Fort Brady; Fort Sedgewick; a gun squad on deck of the Monitor; an Infantry parade near Harpers Ferry, West Virginia; and the Petersburg Lines, 1865.

Arranged: No.

Captioned: No.

Finding Aid: A list of 36 original photonegatives and 44 photoprints from the GAF portion of this collection. It is arranged first by negative number, followed by catalog number and a brief description of the photograph.

Restrictions: No duplication allowed.

PH·9

Robert Capa Collection

Dates of Photographs: 1936–1954

Collection Origins

Andre Friedmann (1913–1954) was Hungarian born, and was educated in Budapest, Hungary, and Berlin, Germany.

Friedmann was exiled from Hungary for political activism. He worked as a darkroom assistant at the Deutsche Photodienst (Dephot) Agency in Berlin in 1930. In 1933 he left Germany to work with Henri Cartier-Bresson and David Seymour in Paris.

In 1936 Friedmann changed his name to Robert Capa. He worked as a freelance photojournalist specializing in documenting political unrest and war.

During the following 18 years Capa documented wars while working for *Colliers,* the *Illustrated London News, Life,* and *Time.* He covered the Republican forces during the 1936 Spanish Civil War, during which his wife and partner, Gerda Taro, was killed.

Capa helped to found Magnum Photos. He served as the president of Magnum from 1951 until his death. Robert Capa died in 1954 while on special assignment in Thai-Binh (Hanoi), Indochina (Vietnam), for *Life.*

The photographs in this collection were donated in 1964 by the artist's brother, Cornell Capa, to the Smithsonian Institution in memory of Robert Capa. A portrait of Robert Capa by Ruth Orkin is included.

Physical Description

The collection consists of 70 silver gelatin photoprints. Some of the prints are dry mounted exhibition prints, apparently from the 1964 "Images of War" exhibit at the Smithsonian Institution.

Subjects

The photographs are photojournalistic images of political tumult and war, with particular emphasis on the Civil War in Spain (1936); the creation of Israel (1948–1950); the Indochina conflict (1954); the invasion of China by Japan (1938); and the U.S. Army's role in World War II.

In particular, the photographs document the U.S. Army during World War II in such locations as London, England; Paris, France; the Invasion of Laurent-Sur-Mer on June 6, 1944; Naples, Italy; and North Africa. There is a series of images of the United States D-Day invasion force amphibious maneuvers and troop landings.

There are also informal portraits of a World War II British pilot; civilian casualties; medics; refugees; soldiers; wounded soldiers; and a formal portrait of Robert Capa by Ruth Orkin.

Arranged: No.

Captioned: With the name of the person or event shown, location, and date.

Finding Aid: No.

Restrictions: No reproduction allowed.

PH·10

Card Photograph Collection

Dates of Photographs: 1860s–1920s

Collection Origins

This collection was assembled by division staff from materials found in other division collections, as well as from donations, exchanges, and purchases.

Photographers and studios represented include N. Abrams; D.D. Adams; J. Albert; E. Anthony; C. Apollony; Baldwins Art Gallery; C.M. Bell; Fred Bell; J.C. Bennett; Dean Blackpool; P. Bourgeois; Mathew Brady; Cadwalladers; N.S. Capen; Central Photograph Gallery; Daniels; Davis; Dietrict; Doggherty; Farach & Lalumia; Chas. D. Fredericks & Co.; H.H. Frye; L.C. Griffin; John D. Grotecloss; O. Hallwig & Co.; A.P. Hart; Dr. Heid; J. Hess; Alfred S. Hood; H.J. Jacoby's; J. Jeanes; W.P. Kendall; Kerfoot; M.H. Kimball; Landeberg; Locke's; McAllister; McCrary & Branson; W. Masters; Eugene Mairoce; Meade Bros; W.J. Miller; Mora; Arthur Nicholls; Nims; Notman & Fraser; Novelty Photo Studio; Oak Gallery; Obermuller & Kern; I.G. Owen; Philip & Solomons; Wilhelm Pollot; Porter & Co.; C.E. Read; C.H. Reutlinger; Richardson; Edmund Risse; R.H. Rose; Sarony; C.H. Sherman; Slee Bros.; Stanton & Butler; J.W. Taber; A.G. Taylor; B. Frank Taylor; Taylor & Preston; W.H. Tipton; W.C. Tuttle; Urlin; J. & W. Vincent; Samuel Walker; Wenderoth & Taylor; W. Woodward & Co.; J.S. Wooley; and P.H. Zorn.

Physical Description

This collection contains 3,500 photographs, including albumen photoprints (some cartes-de-visite and cabinet cards); silver gelatin photoprints (Eastman); and silver gelatin postcards.

Subjects

The photographs document architectural exteriors and interiors; circus performers; landscapes; parades; portraits (informal and studio); photographers; transportation; travel images; and weddings.

There are portraits of Prince Albert; William Cullen Bryant; "Che-Mah, the Chinese dwarf"; The Very Reverend A.P. Stanley; Queen Victoria; and the Dean of Westminister.

Arranged: Some, by photographer or by catalog number.

Captioned: With catalog number, studio name, and/or subject.

Finding Aid: No.

Restrictions: No.

PH·11

Dr. Walter Clark Collection

Dates of Photographs: 1840s–1960s

Collection Origins

This collection was assembled by Dr. Walter Clark, Assistant Director of Eastman Kodak Company's Research Laboratory in Rochester, New York. Clark assembled the collection from diverse sources to illustrate luminaries in the history of photography. This collection was acquired in 1969 from Dr. Clark.

Photographers and studios represented include John G. Capstaff (color dye coupler phototransparencies); Carjak; DAGRON (collodion wet plate pellicles); Eastman Kodak Co.; Francis Frith (a portfolio of silver gelatin photoprints); Andre Kertesz (a series of signed prints); Henri LeSecq; Pierre Petit; and Henri de Toulouse-Lautrec.

Physical Description

There are 500 photographs, including albumen photoprints; collodion wet plate pellicles; color dye coupler phototransparencies; and silver gelatin photoprints (some toned). Other materials include engravings; lithographs; miniature photomechanical portraits (used for correspondence and bookplates); and portrait medallions (42 on six sheets).

Subjects

The photographs are portraits of photographic scientists and inventors of photographic processes and equipment.

There are portraits of D.E. Abbe (1889); Sir William de Wiveleslie Abney; Marcel and Betty Abribat (1938); J. Albert; M. Andresen; H.T. Anthony; Dominique Fois Arago; Frederick Scott Archer; A. Auer (1900); Harry Baines (1946); Beccaria; Edmont Becquerel; George Bennett; Joseph Berres; Ulphonie Bertillon; Bruce Billings; Olaf Bloch; Bolton; and Robert Boyle.

There are also portraits of A. Brayor; Brewster; H.V.A. Briscoe; Vere Brodie; Leslie Brooker; A.J. Bull; John G. Capstaff; Carjak; Emmett K. Carver; Albert K. Chapman; C.Z. Chase; Charles Chevalier; E. Chevieul; William Clark (1943); Cowling; William Crookes; Jacques Louis Daguerre; Disderiz; Louis Ducos du Hauron; Durand; George Eastman; Andre Kertesz; Lumiere; Joseph Petzval; C. Welborne Piper; Giuseppe Pizzighelli; Scott; D.A. Spencer; Harry Springer (1944); and Tom Wedgewood.

Arranged: Alphabetically by last name of subject.

Captioned: With subject information and photographer's name.

Finding Aid: No.

Restrictions: No.

PH·12

George Collins Cox Photograph Collection

Dates of Photographs: 1880s–1890s

Collection Origins

George Collins Cox (1851–1902) began his photographic career in Newark, New Jersey. Between

1884 and 1901 Cox had his own photographic portrait studio at 826 Broadway in New York. He photographed friends, including prominent figures, such as, Edward Everett Hale, General George B. McClellan, and Walt Whitman.

Both American impressionist painter William Merritt Chase and sculptor Augustus Saint-Gaudens are known to have used Cox's photographs as preliminary visual aids or studies for their own work. This collection was acquired in 1962 from Cox's family.

Some of Cox's portraits were reproduced in journals, such as, *The Century Magazine, The Century Gallery of One Hundred Portraits, 1897*, and *Harper's Weekly*. Note: Cox copyrighted his portraits of Walt Whitman.

Physical Description

The collection consists of 1,400 photographs, including platinum photoprints, salted paper photoprints, and silver gelatin photoprints.

Subjects

The photographs are portraits of American actors; artists; celebrities; editors; financiers; painters; poets; sculptors; and writers of the 1880s and 1890s. There are many portraits of William Merritt Chase; Richard Watson Gilder; H.H. Richardson; Augustus Saint-Gaudens; and Walt Whitman. There are also many portraits of anonymous children, men, and women, both in the studio and in their homes.

Arranged: No.

Captioned: No.

Finding Aid: A partial computer-based inventory lists catalog number, size, mount, and description.

Restrictions: No.

PH·13

Daguerreotype Collection

Dates of Photographs: 1840s–1850s

Collection Origins

This collection was assembled by division staff from a variety of sources.

Physical Description

There are 2,000 daguerreotypes ranging in size from sixteenth plates ($1\frac{5}{8}'' \times 2\frac{1}{8}''$) to double whole plates ($8\frac{1}{2}'' \times 13''$). The images are primarily monochrome, only about one-tenth are tinted.

Subjects

The majority of these images are portraits of unidentified American children, men, or women, taken between the 1840s and the 1850s. There are also architectural views, genre scenes, and landscapes.

Identified individual portraits include Abbie Leeds Avery; Spencer Baird; Sally Borrows; James Clark; J.H. Clarke; Henry Clay; Reverend Dall; "Uncle" Samuel Deal; Dorothy C. Draper; Charley Evans; Joseph Henry; William Hoxie; Samuel Houston; and Charles Hubbard.

There are also portraits of Bruno and Eliza Lamoureaux; Frederick Langenheim; Margaret Law; Professor O.J. Mason; Mecheninga—Chief of the Iowas; the Honorable Robert Dale Owen; Peter and Susan Palmer; Rachel Griffith Riggs; the King and Queen of Siam; Mrs. S.G. Stevens; Charles Sumner; William Wadden Tuxer; Charles D. Walcott; Mary Simmons Walker; and Daniel Webster.

Landscapes and cityscapes include the locomotive *Bay State* in a landscape; Niagara Falls; a panorama of San Francisco; the Smithsonian Institution Castle building; a snow scene; and a windmill. Genre scenes show Afro-Americans working; chess players; children with toys; firemen; and musicians.

Arranged: By division catalog number.

Captioned: No.

Finding Aid: A browsing file of photographic copies of daguerreotypes serves as a visual index.

Restrictions: No.

PH·14

Henry Draper Photograph Collection

Dates of Photographs: 1850s–1882

Collection Origins

This collection was assembled by the Draper family including Henry Draper (1837–1882), the second son of John William Draper (1811–1882), a pioneering American chemist and photographer.

Henry Draper was an early astronomical photographer and researcher of stellar spectra. In 1863 Henry Draper made approximately 1,500 photonegatives of the face of the moon. These were primarily collodion wet plate photonegatives. In 1872 he took the first photographs of stellar spectrum lines.

In 1874 Henry Draper became Photographic Department Director of the United States Commission to Observe the 1874 Transit of Venus. In 1876 he served as photographic judge at the Philadelphia Centennial Exposition.

In the spring of 1879 Henry Draper began to use silver gelatin dry plate photonegatives for studying stellar spectra. By 1882 he had produced over 80 spectra studies of astronomical objects, such as, the comet 188 III, Jupiter, Mars, the moon, and the Orion nebula.

Other photographers and studios represented include C. Bierstadt; John Draper; J.H. Schonscheidt; and Underwood and Underwood.

Physical Description

There are 730 photographs, including albumen photoprints and stereographs; collodion wet plate lantern slides and photonegatives; and daguerreotypes (162 total; 118 uncased, most sixth plates, some photomicrographs). Other materials include darkroom equipment, photographic apparatus (including cameras and developing boxes), and photomechanicals (collotypes).

Subjects

The photographs are scientific studies, including astronomical images of comets, Jupiter, Mars, the moon, and the Orion nebula; photomicrographs of the spleen; and spectral studies of the elements and light.

There is also a daguerreotype copy of an early daguerreotype portrait (circa 1840) of Dorothy Catherine Draper made by John Draper.

Arranged: First by type of material, then by size and catalog number. The major divisions of the collection are 1) apparatus; 2) daguerreotypes; 3) stereographs of astronomical bodies, such as, the moon; and 4) lantern slides and photonegatives of the moon and other astronomical bodies.

Captioned: With subject information.

Finding Aid: An inventory lists catalog number, process, size, and description.

Restrictions: No.

PH·15

Fred Eckhardt Collection

Dates of Photographs: 1909

Collection Origins

Fred Eckhardt was an early 20th century photojournalist associated with the *Chicago Tribune*. He exhibited at the Manitowoc Camera Club, according to markings on his prints.

Physical Description

There are 200 silver gelatin photoprints.

Subjects

These photographs are primarily photojournalistic studies taken between 1909 and the 1950s in or near Chicago, Illinois.

These images document civil disobedience; courtroom scenes; crime; disasters; entertainment events; heroes; homeless people; sports; and transportation, including airplanes, boats, cars, and trains.

Activities illustrated include boiling steel at a mill;

a child getting his first haircut; flag-draped women marching; and fire-fighting.

Events documented include the Cherry Mine disaster and the Chicago Streetcar Strike. Entertainment events documented include the American Derby Horse Race; baseball games; the circus; a polo game at a country club; stock cars; and a woman trick-rider on a bronco.

People depicted include American Indians (unidentified); homeless people; a kidnapper and victim; a man and a woman with a bandaged child in the hospital; military police; prisoners in jail; strikers; and a young boy in jail. There are portraits of Colonel Joseph B. Sanborn and Commissioner of Baseball Kereson Landis.

Arranged: In catalog number order.

Captioned: Some, with subject or title.

Finding Aid: No.

Restrictions: No.

PH·16

Harold Eugene Edgerton Collection

Dates of Photographs: 1920s–1980s

Collection Origins

Harold Eugene Edgerton (1903–   ) has taught electrical engineering at the Massachusetts Institute of Technology since 1928 (he is now Emeritus). He is an independent photographer and an inventor of photographic equipment. In 1949 Edgerton founded Edgerton, Germeshausen and Grier (now EG&G, Inc.) which produced technical and scientific products and services.

Edgerton developed stroboscopic high speed motion and still photography equipment. This equipment was the basis of all subsequent electronic flash units. Edgerton also designed underwater camera and electronic flash equipment for use by Jacques Cousteau and the U.S. Navy.

Edgerton's photographs include a number of milestones in high speed image recording. His equipment allowed photography to record objects, such as, bullets, in midflight.

Physical Description

There are 35 photographs, including high speed multiflash color dye coupler photoprints and silver gelatin photoprints.

Subjects

All the photographs are high speed multiflash (stop action) prints showing the sequence of movements in a procedure. There are photographs of circus acrobats in action; a bullet going through a light bulb; a golf swing; a pole vaulter; and a tennis swing.

Arranged: By accession number.

Captioned: No.

Finding Aid: No.

Restrictions: Access restricted.

PH·17

Rudolf Eickemeyer Collection

Dates of Photographs: Circa 1884–1929

Collection Origins

Rudolf Eickemeyer, Jr. (1862–1932) purchased his first camera in 1884 to record his father's inventions for patent model applications. After studying with a local portrait photographer, Eickemeyer became a prolific amateur photographer, submitting his work to international amateur competitions.

In 1895, Eickmeyer joined the Carbon Studio in New York City where he devoted himself to advertising, magazine, and portrait photography, and to the publishing of photographic picture books. He maintained a long association with Eastman Kodak as a photographer for their advertisements, articles, and booklets.

In 1900 Alfred Stieglitz organized a one-man exhibition of Eickemeyer's work at the Camera Club of New York. In 1901 Eickemeyer became art manager of the Campbell Art Studio in New York. In 1905 he bought a half-interest in the Davis and Sanford Studio in New York City. From 1911 to 1915 he was an executive of the Campbell Studio. There he specialized in portraits of the celebrated and rich, such as, a series on Evelyn Nesbit, and in genre images.

In 1911 Eickemeyer was commissioned by William Randolph Hearst to produce portraits of American women who had married into the British peerage. He later worked independently until his death.

Eickmeyer gave a portion of this collection to the Smithsonian Institution in 1929. Upon his death in 1938, the rest of the collection was received from his widow, Isabelle Hicks. One silver gelatin photoprint (bromoil) was a personal gift from Eickemeyer to Smithsonian Curator A.J. Olmstead, who later gave it to the Smithsonian Institution.

Other individuals who contributed Eickemeyer materials to the division include Isabelle Cameron (co-author with Eickemeyer of the *American Book of Beauty*); Eva Eickemeyer; Joel Chandler Harris; and Sadikichi Hartmann.

Eickemeyer's photographs appeared in the exhibition "Platinum Women" (1984 through 1986) at the National Museum of American History. An exhibition of his work was also held at the Hudson River Valley Museum during winter 1986 and spring 1987.

Physical Description

There are 1,500 photographs, including carbon photoprints (including carbon transferred to celluloid, drawing paper, and parchment); gum bichromate photoprints (including gum bichromate on rough Whatman drawing paper and on etching paper); platinum photoprints; silver gelatin photonegatives (some on diacetate and nitrate) and photoprints (bromide); and tintypes. Some photoprints are sulphur toned. There are 2,960 nonphotographic items in the collection. Other materials include clippings; invitations; medals; notes; published books and magazines with photographic illustrations; speeches; and trophies.

Subjects

These are pictorialist photographs of American and British celebrities; commercial products (including some for Eastman Kodak Co.); genre scenes; posed story illustrations for books and magazines; seasonal landscapes; and studies of "types" of individuals, whom Eickemeyer felt represented specific culture groups.

Among his portraits were New York City person-

alities and celebrities including Mrs. Vincent Astor; Sadakichi Hartmann; and Evelyn Nesbit. There are also portraits of American women who married into the British peerage.

Eickemeyer photographed American landscapes at such locations as Winterwood in Bethlehem, Connecticut; Boston, Middlefield, and Royalston, Massachusetts; Barmegal City, New Jersey; New York City; and Hog Island, Virginia. Other specific locales photographed include Halifax; Liverpool; Quebec; and Yarmouth.

Genre scenes include rural individuals posed in story-like settings with titles, such as, "The American Farm," "The Goddess Demeter," and "In and Out of the Nursery." There are sequential scenes of thematic interest with titles, such as, "Attraction, Temptation, and Satisfaction."

Arranged: By catalog number.

Captioned: With subject information (titles).

Finding Aid: An item-level guide with collection history and full subject, date, size, and process information.

Restrictions: No.

PH·18

Elliott Erwitt Collection

Dates of Photographs: Circa 1940–1972

Collection Origins

Elliott Erwitt was born in Paris in 1928. He came to the United States in 1938. Erwitt studied photography while attending Hollywood High School and Los Angeles City College. Following service in World War II, Erwitt went to New York to work as a professional photographer and joined Magnum Photos, Inc., in 1953.

Erwitt's work includes advertising and commercial photographs; documentary motion pictures and photography; and spot news stories, such as, the "Kitchen Debate" between Nixon and Khrushchev.

This collection was a gift of the photographer.

Physical Description

There are 225 silver gelatin photoprints. Many are oversized and mounted on masonite panels.

Subjects

The photographs document contemporary life in the United States. They often are ambiguous, humorous, or ironic images of animals or people photographed in public places during an impromptu moment.

Among the animals documented are dogs on the street; a horse in a corral; a lioness carrying her prey; a seagull on a beach; and zoo scenes.

Among informal portraits of people are museum-goers; musicians; pedestrians; and people on a beach.

Arranged: In catalog number order.

Captioned: No.

Finding Aid: No.

Restrictions: For reference only. No reproductions allowed.

PH·19

Sam Falk Photograph Collection

Dates of Photographs: 1940s–1960s

Collection Origins

Sam Falk joined the staff of the *New York Times* in 1925. Much of his early photographic work for them was feature photography of well-known personalities. In the 1940s Falk pioneered the use of 35mm photography at the *New York Times*. Later in his career, he worked for the *New York Times Magazine*. In 1965 Falk was featured in a Smithsonian Institution exhibition. He retired in 1969. An exhibition of his work was held in 1981 at the Midtown Gallery in New York.

Falk donated this collection to the Smithsonian Institution in two portions. The first accession was in 1965 and the second was in 1968.

Physical Description

There are 5,000 photographs, including color dye coupler phototransparencies and slides, and silver gelatin photonegatives and photoprints.

Subjects

The photographs document public figures and street life in the United States, and, to a lesser extent, in Austria (around 1953); England; Paris, France; and Italy from the 1940s to the 1960s. Falk documented landmarks of New York City, such as, Central Park; Chinatown; Grand Central Station; Greenwich Village; Harlem; Kennedy International Airport; and Times Square.

Among the people documented are Edward Albee; Bernard Baruch; Albert Einstein; Dag Hammerskjold; Julie Harris; Mayor Fiorello La Guardia of New York City; John D. Rockefeller; Eleanor Roosevelt; Franklin Delano Roosevelt, Jr.; Arthur Rubinstein; Beverly Sills; Arturo Toscanini; the United Nations General Assembly; and Andy Warhol.

Other people documented are anonymous patrolmen; bar habitues; children visiting the zoo; museum-goers; participants in public events, such as, parades; racetrack crowds; shoppers; subway riders; and union members in Detroit.

Arranged: No.

Captioned: With subject information, such as, name and location.

Finding Aid: 1) A partial inventory of prints within the collection arranged by Smithsonian catalog number, including caption information and the size of the photonegative. 2) A concordance of division prints with the illustrations from Gilbert Millstein and Sam Falk's book *New York: True North*. Garden City, New York: Doubleday, 1964. (The book is marked as to which items the division owns.)

Restrictions: For reference only. No reproductions allowed.

PH·20

Andreas Feininger Collection

Dates of Photographs: 1936–1982

Collection Origins

Andreas Feininger (1906–   ), the son of artist Lyonel Feininger, was born in Paris, France. He studied with Walter Gropius at the Bauhaus, and at the Bauschule in Weimar and Zerbst, Germany, where he graduated summa cum laude as an architect in 1928.

Feininger's early professional career (1928–1933) was as an architect in Germany and with Le Corbusier in France. In 1933 Feininger moved to Sweden and became an architectural photographer.

In 1939 Feininger moved to New York. He was a *Life* magazine staff photographer from 1943 to 1962 and a columnist for *Modern Photography* from 1957 to the present. He has produced numerous photographic books and museum exhibitions. He has been associated with Black Star Picture Agency. He is a founding member of the American Society of Magazine Photographers.

Feininger has published extensively. There have been one-man shows of his work at the American Museum of Natural History, New York; the Carl Simbab Gallery, Boston, Massachusetts; the Pratt Institute, New York; and the Smithsonian Institution.

This collection is the result of several separate donations by Feininger.

Physical Description

There are 110 silver gelatin photoprints (some oversized and mounted).

Subjects

The photographs are abstracts; architectural studies; cityscapes; landscapes; motion studies; nature studies; portraits taken between 1936 and 1982; sculpture studies; and seascapes. The cityscapes include New York City, Paris, Sweden, and Weimar, Germany.

Arranged: By size and catalog number.

Captioned: With subject information.

Finding Aid: No.

Restrictions: For reference only. No reproductions allowed.

PH·21

Wolfran C. Fuchs Collection

Dates of Photographs: 1897–1903

Collection Origins

Wolfran C. Fuchs, a medical photographer and radiologist, lived in Chicago, Illinois. Several of Fuchs's photographs were exhibited as transparencies at the St. Louis World's Fair in 1903.

Physical Description

There are 105 original silver gelatin radiographs (celluloid) bound in a red leather album.

Subjects

The photoprints are medical radiographs (x-rays) of damaged or diseased human tissue.

The photographs document abnormal growth of the dura; appendicitis abcess; biliary caluculi; cholesterin stone in gall bladder; cystic tumor of the brain; diseased hip joint; dislocated shoulder joint; empyema; foetus in utero; and a fracture of the dorsal vertebrae.

There are also photographs of a fracture of the ischium; fracture of the neck of a left femur; fractured pelvis; gumma; a hatpin in child's esophagus; inga cerebralia-normal head; lateral view with bullet; osteosarcoma of vertebrae; normal shoulder; pericarditus with effusion; renal calculus; sarcoma of the kidney; skull with hardened dura matter; stones (4–5) in the kidney; stones in ureter; tuberculosis of lung; and tumor on the sella turcica.

Arranged: No.

Captioned: No.

Finding Aid: A list of subjects.

Restrictions: No.

PH·22

Thomas Gaffield Collection

Dates of Photographs: Undated, probably 1870s

Collection Origins

This collection was assembled by S.R. Koehler of Boston, Massachusetts. It documents Thomas Gaffield's (1822–   ) photographic research with colored glass filters.

The collection contains photographic test strips made by Thomas Gaffield on sensitized paper under light shielded by the following: blue glass; green glass; ground glass; orange glass; purple glass; red glass; and red flashed glass with etched cut figures.

Physical Description

There are 80 images, including albumen photoprints and platinum photoprints.

Subjects

The photographs illustrate unidentified botanical specimens, such as, branches and roots of trees. Some of the images were made under light shielded by special filters.

Arranged: By the size of the print and catalog number of the photograph.

Captioned: With type of filter used, and some with subject.

Finding Aid: No.

Restrictions: No.

PH·23

Glass Negative Collection

Dates of Photographs: 1850s–1890s

Collection Origins

This collection was assembled by the division staff from a variety of donations and purchases. Photographers and studios represented include Capstaff and the GAF Collection.

Physical Description

There are 3,800 photographs, including albumen photonegatives, collodion wet plate photonegatives, and silver gelatin dry plate photonegatives. All have glass bases.

Subjects

The photographs include architectural studies; art historical studies (photographic reproductions) of painting and sculpture; astronomy and biology study images; commercial still lifes of products; genre scenes of children playing and of women with children; scenes of early manufacturing and technology, such as, automobiles, boat building, construction sites, and factories; and unidentified city scenes worldwide.

Arranged: By size. Accessioned negatives are then arranged by the catalog number of the photonegative.

Captioned: No.

Finding Aid: No.

Restrictions: No.

PH·24

Mrs. Leopold Grey Collection

Dates of Photographs: 1863–1864

Collection Origins

These two albums of photogenic drawings were created by Mrs. Leopold Grey. According to the album inscriptions they are "ferns printed from nature," created at Bedford Lodge in 1863 and 1864.

Physical Description

There are 225 salted paper photograms mounted in two leather albums.

Subjects

The photographs are photogenic drawings of ferns. The ferns are arranged to suggest movement and life. Specific ferns included are Allosporus Crispus British; Asplenium Marinum; Decurtatum Brazil; Decustatum; Molte Spinortosum; and Scolopendoium Vulgare British.

Arranged: No.

Captioned: With the name of the fern pictured.

Finding Aid: Individual album indexes with a number and botanical name for each image.

Restrictions: No.

PH·25

Charles Harbutt Collection

Dates of Photographs: 1956–1972

Collection Origins

Charles Harbutt (1935–   ) was born in Camden, New Jersey. He received a B.S. in journalism from Marquette University in Milwaukee, Wisconsin. Harbutt served as an editor and writer for *Jubilee Magazine*. He made numerous documentary photographs of the southern United States.

Harbutt worked as a freelance magazine photographer until 1963 when he joined Magnum Photos, Inc. From 1968 to 1970, he was director of photography for the New York City Planning Commission's *Plan for New York City*.

Harbutt taught photography at both the Cooper Union and the Pratt Institute School of Visual Arts in New York City in 1970. In 1975 he was the photographer for the United States Bicentennial Commission touring exhibit.

Harbutt won the Arles Prize for his book *Travelog*, and a gold special award at the Atlanta International Film Festival for his film *America*. Harbutt has created numerous films which utilize his still photographs and a slot-machine image projection device called a "picture bandit."

Physical Description

There are 100 silver gelatin photoprints.

Subjects

These photojournalistic photographs document the political and social history of the United States between 1956 and 1972. There are photographs of the Civil Rights Movement; elections; migrant farmworkers; the Peace Movement of the 1960s; the South; and wars. Also included are studies on such topics as desolation, fear, the home, loneliness, and the American school.

Arranged: By catalog number.

Captioned: No.

Finding Aid: No.

Restrictions: For reference only. No reproductions allowed.

PH·26

Ken Heyman Collection

Dates of Photographs: 1950s–1960s

Collection Origins

Ken Heyman (1930–   ) attended Columbia University, where he received a B.A. in 1953. A student of anthropologist Margaret Mead, Heyman documented Mead's field work in Bali well into the 1970s. From 1956 to 1962 Heyman worked for *Life* magazine. He has been affiliated with the Rapho Guillumette Agency and Magnum Photos, Inc.

Heyman had a one-man exhibition at the Smithsonian Institution in 1965 and a one-man show in 1966 at the Hallmark Gallery. Between 1966 and the 1980s Heyman has been the president of Meridian Graphics. He published two books in 1963, *Willie* and *Clyde of Africa*. Heyman collaborated on two books with Margaret Mead, *Family*. New York: Macmillan, 1965; and *World Enough: Rethinking the Future*. Boston: Little, Brown, 1975.

This collection was gift from the photographer in 1964.

Physical Description

There are 90 large format silver gelatin photoprints mounted on board.

Subjects

The photographs document children in cities, schools, towns, and at play worldwide. Most of the pictures emphasize the child's cultural, natural, or social context. For example, there are images of a boy gazing at a dead man lying on the ground; a child sweeping a street; a seated girl with a broken doll; and a child in diapers running through grass.

Among the nationalities represented are American; Balinese; Chinese; Jamaican; Mexican; Nigerian; and Spanish.

Arranged: By the size of the print, and then by catalog number.

Captioned: With subject information, such as, location.

Finding Aid: No.

Restrictions: For reference only. No reproductions allowed.

PH·27

Hillotype Collection

Dates of Photographs: 1850s

Collection Origins

Levi Hill (1816–1865) claimed to have invented one of the first color photographic processes.

As a boy, Hill worked as a printer. He later ran a Baptist book printing operation. After leaving the Baptist ministry in Westkill, New York, because of severe bronchitis, Hill discovered that the fumes from the daguerreotype process helped alleviate his breathing problem.

He worked as an itinerant daguerreotypist, traveling the countryside taking portraits. In 1850 he authored a successful daguerreotype manual *A Treatise on Daguerreotype: The Whole Art Made Easy*.

In 1850 Hill publicly announced the hillotype, a color daguerreotype process. The news was widely published in the photographic journals. As time passed, the promised details of Hill's process were not revealed and it proved impossible for anyone else to reproduce his results. In 1856 Hill revealed his secret process in a new manual entitled *A Treatise on Heliochromy*.

The collection was donated by a private donor.

Physical Description

There are 60 daguerreotypes (or heliochromes or hillotypes) measuring $6\frac{1}{2}" \times 8\frac{1}{2}"$. Note: Most were made by superimposition.

Subjects

There are portraits of anonymous individuals, reproductions of illustrations, and still lifes. Some of the plates are blank.

Arranged: By division catalog numbers.

Captioned: No.

Finding Aid: No.

Restrictions: No.

PH·28

Frederick Ives Collection

Dates of Photographs: 1880s–1930s

Collection Origins

Frederick Eugene Ives (1856–1937) was a pioneer of practical three-color photography and photomechanical reproduction. In 1892 he introduced the first of a series of three-color cameras, the Photochromoscope; and in 1893 he introduced a stereoscopic version, the Kromskop.

In the 1920s Ives patented a number of basic ideas for materials using dyes for the subtractive synthesis of color. This method was later used in Kodachrome film, which was introduced in 1935.

This collection was received from the heirs of Frederick Eugene Ives.

Physical Description

There are 160 photographs, including color screen plate phototransparencies, color separation photoprints and phototransparenices, and silver gelatin dry plate lantern slides (some in stereograph format). Other materials include a Kromoskop projector.

Subjects

Most of the photographs are travel images or scenic views of Egypt; France; Japan; Spain; and the United States. Places documented include an old mission in Santa Barbara, California; the Washington Monument in Washington, D.C.; Festival Hall and Hypostyle Hall of Thutmos III at Karnak, Egypt; Luxor, Egypt; Funchei; the Narrows and the High Bank, Gaspe Peninsula; a Japanese Tea Garden in St. Louis, Missouri; and Coronado and Madeira, Spain.

Arranged: By type of material.

Captioned: With subject information.

Finding Aid: No.

Restrictions: No.

PH·29

Gertrude Kasebier Collection

Dates of Photographs: 1898–1900s

Collection Origins

Gertrude Kasebier (1852–1934) was born in Des Moines, Iowa. She was educated at the Moravian Seminary for Girls in Bethlehem, Pennsylvania, and at the Pratt Institute in Brooklyn, New York. Following her schooling, Kasebier apprenticed first to a German chemist and then to a commercial portrait photographer in Brooklyn.

After raising her family and studying painting in New York and Paris, Kasebier set up her own photography studio in New York in 1897. Her early work included assignments for *Camera Notes, The Craftsman, McClure's, The Monthly Illustrator, The Photographic Times,* and *Scribner's.* Kasebier was a founding member of the Photo-Secession (1902), and the Pictorial Photographers of America (1916). She was the first woman elected to the Linked Ring (1900).

This collection consists of images of American Indians from Buffalo Bill's Wild West Show taken by Kasebier in New York between 1898 and 1901. There are also drawings by various Dakota Sioux Indians. Note: Charles James Fox took the portrait of Thomas A. Edison (73.4), which was owned by Kasebier.

Most of this collection was donated to the Smithsonian Institution in 1969 by the photographer's family.

Physical Description

There are 110 photographs, including gum bichromate photoprints; platinum photoprints; salted paper photoprints; and silver gelatin photoprints (some bromoil). Many prints are mounted and signed. Several are duplicate prints. Other materials include photomechanical reproductions of drawings and photographs.

Subjects

The photographs are primarily portraits of Dakota Sioux Indians from Buffalo Bill's Wild West Show, 1898–1901. There are also a few pictorialist images of Europeans, such as, a girl with a mirror, and Baron De Meyer.

The Sioux Indians are shown with a book, with a drawing board, with guns and feather headdresses outside of teepees, smoking cigarettes, and with a violin. They are also seen on horseback, and on horseback with a sledge of children behind. The portraits include busts; full-face shots; full-figure shots; groupings of individuals; profiles; and three-quarter views.

There are three shots of Sioux Indians from Buffalo Bill's Wild West Show troupe taken in Gertrude Kasebier's studio. There are many portraits of the following individuals: Black Cat; Joe Black Fox; Black Horse; Has-No-Horses; Samuel Lone Bear; Little Finger; Shooting Pieces; Short Man; Spotted Tail; Philip Standing-Soldier; Whirling Hawk; and Zit-Ka-La-Sa.

There is also a portrait of Thomas Edison.

Arranged: By catalog number.

Captioned: Many are signed and captioned with the subject's name and the date.

Finding Aid: No.

Restrictions: No.

PH·30

Victor Keppler Collection

Dates of Photographs: 1930s–1961

Collection Origins

Victor Keppler (1905–   ) was born in Manhattan and attended the College of the City of New York. Keppler pioneered the use of color photography in advertising in the 1930s.

Keppler's work was used by the American Tobacco Company; DuPont; General Electric; Koppers; Lever Brothers; Schaefer Brewing Company; Seagrams; U.S. Steel; and Viking.

During World War II, Keppler was a consultant to the War Savings Staff for the Office of the United States Treasury. He produced a series of war posters. From 1946 to 1961 he was a commercial and editorial photographer.

In 1961 Keppler sold his studio to become head of the Famous Photographers School, a home-study school. He retired in 1969.

This collection was acquired in 1961.

Physical Description

There are 575 photographs, including carbro photoprints; color dye coupler photoprints and phototransparencies; color dye transfer separation photonegatives; silver gelatin dry plate photonegatives; and silver gelatin photoprints. Other materials include an ANSCO film pack; awards; a book; a book galley proof; a book outline; color tear sheets; groups of book illustrations; and one-shot cameras.

Subjects

The photographs include cityscapes; commercial advertising photographs; editorial photographs; landscapes; nudes; and still lifes.

People shown include a baby with a telephone, a cowboy smoking a cigarette, Santa Claus, skaters, and train men. There are also images of puppies in a basket.

Many of the still lifes are of commercial products, flowers, or food. Foods illustrated includes bread and wheat; fish and meat; raspberry shortcake; shellfish; and tomatoes on a vine.

Arranged: The collection has been dispersed and housed by type of material.

Captioned: With titles and subject information.

Finding Aid: No.

Restrictions: For reference only. No duplication allowed.

PH·31

Lantern Slide Collection

Dates of Photographs: 1850–1910

Collection Origins

This collection was assembled by division staff from a variety of gifts and purchases.

Distributers, photographers, and photographic publishers represented include E. & H.T. Anthony; Caspar W. Briggs; Chicago Lantern Slide Collection; Frank B. Dante; McAllister Manufacturing Optician; C.T. Milligen; Frederick and William Langenheim; and T.C. Roche.

Physical Description

There are 2,000 photographs, including collodion wet plate lantern slides and silver gelatin dry plate lantern slides. The lantern slides include comic slips, slipping slides, and a few panoramas.

Subjects

The photographs document architecture, art works, science, and travel from the 1840s to the 1910s. There are art reproductions of architecture, paintings, and sculpture; astronomy slides of the stars and planets; biological study specimens; disaster slides of train and ship wrecks; genre scenes of American life; magic lantern and vaudeville announcements including header and trailer slides (announcements); sports scenes; and travel images of exotic animals and lands.

Architecture and cities documented include England (Windsor Castle); Italy (Rome); and the United States (the Library of Congress Jefferson Building, Washington, D.C., and Arlington, Virginia).

Among the people shown are: American farmers; American Indians; American street vendors; children playing; nuns and priests; and an unidentified king on a horse. Sports documented include football, horse racing, and pole-vaulting.

Science images include astronomy slides of Mars, Saturn and Venus; biological studies of an exogenous growth; and the leg of a blowfly. Among the animals illustrated are dogs, leopards, monkeys, and sea lions.

Arranged: No.

Captioned: With subject and date information.

Finding Aid: No.

Restrictions: No.

PH·32

Lock and Whitfield Collection
A.K.A. *Men of Mark: Contemporary Portraits of Distinguished Men*

Dates of Photographs: 1876

Collection Origins

The photomechanicals (Woodburytypes) in this collection came from the book *Men of Mark: Contemporary Portraits of Distinguished Men of the Senate, Church, Science, Literature and Art, the Army, Navy, Law, and Medicine.* This is a three-volume work published by Sampson, Low, Marston, Searle, & Rivington in London in 1876.

Photographers represented include Lock and (George C.) Whitfield. Note: Biographies accompanying the portraits were written by Thompson Cooper, FSA.

Physical Description

There are 110 photomechanicals (Woodburytypes) tipped-into the three volumes. Each oval portrait has decorative scroll work around it.

Subjects

The images document Englishmen in the arts, the church, the government, the law, and the sciences. There are photographs of Lord Airey; Bishop of London; Charles Robert Darwin; Earl of Dufferin; Joseph Durkam, ARA; Sir Wm. Ferguson; M. Lord Lytton; Samuel Plimsol; Richard Redgrave, Esq.

RA; and Jules Verne. Most images are 3/4 length busts. Some are shown in profile.

Arranged: No.

Captioned: With the person's name and a one- or two-page biographical sketch.

Finding Aid: No.

Restrictions: No.

PH·33

Master Photographer Collection

Dates of Photographs: 1840–Present

Collection Origins

This collection was assembled by the division staff from a variety of donations and purchases. The collection began in 1882 with the accession of a group of photographs by Frederick Gatekunst. In 1888 the division began to collect apparatus with the acquisition of Samuel F.B. Morse's daguerreotype camera. From 1913 to 1966, photographic exhibitions appeared in the U.S. National Museum, now called the Arts and Industries Building.

There are 1,150 photographers represented in this collection. Photographers (and the number of their representative photographs) represented include Berenice Abbott (18); Ansel Adams (25); Lucien Aigner (7); Josef Albert (5); James Alinder (2); Paul Anderson (34); J. Craig Annan (17); E. & H.T. Anthony (17); Diane Arbus (5); Eugene Atget (14); Hippolyte Bayard (25); Cecil Beaton (1); Richard Beattie (6); Zaida Ben-Yusuf (1); Freres Bisson (1); Louis Desire Blanquart-Evrard (22); Clark Blickensderfer (3); A. Aubrey Bodine (14); Charles Booz (17); Margaret Bourke-White (25); Bill Brandt (6); Brassai (Gyula Halasz) (20); Adolphe Braun (9); Anne Brigman (2); Lucien Georges Bull (30); Wynn Bullock (5); Harry Callahan (10); Julia Margaret Cameron (14); Paul Caponigro (3); Lucien Clergue (5); Alvin Langdon Coburn (3); Van Deren Coke (5); Will Connell (61); Leon Cremiere (36); Imogen Cunningham (33); L.J.M. Daguerre (1); Bruce Davidson (7); F. Holland Day (2); Robert Demachy (1); Baron Adolph De Meyer (1); Andre Disderi (3); Alfred Eisenstaedt (9); Frank Eugene (3); Walker Evans (35); Henry Fitz, Jr. (24); Robert Frank (6); Lee Friedlander (5); Francis Frith (36); Alexander Gardner (17); Arnold Genthe (13); Mario Giacomelli (5); Laura Gilpin (3); Franz Hanfstaengl (66); Harris and Ewing (53); and David Octavius Hill and Robert Adamson (7).

Other photographers include Lewis W. Hine (20); George Hubbard Holt (68); Eikoh Hosoe (5); William Henry Jackson (19); Frances Benjamin Johnston (6); André Kertész (10); Dorothea Lange (19); W. & F. Langenheim (13); Clarence John Laughlin (59); Robert MacPherson (4); Frederich von Martens (6); Margrethe Mather (5); Ray K. Metzker (12); Duane Michals (8); Lisette Model (5); Laszlo Moholy-Nagy (10); Barbara Morgan (21); Paul Nadar (2); Arnold Newman (29); Janine Niepce (50); Wallace Nutting (1); Paul Outerbridge, Jr. (11); Irving Penn (5); David Plowden (45); Carlo Ponti (40); Guido Rey (22); Henry Peach Robinson (17); Napoleon Sarony (39); Harry B. Shaw (9); Aaron Siskind (10); Thomas A. Smillie (19); W. Eugene Smith (1); Southworth & Hawes (1); Edward Steichen (6); Alfred Stieglitz (6); Jerry Uelsmann (20); Amelia Van Buren (4); Roman Vishniac (4); Cole Weston (1); Edward Weston (43); Clarence White (7); Minor White (14); J.W. Whitesell (15); and Garry Winogrand (15).

Physical Description

There are 23,000 photoprints, including albumen photoprints; carbon photoprints; carbro photoprints; diazo photoprints; gum bichromate photoprints; gum platinum photoprints; Kallitypes (Vandyke brown photoprints); a Kwic-Print; pannotypes; platinum photoprints; salted paper photoprints; and silver gelatin photoprints (some bromoil). Note: Most images are silver gelatin photoprints.

Color processes represented include color dye bleach photoprints (Gasparcolor and Utocolor); color dye coupler images (including Agfachrome slides, Ektachrome slides, Ektacolor photoprints, Kodachrome slides, and Kodacolor photoprints); color dye diffusion transfer images (including Cibachrome photoprints, Polacolor photoprints, and Polaroid SX-70 photoprints); color screen plate phototransparencies (including Autochromes, Dufay and Finlay phototransparencies, and the Joly process); dye transfer photoprints (Pinatype); and three-color separation process (technicolor).

Subjects

The photographs include abstract photography; architectural photography; cityscapes; documentary photography; genre scenes; individual and group portraits; landscapes; nature studies; news photography; nudes; panoramas; pictorialist studies of shadows and forms; seascapes; and still lifes.

Arranged: Alphabetically by the last name of the photographer.

Captioned: With photographer's name, accession number, and title.

Finding Aid: A list, arranged by photographer's last name, gives the number and type (process and format) of images.

Restrictions: Some materials are for reference only.

PH·34

Morrison Studio Collection

Dates of Photographs: Circa 1893

Collection Origins

The Morrison Studio is a commercial photographic studio which has operated in Woodstock, Virginia, since the 1870s. This collection consists of the photographs, props, and studio furniture donated to the division by the firm.

Physical Description

There are 500 photographs, including a collodion wet plate photonegative, silver gelatin dry plate lantern slides and photonegatives (the bulk of the collection), and silver gelatin photoprints (DOP bromide).

Subjects

All the photographs are exterior and interior images of the World's Columbian Exposition held in Chicago in 1893. Architectural studies, concession stands, exhibitions, and exposition participants and visitors are shown.

Among the exhibits documented are the exterior of a building labeled "famous 1st century Arab home"; a Colorado Gold mine mock-up (10 cents a visit); a German beer garden; paintings of Indian women by Ravi Varma of Travancore, India; a Turkish rug exhibit; and costumed women reclining in a mock harem room.

Arranged: By accession number.

Captioned: With subject information.

Finding Aid: No.

Restrictions: No.

PH·35

Fred Mueller Collection

Dates of Photographs: 1913, 1914

Collection Origins

Fred Mueller (circa 1910–June 1964) was a Baltimore builder, carpenter, inventor, and commercial photographer. The Mueller family built many of the homes near the John Hopkins Hospital in Baltimore at the turn of the century.

Mueller developed and patented a camera which made 360 degree "dome" pictures of the horizon and the sky; as well as panorama and 360 degree cyclorama cameras.

Mueller was one of the first photographers to take aerial pictures from a plane. His early aerial photographs convinced him that it was possible to make accurate land measurements from photographs. Britain, France, Germany, and the United States bid on his aerial camera. The sale of his cameras to Germany was blocked by the government when World War I began.

This collection was given to the division by the Mueller's heirs.

Physical Description

There are 125 photographs, including platinum photoprints, and silver gelatin photonegatives (some on nitrate) and photoprints. Other materials include a flier labeled "Cycloramic Photography."

Subjects

Most of the photographs are panoramic city-scapes of Baltimore and other unidentified cities and towns, some with a 360 degree fisheye perspective. There are also experimental images of the Baltimore city horizon; the Baltimore harbor; the sky; and wooded landscapes.

Some of the photographs were taken from balloon gondolas, dirigibles, and tall buildings. There are images of Charles Street in Baltimore taken the day after the fire of 1904 destroyed much of the city (copyrighted); a partially submerged submarine; and an unidentified parade in Baltimore.

There are also informal portraits of John Garret and unidentified people.

Arranged: No.

Captioned: Some with technical information, such as, light level, wind direction, date, and time.

Finding Aid: No.

Restrictions: No.

PH·36

Eadweard Muybridge Collection

Dates of Photographs: 1884–1920

Collection Origins

This collection was assembled by division staff from four distinct accessions of Muybridge materials.

In 1920, one accession came to the division from the Commercial Museum in Philadelphia. This consisted of vintage materials produced by Muybridge for distribution. The collotypes and cyanotypes were purchased by a private donor at a New York City auction in 1879 and were donated to the Smithsonian in 1930. The lantern slides were purchased by the division from a private source in 1923. Other materials in the collection were purchased by the Bureau of American Ethnology in the 1880s and later transferred to the division.

Eadweard Muybridge (1830–1904) emigrated from England to the United States in 1852. He be-

came the representative of the London Printing and Publishing Company.

While in California in 1856 Muybridge studied the daguerreotype process under Silas Selleck and worked for Carleton E. Watkins. He photographed the Pacific Coast for the United States government and for Thomas Houseworth. He also photographed Yosemite, and accompanied the official United States expedition to Alaska when it was acquired from Russia.

In 1872 Muybridge was commissioned to photograph Leland Stanford's horse, Occident, in stop motion photography. Muybridge photographed animal movement at Stanford's Palo Alto Ranch again from 1877 to 1879. In 1881 he produced his volume *The Attitudes of Animals in Motion*, and traveled and lectured in Europe.

Between 1883 and 1885 he continued his photographic research at the University of Pennsylvania, where his advisory committee included University Provost William Pepper and painter Thomas Eakins. Between 1884 and 1885 Muybridge produced 30,000 photonegatives. Copy sets of the images were sold to libraries throughout the country. His work was published in 781 bound collotype plates entitled *Animals in Locomotion* in 1887.

Physical Description

There are 48,600 photographs including albumen photoprints; collodion lantern slides; cyanotypes; and zoopraxiscope silver gelatin phototransparencies. Other materials include a lens boards; multiple plate curtain slide holders; negative holders; a rotary shutter; an electrically controlled timing device; and 1,356 photomechanical interpositives (collotypes).

Subjects

Most of the photographs document animals or people in motion, for example, engaged in sports activities, running, or walking. All scenes show a sequence of motions in serial fashion, much like a cartoon strip or motion picture film footage.

Images of women include a a nude woman striking a pose entitled "Shame"; a nude woman with a towel; a woman carrying a nude baby; a woman in an Empire-style dress; and a woman raising and opening a closed parasol.

Images of men include a man dropping off a mule and pulling its tail; a man in a high hat riding a kicking mule; a man throwing a stick; a man tipping his hat; and a man in white trousers riding a spirited horse.

Images of animals include a male goat walking; a mule alternately raising his front and back feet; and a horse on a seesaw.

Arranged: In plate number order.

Captioned: The plates have penciled plate numbers on top.

Finding Aid: In production.

Restrictions: No.

PH·37

Charles Negre Collection

Dates of Photographs: 1960s

Collection Origins

Born in 1820 in Grasse, France, Charles Negre was a student of J. Ingres and Paul Delaroche in Paris. Negre made daguerreotype records of his paintings in 1844, and later produced daguerreotype landscapes. Negre studied the calotype process under Gustave Le Gray, and produced calotypes as preliminary sketches for his paintings.

In 1851 Negre's first exhibition of photographs was held at the Societe Heliographique. In 1852 he taught at the Ecole Superieur du Commerce in Paris. Negre ran a portrait studio in Paris and also did work on commission. He took a series of photographs of the Imperial Asylum at Vincennes for Napoleon III.

Seeking a medium that would be both permanant and inexpensive, Negre experimented with transferring silver gelatin photoprints to zinc plates, as well as to steel photomechanicals (photogravures).

Negre made many unposed photographs of Parisian street people and tradesmen during the 1850s. He also photographed French monuments such as Chartres Cathedral. Later in his life he continued to produce photographs of landscapes and monuments, sometimes making albumen photoprints, calotypes, and salted paper photoprints of great size. He died in Grasse in 1880.

This collection was acquired by the Smithsonian Institution in 1965 and 1966 through a purchase from a private individual in Paris.

The modern photoprints were made by Andre

Jammes from Negre's original images which are housed in the Societie Francaise de Photographie.

Physical Description

There are 120 photographs, including an original calotype photonegative and modern silver gelatin photoprints. Most of these photoprints were made from calotype photonegatives, although a few were made from collodion wet plate photonegatives.

Subjects

The photographs are French cityscapes, genre scenes, landscapes, portraits, and views of the monuments of Chartres, Grasse, Marseilles, Nice, and Paris between the 1850s and the 1860s.

The portraits are largely studies of street people and tradesmen, such as, a portrait of a gardener with two wheelbarrows and a portrait of a young girl on a bench in Paris, France, around 1860.

Arranged: No.

Captioned: With Smithsonian accession number, date of the original print, topical information, and original process.

Finding Aid: No.

Restrictions: No.

PH·38

Paris Salon of Women Photographers, 1900

Dates of Photographs: 1890s

Collection Origins

This collection was assembled by Frances Benjamin Johnston (1864–1952) of Grafton, West Virginia.

Johnston assembled it between 1899 and 1900 for an exhibition entitled "Photographs by American Women" held at the Paris Salon of Women Photographers in 1900. Johnston was an apprentice of Thomas William Smillie, director of the Smithsonian Institution's Photographic Division.

Women photographers represented include Alice

Austin; Mary A. Bartlett; Zaida Ben-Yusuf; Sara Jane Eddy; Emma Justine Farnsworth; Mary Paschall; Mary Schaffer; Alta Belle Sniff; Amelia Van Buren; and Eva Lawrence Watson. Note: The images in this collection are housed by creator in the Master Photographer Collection.

Physical Description

There are 95 photographs, including albumen photoprints, calotype photonegatives, platinum photoprints, salted paper photoprints, silver gelatin photoprints, and theodolites. Other materials include photomechanicals (Woodburytypes).

Subjects

Most of the photographs are pictorialist, including soft-focus shots of children in costume; children on holidays; flowers; landscapes; and portraits of individuals (mostly unidentified women and children). There is also a portrait of William Rau.

Arranged: By the photographer's last name (in the Master Photographer Collection).

Captioned: With subject information or titles.

Finding Aid: A guide to the "Photographs by American Women" exhibition of 1900 is arranged by photographer's name. It lists the number of prints shown; active dates of the photographer; name of the work; and contemporary location of the print.

Restrictions: No.

PH·39

Titian Ramsay Peale Collection

Dates of Photographs: Circa 1855–1885

Collection Origins

Titian Ramsay Peale (1799–1885) was born in Philadelphia, Pennsylvania, where he was educated by his father, Charles Wilson Peale, in the Peale Museum.

Titian Ramsay Peale served as explorer, naturalist, and scientist on the United States Exploring Expedition (also known as the Wilkes Expedition).

In 1848 Peale joined the U.S. Patent Office. He became principal examiner in the Division of Fine Arts and Photography in 1858. Due to his interest in new patents and technology, Peale became one of the earliest users of the collodion wet plate process. Among Peale's early experiments were attempts to modify the collodion wet plate process for ease of printing. He tried adding chemicals and food to his emulsions to make them dry more slowly and to increase their sensitivity. Peale was interested in producing a collodion process variant which would be sensitive even when dry. He also experimented with panorama production and stereo photography.

Peale frequently listed in his photo albums the equipment and photographic processes he used. He often noted the light conditions, location, time of day, weather conditions, and other variables which effected his photographs. Many of his subjects were repeatedly photographed over a long period of time.

The collection came to the Smithsonian from a private donor in 1965.

Physical Description

There are 200 photographs, including albumen photoprints (from collodion wet plate photonegatives); albumen stereographs (24); albumen and silver gelatin photoprints using a variety of experimental additions to the photographic emulsion, such as, beer, glycerin, honey, milk, and tannin (also called the culinary processes); and carbon transfer photoprints. The photographs are in two albums. Other materials include photomechanicals (Woodburytypes).

Subjects

The photographs include images of Washington, D.C., architecture, cityscapes, engineering projects, and landscapes from 1855 to 1884. There are also portraits of Peale's friends and relations.

Places illustrated include Henry Burr's cottage; General Daniel Butterfield's headquarters; the Chesapeake & Ohio Canal; the feed store at 259 G Street; the Georgetown College Observatory; Mount Vernon; Pierce's Mill in Rock Creek Park; the U.S. Patent Office; Washington, D.C., churches, including Rock Creek Church and Saint John's Church; and the Washington, D.C., Aqueduct and bridge construction.

There is an eight-plate photographic panorama of Washington, D.C., taken from the towers of the Smithsonian Institution Castle Building. There are images of the Joseph Henry family quarters in the Smithsonian Castle building, of the Smithsonian Institution, and of the Mall.

There are also a number of photographs of the architecture and landscapes of the Delaware Water Gap; Red Bank, New Jersey; and Montrose and Philadelphia, Pennsylvania. There are several miscellaneous photographs of museum specimens, such as, arrowheads.

Portraits include Dorothea Dix; Mr. and Mrs. Joseph Henry and their family; Mary and Carrie Henry; General and Mrs. Montgomery Meigs and their family; Francis Peale; Franklin and Caroline Peale; Lucy Peale; and Mr. and Mrs. Frederick Seward. There are also images of the inauguration of President Abraham Lincoln.

Arranged: The photograph albums are in catalog number order (which is also chronological order).

Captioned: Captions may include the following: subject identification; date of the photograph; process used; type of printing paper; weather and light conditions; and other factors.

Finding Aid: No.

Restrictions: Certain materials within the collection are restricted and may not be photographically or xerographically copied.

PH·40

Joseph Petrocelli Photograph Collection

Dates of Photographs: 1921–1928

Collection Origins

Joseph Petrocelli (–1928) was a pictorialist photographer and a long-term member of the Brooklyn Institute of Arts and Sciences in New York.

During his life, Petrocelli was widely exhibited in both Europe and the United States, including a one-man show at the Smithsonian Institution and exhibitions at the Brooklyn Institute.

This collection of pictorialist photographic prints was donated by Petrocelli's widow, Mary, in January 1933.

Physical Description

There are 90 photoprints, including gum bichromate photoprints, silver gelatin photonegatives and photoprints (bromoil).

Subjects

The photographs are pictorialist soft-focus cityscapes, genre scenes, landscapes, portraits, and still lifes. There are also posed portraits of children, men, and women symbolizing various stages of life, and "types" (or individuals felt to be representative of their nationality or ethnic backround). Many images are of rural individuals posed to illustrate a theme, such as, "Summer Rain" or "A Witty Story."

Geographic areas shown include Tunis, Tunisia; Egypt; Paris, France; Abend, Munich, Nuremberg, and Rothenburg, Germany; Hawaii; India; Ireland; Florence, Pompeii, and Venice, Italy; Saudi Arabia; New York City; and Dalmatia, Yugoslavia.

Arranged: In catalog number order.

Captioned: With subject information, such as, nationality or locale.

Finding Aid: No.

Restrictions: No.

PH·41

Photographic Illustrations File

Dates of Photographs: 1970s–Present

Collection Origins

This collection was assembled by division staff from OPPS copy and duplicate photoprints to serve as a browsing file for researchers. It consists of copy images of photographs in other collections, such as, the Gertrude Kasebier Collection.

Photographers represented include Walter Clark; George Collins Cox; George Eastman; Sir John Herschel; Gertrude Kasebier; Eadweard Muybridge; and Titian Ramsay Peale.

Physical Description

There are 7,000 copy silver gelatin photoprints (all copies or duplicates).

Subjects

The photographs are copies or duplicates of the images in other collections of the Division of Photographic History.

The images document architectural studies; art works; cityscapes; corporate leaders and public figures; culture groups such as, American Indians; domestic interiors; landscapes; news photographs; photographic apparatus such as, cameras, lenses, and shutters; portraits of children, men, and women; scientific imagery, including astronomical and medical images; seascapes; sports groups; and still lifes.

Arranged: By division catalog number.

Captioned: With the original image's catalog number and OPPS negative number.

Finding Aid: No.

Restrictions: No.

PH·42

Photographic Patent Models

Dates of Photographs: 1840–1905

Collection Origins

The U.S. Patent Office assembled this collection from examples of photographic processes submitted with photographic patent applications. The images were transferred to the Smithsonian Institution from the U.S. Patent Office around the turn of the century.

The photographs are examples of early photographic procedures, processes, or techniques that have received a patent.

Photographers represented include Joseph Albert Edward Bierstadt; Bisbee; Daniel Davis, Jr.; Herman Decker; P.A. Despaqries; P.F. Dodge; Ernest Edwards; M.R. Freeman; Gilbert & Bacon, Philadel-phia; Jeremiah Gurney; Alfred A. Hart; O.P. Howe; Edward Howell; D.F. Hulbert; S.D. Humphrey; J.B. Isnirung; John Jacobson; J.A.F. Lair; E.B. Lancher; Frederick Langenheim; Lefeora; L.E. Levey; Lewis; G.S. Lucas; F. Mauravour; C.A. Miller; Eadweard Muybridge; W.D. Osborn; J.W. Osborne; Joseph A. Schultz; William Henry Fox Talbot; Thompson; Leon Vidal; Horace W. Waide; W.F. Watson; E. & H.C. White; J.F. Whitley; F. Williams; G.M. Williams; Simon Wing; Thomas E. Wood; W.B. Woodbury; and W. Yarnell.

Physical Description

There are 100 photographs, including albumen photoprints; carbon transfer photoprint (metalograph); collodion photoprints (enamel); daguerreotypes (some with applied carbon transfers); salted paper photoprints; silver gelatin photoprints (DOP and POP); and tintypes. Many of the images are in stereographic format or in cases, frames, holders, or viewing apparatus.

Many of the images included are examples of specific format, process, or technique variants which were never commercially available. These include attempts at obtaining photographic permanence; case and mount possibilities; coloring processes; enameled photographs; enlarged or reduced images; halftone production; motion photography; multiple images from a single sitting; panorama production possibilities; photographic transfers; photographs on glass; printing using artificial light; relief printing; stereoscopic images; and surface preparations, such as, embossing or burnishing. Other materials include albums; bellows; camera stands; cameras; developing tongs; lenses; magic lantern projectors; photomechanical processes (such as, Albertypes and photomechanical stereographs [collotypes]); plate holders; portable dark rooms; print cutters; printing frames; reflectors; retouching equipment; rollers; screens; shutters; stereoscopes; vignetting equipment; and other photographic apparatus.

Subjects

The photographs are architectural exteriors and interiors, informal portraits of unidentified children, men, and women; and landscapes.

Arranged: No.

Captioned: With number, catalog number, accession number, patent description, and date.

Finding Aid: A printout with inventor's name, invention description, secondary inventors involved, and patent number.

Restrictions: Fragile materials are restricted.

PH·43

Photographic Techniques and Processes Collection

Dates of Photographs: Circa 1840–1980s

Collection Origins

This collection was assembled by division staff for study purposes from diverse discoveries, donations, and purchases. This collection's primary purpose is to serve as examples of specific photographic formats, processes, and techniques.

Physical Description

There are 5,000 photographs, including albumen photoprints; carbon photoprints; carbon transfer photoprints; carbro photoprints; cyanotypes; gum bichromate photoprints; palladium photoprints; platinum photoprints; salted paper photoprints; silver gelatin photonegatives on gelatin (Eastman); and silver gelatin photoprints (bromoil) and radiographs; tintypes; and various printed-out photoprints on paper, such as, silver gelatin photoprints (POP chloride).
   Note: The collection contains phototransparencies; positive photoprints; direct positive photoprints and photonegatives on glass, metal, paper and alternative supports, such as, cloth, leather, and porcelain.
   Color processes included are color patent models; color screen plate processes (Dufaycolor or Finlay color phototransparencies); color dye coupler processes (Ektachrome and Kodachrome); dye diffusion processes (Polacolor); dye transfer separation processes (Pinatypes); and technicolor motion pictures.
   Formats include holograms; panoramas; photomicrographs; snapshots; stereographs; underwater photoprints; and wire photoprints. Other materials include graphic art apparatus and prints; motion

pictures; and photomechanical processes, such as, Woodburytypes and xerographic copies.

Subjects

The photographs are cityscapes, landscapes, portraits, seascapes, and still lifes. Most are unidentified as to name and locale.

Arranged: By process, technique, or format.

Captioned: With the name of the process and format, and occasionally with the photographer's name and date. Some of the images have catalog numbers.

Finding Aid: No.

Restrictions: No.

PH·44

M.P. Rice Negative Collection

Dates of Photographs: 1850s–1870s

Collection Origins

There is no information about the provenance of this collection. Note: Internal evidence suggests that the images may have been created by the Rice Studio, which was located at 1217–1219 Pennsylvania Avenue, Washington, D.C., from 1891 to 1901 (according to Library of Congress records).

Physical Description

There are 15 collodion wet plate photonegatives which measure roughly $13'' \times 15\ 1/2''$.

Subjects

The collection consists primarily of bust-length portraits of unidentified men in uniforms of the United States Armed Forces.

Arranged: By size of negative.

Captioned: Several are labeled with name and rank (undecipherable).

Finding Aid: No.

Restrictions: No.

PH·45

Arthur Rothstein Collection

Dates of Photographs: 1935–1961

Collection Origins

Arthur Rothstein was born and educated in New York City. He earned a B.A. from Columbia University, where he worked with Roy Stryker. Rothstein later joined Stryker at the Farm Security Administration where he served as a photographer primarily in the South and the West from 1935 to 1940.

Rothstein was a picture editor for the U.S. Office of War Information and a photo officer in the U.S. Army Signal Corps. After World War II, Rothstein joined *Look* magazine as director of photography. In 1972 he became photography director at *Parade* magazine.

Arthur Rothstein is primarily a documentary photographer and a photojournalist. He helped found the American Society of Magazine Photographers, whose journal, *Infinity*, he edited for many years.

This collection was a gift of the photographer to the Smithsonian Institution in 1962.

Physical Description

There are 300 photographs, including color dye coupler slides (Ektachrome) and silver gelatin photoprints.

Subjects

Most images are photojournalistic cityscapes (including slums and taverns), landscapes (including river images), portraits (including people at work), and still lifes.

Areas documented include China; India; and the United States (including the American South and West during the 1935 to 1940 Dust Bowl period;

and the Mid-Atlantic states, including Maryland, Vermont, and Virginia).

There are images of artists, cowhands, entertainers, factory workers, farmers, an Indian army captain, miners, a Chinese peddler, Chinese refugees, politicians, a postmaster, refugees, sharecroppers, sheepherders, soldiers, and welders.

Celebrities documented include Jimmy Durante, Eartha Kitt, Tanaquil LeClerq, John Marin, and Grandma Moses.

Arranged: By catalog number.

Captioned: With location, subject, and date.

Finding Aid: No.

Restrictions: For reference only. No reproductions allowed.

PH·46

Kosti Ruohomaa Collection

Dates of Photographs: 1940s–1950s

Collection Origins

Kosti S. Ruohomaa (1914–1961) was born in Quincy, Massachusetts. He worked first as a commercial artist in Boston and New York, and then as an animator for Walt Disney in Hollywood, California.

While in Hollywood, Ruohomaa took up photography. During the 1930s, he photographed for *Life* magazine. He became a freelance photographer for Black Star in the 1940s and worked for *Collier's, Down East, How America Lives, Ladies' Home Journal, Parade, This Week,* and *Yankee.*

This collection came to the division in 1964 from the Black Star Publishing Company in New York.

Physical Description

There are 115 silver gelatin photoprints.

Subjects

The photographs are of New England landscapes; people, such as, doctors, farmers, and fishermen; rural exteriors and interiors; and seascapes.

Landscapes and rural scenes illustrated include a barn; Cape Hatteras; a country store; a farmer and wagon silhouetted against a sky; forests; a horse in a corral; a snowstorm; and a town square with a statue of Paul Revere.

Arranged: By catalog number.

Captioned: With subject information.

Finding Aid: No.

Restrictions: For reference only. No duplication allowed.

PH·47

Erich Salomon Collection

Dates of Photographs: 1927–1938

Collection Origins

Erich Salomon (1886–1944) was born in Berlin, Germany. He received a doctorate of law from the University of Munich.

During World War I Salomon was a prisoner of war for four years. He began to photograph in 1927. He was one of the first photographers to use a miniature Ermanox camera; and later used an Er-Nox, then a Leica.

Salomon's work was called "candid camera" photography. Often he kept his cameras hidden from view while shooting. He established a style of informal glimpses of important figures which influenced later photojournalists. Salomon died in Auschwitz concentration camp.

Physical Description

There are 140 silver gelatin photoprints. They are oversized dry mounted images.

Subjects

The photographs are candid and informal portraits of politicians. There are photographs of the Dutch cabinet in session at The Hague, Netherlands (October 1932); Lord Snowdon making an announcement at the second Hague Conference (January 1930); the President's Box at the State Opera in Berlin (1928); and unidentified men sitting at tables in a meeting.

Arranged: No.

Captioned: No.

Finding Aid: No.

Restrictions: No.

PH·48

Stereograph Collection

Dates of Photographs: 1850s–1930s

Collection Origins

This collection was assembled by division staff from disparate sources within the Smithsonian Institution. When the Division of Photographic History was first founded, photographic materials were taken from other divisions. A second major collection component of 1,423 stereographs was assembled and given to the Smithsonian Institution by Albert Boni of New York City. (See the Boni Collection report PH7).

Among the stereographic manufacturers and distributers represented are American Stereoscopic Views; Appleton Stereo Photo Co.; Baker & Record; Baldi and Wurthle; Baldwin Photo; George Barker; Barnum Photographer; Bay State Publishing Co.; Beal's Art Gallery; Bebitte and Herre; Francis Bedford; C. Bierstadt; Bolles and Frisbie; Caswell and Dary; Centennial Photographic Co.; W.M. Chase; Climo's Stereographs; Continent Stereo Co.; Cook and Seely; Copelin and Hine; Cosmos Series; Detlor and Dow's; Detlor and Waddell's; DeYoung's Palace Dollar Store; Dodge, Colt, and Perkins; Edinburgh Stereographs Co.; European and American Views; Everett and Co.; Everett and Lindsey; and the Eye Comfort Series.

Also included are A. Frankfield and Co.; Gardner's Photographic Art Gallery; Globe Photo Art Co.; Halsey and Coffin; Hemple's Photographic Rooms; Wm. B. Holmes and Co.; Horne and Thornthwaite; Thomas Houseworth and Co.; Hurd and Smith; Hurd and Ward; Hurst and Son; Infernal Fancies and Co.; International Stereograph Co.; International Stereoscopic View Co.; Italy Through the Stereoscope; Kelley and Chadwick; Ketchun and Co.; Keystone View Co.; Kilburn Brothers; Knowlton Bros.; Lawrence and Houseworth; Liberty Brand Stereo Views; Liersch, Gustav and Co.; Littleton View Co.; Loescher and Petsch; Frederick Loeser and Co.; London Stereoscopic Co.; Lovejoy and Foster; and Melander and Henderson.

Also included are Metropolitan Syndicate Press; J.S. and J.W. Moulton; New England Series; New York Stereoscopic Co.; Northrup's Wonder Store; Original Boston 99 Cent Store; Pauly, Geschwister, Peabody, and Tilton; Peter, Paul and Bro.; Picturesque America New Series; Poulton and Co.; Powell and Thompson; Presko Binocular Co.; Purviance Photo; Putnam and Valentine; Ripple Bros.; Roberts and Fellows; Savage and Ottinger; Schurch and Co.; Shaw and Chamberlin; Slee Bros.; Smith and Sayles; Standard Series; Stereo Photo Co.; Stereo Travel Co.; Stereoscope View Co.; Stereoscopic Views; Strohmeyer and Wyman; Swisse et Savoie; Townsend and Gould; Underwood and Underwood; U.S. Stereoscopic View Co.; Vernon Portrait and Ferrotype Gallery; Webster and Albee; Whiting View Co.; Whitney and Zimmerman; and Woodward and Albee. Many other firms are represented.

Physical Description

There are 10,000 stereographs, including albumen photoprints and phototransparencies; collodion wet plate phototransparencies; salted paper photoprints; and silver gelatin photoprints and phototransparencies. Stereographic formats represented include parallax stereographs and tissue stereographs. Other materials include lithographic prints.

Subjects

These stereograph cards document world architecture; art objects; disasters; nature; portraits; stage scenes; and travel.

Among the activities and events illustrated are: art exhibits; celebrations; Centennial scenes; Chicago fire scenes; disasters; farming; fishing; hunting; mining; sports; transportation on land; and war (particularly World War I).

Among the objects shown are graphic prints, monuments, paintings, and sculpture.

Among the travel images included are: architecture (exteriors and interiors—many of cathedrals); cityscapes; parks; plants; landscapes (predominantly scenic views of America and Europe); and railroads.

Among the people shown are celebrities; comics and humorous groups; the military (particularly the U.S. Navy); and political figures. Note: The comics and humor categories often document historical attitudes toward culture groups, minorities, political groups, and occupations.

Among the photographic genres included are animal portraits (including eagles); fairy tales; genre scenes of life in America; landscapes; occupational shots; portraits; spirit photographs; and still lifes.

Arranged: Alphabetically by either 1) Name of the maker, manufacturer, or distributer; 2) Series; 3) Geographical locale; or 4) Image subject.

Captioned: Many were captioned by the manufacturer. The captions are humorous, or descriptive, or they tell the name of the manufacturer and the series number.

Finding Aid: There is an index to this collection which lists photographers; image manufactures and distributors; geographical locales; and subjects in a single nine-page alphabetical list. Following the name, location, or subject heading is the housing location of the stereograph card.

Restrictions: No.

PH·49

William Henry Fox Talbot Collection

Dates of Photographs: 1839—Mid-1840s

Collection Origins

William Henry Fox Talbot (1800—1877) was born in Melbury, Dorset, England. He received an M.A. from Cambridge University in 1825. Talbot joined the Royal Astronomical Society in 1822 and became a fellow in 1832. He served as a Member of Parliament. Also famous as an Assyriologist, Talbot was involved in deciphering the cuneiform inscriptions from Ninevah in conjunction with Edward Hincks and Sir Henry Rawlinson.

William Henry Fox Talbot was a pioneer photographic scientist who invented the photogenic drawing process. (A more contemporary term is photogram, which is an image made by placing an object over light sensitive paper and exposing it.) In 1841 he patented the first negative/positive process (the calotype process). In 1843 Talbot began the first mass production of photographic prints for the publication of his book *The Pencil of Nature*, the first book ever illustrated with photographs.

In 1851 he developed a method for taking instantaneous pictures. This was followed in 1852 with his development of a photoengraving process, and his creation of his special collodian wet plate traveler's camera in 1854. Talbot produced over 600 photographs during his lifetime. Talbot died at Lacock Abbey in 1877 while in the process of writing a history of his photographic inventions.

Much of the Talbot collection came to the Smithsonian Institution between 1927 and 1928, from his sister, Mrs. Katherine Burnett Brown, and other family members.

Physical Description

There are 100 photographs, including calotypes—with one complete edition of the 24 calotypes in *The Pencil of Nature*—and salted paper photoprints. Note: One photograph is one of the earliest extant Talbot calotypes. Other materials include a label from W. and F. Langenheim's talbotype establishment in Philadelphia, Pennsylvania; manuscripts; photographic equipment, including Talbot's camera; and about 82 photomechanicals (some photogravures).

Subjects

The photographs are architectural studies of abbeys, churches, and monuments of England, France, and Scotland, between 1839 and the middle 1940s; as well as genre scenes; landscapes; portraits of William Henry Fox Talbot and his acquaintances; and still lifes. Architectural studies and landscapes include Balliol College, Oxford; the bridge and Castle of St. Angelo; Dryburgh Abbey, Scotland; and Lacock Abbey's environs and north court from the northwest. *The Pencil of Nature* is also included in one complete and one partial edition.

Arranged: By type of material and then by process or format. Cameras and equipment are housed in one area, and prints and negatives in another.

Captioned: With subject information.

Finding Aid: A new finding aid lists catalog number; maker; date; description; and size.

Restrictions: No.

PH·50

Tokutaro Tanaka Collection

Dates of Photographs: 1940s–1960s

Collection Origins

Tokutaro Tanaka (1909–   ) is a Japanese author and photographer who has published several books on white herons. Two titles are *Forest of White Herons*, Series 20 of Akane Publishing Company (Science for Grade School Children Series), 1972; and *Poem of White Herons*, Series 3 of Iwanami Publishing Company, 1982.

Physical Description

There are 60 silver gelatin photoprints. Many are oversized and/or framed.

Subjects

The photographs document white herons in Japanese landscape settings. The herons are shown flying silhouetted against the sky, in forested landscapes, in nests, and standing alone and in groups.

Arranged: By the size of the print and by the catalog number of the photograph.

Captioned: With partial subject information.

Finding Aid: No.

Restrictions: For reference only. No reproductions allowed.

PH·51

Dain Tasker Collection

Dates of Photographs: 1950s–1961

Collection Origins

This collection was assembled by a private donor from images taken by photographer Dain Tasker between the 1950s and 1961. It was given to the division in 1965.

Physical Description

There are 630 photographs, including color dye coupler photoprints, and silver gelatin photoprints and radiographs.

Subjects

The photographs primarily document flowering plants, shrubs, and trees; as well as a few landscapes; and still lifes. Among the plants included are amazon lily; anthurium; aztec lily; bleeding heart; calla lily; canary bird bush; canterbury bells; columbine; copa de ora (three in a group); desert candle; desert holly; double fuschia; epiphlium; formosan lily; freesia; fuschia; hadley rose; hibiscus; hollyhock; iris; lotus; mistletoe; monstera delicosa; angel wings; narcissus; nasturtium; passion vine; peruvian daffodil; pussy willow; regal lily; strelitzia; succulent; tulip (two in a group); tulip tree; watsonia; wisteria; and yellow calla lotus.

Arranged: By the size and type of the print.

Captioned: With the plant's name.

Finding Aid: No.

Restrictions: No.

PH·52

Tintype Collection

Dates of Photographs: 1856–Early 1900s

Collection Origins

This collection was assembled by division staff from a variety of donations, exchanges, and purchases.

Physical Description

There are 2,000 tintypes in this collection. There are both cased and uncased tintypes from "gem" size to 8″ × 10″.

Subjects

Most of the photographs are individual portraits of American children, men, and women taken between 1856 and the late 1880s. The people in these portraits are shown in full-length studio portraits; or in bust-length, full-face, or profile shots. The photographs include images of American Indians, Civil War soldiers, factory workers, families, and farm workers in a variety of individual and group poses. There are several photographs of factories, farms, and houses.

Arranged: In catalog number order.

Captioned: No.

Finding Aid: A visual browsing file of xerographic copies of the tintypes, labeled with catalog and negative numbers is available. It is arranged in catalog number order.

Restrictions: No.

PH·53

Topical Photograph Collection

Dates of Photographs: 1860s–1970s

Collection Origins

This collection was assembled by division staff from photographs removed from other division photograph collections.

Photographers and studios represented include E. & H.T. Anthony and Co., New York City; Baldwin & Buell, Malone, New York; C.M. Bell, Washington, D.C.; Bennett & King, Naughty Nifties Co.; C.B. Bogle, New York City; M. Brady and Co., Washington, D.C.; Carriere; George M. Christy, New Haven, Connecticut; H.D. Curtis; Dr. S.P. Davis, Danielsonville, Connecticut; Eureka Studio, New York City; Fairchild Aerial Surveys, Inc., Los Angeles, California; and Samuel Fry and Co.

Also represented are Gardner's Photographic Art Gallery, Washington, D.C.; The Edward N. Gibbs X-Ray Laboratory; C. Gilhonsen; Jesse A. Graves;

De Lancey Gill; Frederick Gooch, Washington, D.C.; Harvard Observatory; Sir John F.W. Herschel; Thomas Houseworth and Co., San Francisco; International Press Photo Co., New York City; J.F. Jarvis; Amandus Johnson; Italica ARS Studio, New York City; and J.E. Keeler.

Also represented are LaRoche, Photo; Morris and Bendien, New York; Perkin-Elmer Corp.; Rice Bros., Washington, D.C.; S.S. Richards, Carthage, New York; H.P. Robinson, Photo; Louis M. Rutherford; J.F. Ryder, Cleveland, Ohio; Scio, Ohio; Albert Siebert; George Simpson; Will G. Singh, Bainbridge; Thomas A. Smillie; John P. Soule, Boston; the South Philadelphia Works, Photo Department; W.G. Spiker, St. John Photo, Hartford, Connecticut; Sussman, Minneapolis; and Sweeny.

Also represented are Torpedo Station, Newport, Rhode Island; F. Treble, Salisbury; Fred K. Ulrich, New York; Underwood and Underwood, Publisher; United Press International; the U.S. Army Medical Museum, Surgeon General's Office; U.S. Army Photo; U.S. Army Signal Corps; U.S. Geological Survey; William Vandivert, New York City; Dr. Vansant; Wayne Color Print; Dr. Lewis Wolberg; Yerkes Observatory; D. York, Alameda; and Carl Zeiss in Jena.

Physical Description

There are 1,160 photographs, including albumen cabinet cards, cartes-de-visite, imperial cards, and stereographs; collodion microphotographs (pigeon post pellicle); color dye bleach photoprints (Cibrachrome); color dye coupler photoprints (Kodak); cyanotypes; infrared photoprints; microfilm; platinum photoprints; radiographs; salted paper photoprints; silver gelatin dry plate lantern slides (some tinted); silver gelatin photonegatives (some on diacetate or nitrate film); original and copy silver gelatin photoprints (including SEM photoprints); and tintypes.

Subjects

The photographs include the following photographic genres, production modes, and vantage points: aerial; architectural; astronomical; documentary (news); erotic; holograms; landscapes; medical; microphotography; panoramic; portraits; scenic views; space; stereographic; travel; and underwater photography.

Architecture and buildings illustrated include the Eastman Kodak Factory (exterior, circa 1896); the Smithsonian Institution Castle and Arts & Industries Building (in the 1880s); Georgetown University; A. Hart's house in Kensington, Maryland; Harvard College Observatory; Stratford Hall (Robert E. Lee's birthplace); U.S. Marine Hospital, San Francisco, California; and the U.S. Patent Office (1880s).

Cityscapes and landscapes documented include the American West; Civil War battlefield and camp scenes; European travel scenes; Great Falls on the Potomac River; London during a World War II air raid; lower Manhattan and the Statue of Liberty (aerial views); and Rock Creek Park, Washington, D.C.

Expositions illustrated include the Cleveland, Ohio, Photographic Exposition (1870); the Smithsonian Astronomical Exposition in Wadesboro, North Carolina (1900); and the World's Columbian Exposition (1893).

People shown include American Indians in studio portraits (e.g., Apache, Arapaho, Dakota, Pawnee); Lauren Bacall; President Cleveland (at his inauguration); August and Louis Lumiere; Senator Joseph McCarthy; military personnel; photographers at work; President Truman and General MacArthur; and unidentified women in erotic poses.

Also documented are early photographic laboratories, including Alexander Gardner's darkroom wagon; studios, primarily interior shots of turn of the century photograph studios; and photographic apparatus.

Other topics documented are astronomical objects including Halley's Comet (June 6, 1910), planets, and stars; news events; transportation; and x-rays of human abnormalities.

Arranged: By subject into 25 series.

Captioned: A few with subject information and dates.

Finding Aid: No.

Restrictions: No.

PH·54

Underwood and Underwood News Collection

Dates of Photographs: 1920s–1940s

Collection Origins

This collection was assembled by the Underwood and Underwood firm of Ottawa, Kansas, between 1920 and 1940. The Underwood and Underwood firm was started by Bert Elias Underwood (1862–1943) and Elmer Underwood (1860–1947), brothers who were news photographers and businessmen from Oxford, Illinois.

The firm was started in Kansas in 1882 as a stereograph sales office. It was selling stereographic views on the Pacific coast in 1884. The firm had a large door-to-door sales force, which led to huge volume sales. Underwood and Underwood also pioneered the sale of boxed sets of images on a particular locale or theme, such as, Egypt or the Grand Canyon.

By 1886 Underwood and Underwood had opened offices in Baltimore, Chicago, New York, and Toronto. A nephew of the founders, C. Thomas Underwood, headed their New York illustrations office. In 1896 the firm began providing news photographs to the *Illustrated London News* and *Harper's Weekly*. Bert Underwood covered the Greco-Turkish War and the coronation of King Edward VII and Queen Alexandra (of England).

This collection was donated to the Smithsonian Institution in 1934. Note: The University of California in Riverside has the Keystone-Mast Collection of Underwood and Underwood negatives as well as original logbooks which document the Smithsonian's holdings.

Physical Description

There are 20,000 photographs, including silver gelatin dry plate photonegatives (16,000) and silver gelatin photonegatives (4,000). Many of the silver gelatin photonegatives are nitrate.

Subjects

These news photographs document world events between the 1920s and the 1940s. In particular they document architecture; celebrities (including movie stars and sports figures); cityscapes; clothing and fashion; cultural history; disasters; engineering and technology; industry; military history; politics and political history; and transportation. A great number of the images are from the Chicago area.

Among the individuals and groups portrayed are the Chicago Boys Clubs; President Calvin Coolidge; General Kincaid; and the Pan-American Congress.

Arranged: The photonegatives are organized by the Underwood and Underwood assigned negative number. Some of these images have also been assigned division catalog numbers, which run in the same sequence as the Underwood and Underwood negative numbers. The first 2,300 negatives in sequence have been tab-indexed by subject.

Captioned: The negatives have narrative subject captions that include the names of individuals shown, location, date, and the negative number.

Finding Aid: No.

Restrictions: No access.

PH·55

Burk Uzzle Collection

Dates of Photographs: Circa 1950–1971

Collection Origins

This collection was assembled by division staff from two separate accessions. Fourteen of the photographs were donated by the artist in 1964. The other 105 were given by a private donor in 1971.

Burk Uzzle was born in Raleigh, North Carolina, in 1938. He studied under Gjon Mili. From 1962 to 1968 Uzzle freelanced with the Black Star agency in Atlanta, Chicago, and Houston. During this time, he also worked as a contract photographer for *Life* magazine. Since 1967 he has been an active member of Magnum Photos and became its president in 1979. Uzzle received a Page One Award from the

Newspaper Guild of New York in 1970 for an essay on the U.S. Marines.

Physical Description

There are 119 silver gelatin photoprints.

Subjects

The images are news photograph studies and photo-essays on ambiguous and sometimes humourous American themes, such as, adolescents in school; children fishing; cityscapes of New York City; the corporate world; the cowboy in American society (including some images of men and horses); and sheep herding.

Arranged: No.

Captioned: No.

Finding Aid: No.

Restrictions: For reference only. No duplication allowed.

PH·56

Waterbury Collection of Union Miniature Cases

Dates of Photographs: 1840s–1860s

Collection Origins

Unknown.

Physical Description

There are 750 photographs, including albumen photoprints, ambrotypes, daguerreotypes, and tintypes. About ten percent have been tinted. Other materials include 1,500 union miniature cases.

Subjects

The photographs are primarily portraits of unidentified individual American children, men, or women. There are also a number of architectural

studies; genre scenes (children playing and women with children); and several unidentified landscapes.

Arranged: By catalog number.

Captioned: No.

Finding Aid: Browsing notebook of duplicate photographic images.

Restrictions: No.

PH·57

Weegee (Arthur H. Fellig) Collection

Dates of Photographs: 1950s–1960s

Collection Origins

Arthur H. Fellig (1899–1968) was born in Austria, but raised on New York's Lower East Side. At age 14 Fellig quit school to become a street photographer, and later freelanced for New York newspapers.

Fellig used a police band radio in order to be the first photographer on the scene of disasters. He built upon this reputation by selecting the name Weegee, a reference to the Ouija board fortune-telling game.

Based at the Manhattan Police Headquarters, Weegee took images of both everyday life and sensational stories. He often supplemented his images with commentary, for example, a picture of a murder scene with onlookers is titled, "enjoying the murder."

Physical Description

There are 150 silver gelatin photoprints.

Subjects

These photographs document city jails; disasters and their survivors (including city fires); drunken people; entertainers and their audiences; homeless people; teenagers; and violent crimes. Many of the images are of the homeless sleeping on the streets;

lovers at Coney Island; onlookers to crimes or disasters; and the urban poor.

Hollywood and sports figures and events documented include autograph seekers at a Hollywood premier (1955); boxing heavyweight title fight between Joe Walcott and Rocky Marciano (March 7, 1953); a circus acrobat being shot out of cannon; female strip tease performers in New Orleans; Marilyn Monroe (distorted lens images); Radio City Music Hall opening night; a rock music concert audience of screaming teenagers; and Frank Sinatra with a swooning teenage audience.

There is also an image of the exterior of an Harlem herbal store advertising dreambooks, lodestones, and the "6 & 7 books of Moses."

Arranged: No.

Captioned: With titles and/or subject information.

Finding Aid: No.

Restrictions: No.

PH·58

Edward Weston Collection

Dates of Photographs: 1918–1936

Collection Origins

This collection was assembled by division staff from gifts and purchases from Edward Weston and others.

Edward Weston (1886–1958) was born in Illinois and moved to California around 1906. Weston started as an itinerant portrait photographer, traveling door to door. In 1911 he opened his first studio in Glendale, California. His early work, until about 1922, was in the soft-focus pictorialist vein.

After 1922 Weston's work was in a sharp-focus precisionist style. Working with Tina Modotti, Weston operated a portrait studio in Mexico. Around 1927, after Weston's return to Carmel, California, he began producing studies of artifacts, such as, nautilus shells, taken out of their surrounding contexts.

In 1937 and 1938 he received a Guggenheim Fellowship, allowing him to travel and photograph in the Southwest and the West. In 1946 a major exhibition of his photographs was mounted at the Museum of Modern Art in New York City. With the help of his sons, Brett, Cole, and Neill, Weston continued to work until the end of his life in 1958.

Weston was the subject of a film, *The Photographer*, in 1948. His photographs are featured in: Charis Wilson Weston and Edward Weston. *California and the West*. New York: Duell, Sloan, and Pearce, 1940; and *My Camera at Point Lobos*. Edited by Ansel Adams. New York: 1950. From 1923 until around 1943, Weston kept a daily journal, which was published posthumously as the *Daybooks*. Edited by Nancy Newhall. Rochester, New York: George Eastman House, 1961–1966.

Physical Description

There are 43 photographs, including platinum photoprints (18), and silver gelatin photoprints (25). Many are signed, matted, and toned.

Subjects

The photographs are titled fine arts studies, including abstracts, architectural interiors, nature studies, nudes, portraits, and still lifes.

The following titled studies are included: "The Ascent of Attic Angles" (1925); "Daniel in His Attic"; "Epilogue (Girl With Fan and Vase, 1918)"; "Fragment of a Nude" (1925); "Girl in Canton Chair" (1922); "Head of Italian Girl" (1921); "Mountain" (1936); "Nude, E.W." (1936); "Portrait of Edward Weston" (1920s); "Prologue to a Sad Spring" (1920s); "Rafael Sala" (Mexico, 1924); "Reclining Men"; "Rock Study" (1930); "Seashore" (1938); "The Source" (1921); "Three Pots" (1926); and "Water" (1938).

Arranged: By the print size and then by the catalog number.

Captioned: With title and date.

Finding Aid: No.

Restrictions: For reference only. No reproduction allowed.

PS

Division of Physical Sciences

Division of Physical Sciences
National Museum of American History
Smithsonian Institution
Washington, D.C. 20560
Deborah Warner and Jon Eklund, Curators
(202) 357-2482
Hours: Monday—Friday, 10 a.m.—4 p.m.

Scope of the Collections

There are seven photographic collections with approximately 3,600 images in the Division of Physical Sciences.

Focus of the Collections

These photographs document the history of astronomy; astrophysics; cartography; chemistry; classical physics; geology; industrial chemistry; meteorology; and metrology. There are also photographs of chemical apparatus production and sales; the development of synthetic polymers; scientists and their discoveries; scientific surveying and mapping instruments used in the exploration of America; and scientific teaching instruments from the 19th and 20th centuries.

Photographic Processes and Formats Represented

Photographs include standard 20th century slide, photoprint, and photonegative processes. Early photographic processes include albumen photoprints (some stereographs), ambrotypes, collodion gelatin lantern slides, and daguerreotypes. There are also photomechanical reproductions.

Other Materials Represented

This division collects cartography; chemical apparatus; engraved cards; engravings; ink sketches; measuring devices; navigational instruments; surveying instruments; watercolor sketches; weights and measures; woodcuts; and other instruments of science and technology.

Access and Usage Policies

This division's collections are open to the public by appointment. Researchers are asked to call or write for an appointment in advance of their proposed visit. There is a division accession card file which serves as a finding aid to the accessioned photographs. Copy photographs may be obtained through OPPS at the prevailing rates.

Publication Policies

In addition to obtaining permission from the Smithsonian Institution to reproduce a photograph, researchers may have to obtain permission from the copyright holder. The Smithsonian Institution is not necessarily the copyright holder. The preferred credit line is: "Courtesy of the National Museum of American History, The Smithsonian Institution."

PS·1

Accessioned Objects Photograph File

Dates of Photographs: 1960s–1980

Collection Origins

This collection was assembled by division staff to document objects in division collections.

Physical Description

There are 1,040 silver gelatin photoprints (including 990 mounted and 50 unmounted images).

Subjects

Most of the photographs document objects in the division collections, including the Bleakney shock tube, electric furnaces, French balances, pyrometers, sniperscopes, and stone weights. Some images are photographic reproductions of original graphics.

There are also photographs of Dibner Library exhibits (NMAH), the Fairbanks Steel Yard, the Patterson Laboratory, and Pebble Mill.

Arranged: By subject.

Captioned: With subject heading, and the catalog and negative numbers.

Finding Aid: No.

Restrictions: No.

PS·2

American Optical Company Photograph Album

Dates of Photographs: 1914–1929

Collection Origins

This album was assembled by unidentified staff of the American Optical Company to illustrate the company's activities, physical plant, products, shops, and staff.

Physical Description

There are 90 silver gelatin photoprints in an album.

Subjects

The photographs document the personnel, physical plant, products, and sales activities of the American Optical Company from 1914 through 1924.

Arranged: By subject.

Captioned: No.

Finding Aid: A partial index arranged by subject.

Restrictions: No.

PS·3

Draper Family Collection

Dates of Photographs: 1840–1856, 1863, 1869–1882, 1892–1908

Collection Origins

This collection was assembled by the Draper family of New York City. Draper family members were actively involved in astronomy, chemistry, medicine, meteorology, and photography during the 19th and early 20th centuries.

John William Draper (1811–1882) was primarily a chemist, but he also did pioneer work in photography and on the chemical effects of radiant energy. He took a very early photograph of the moon in 1863 (which is included in this collection) and the first photograph of the diffraction spectrum. His son, Henry Draper (1837–1882), was also an astronomical photographer, a researcher into stellar spectrum, and a surgeon.

This collection contains correspondence, photographs, and publications which were assembled by family members during their lifetimes. Note: A portion of this collection may be transferred to the Archives Center (AC) and the Physical Sciences Accessioned Artifact Collection (PS5).

Physical Description

There are 12 photographs, including albumen photoprints, daguerreotypes (1840–1863), and early silver gelatin photoprints. Three of the daguerreotypes and six of the early photoprints are displayed in the "Draper Memorial," a flat display panel measuring 32″ × 35″. Other materials include correspondence addressed to Daniel Draper; publications of the New York Meteorological Observatory; publications of the University of the City of New York; and reprints.

Subjects

The photographs document the family and work of chemist John William Draper. There are daguerreotype portraits of John Draper and his sister, Dorothy C. Draper.

There are several astronomical photographs including John Draper's daguerreotype of the sun taken November 26, 1860, and a daguerreotype of the moon taken on September 3, 1863, by Henry Draper.

Arranged: The "Memorial," an exhibit board with mounted photographs and textual material, is stored separately from the astronomical photographs and the papers. The astronomical photographs have been physically removed from the Draper Family Collection and are housed with the Physical Sciences Photograph Accessioned Artifact Collection (PS5).

Captioned: With date and subject information.

Finding Aid: The astronomical photographs are included in the small card catalog called "Specimen Catalog Cards for Accessioned Items."

Restrictions: No.

PS·4

Julien Pierre Friez Papers

Dates of Photographs: 1887–1894, 1896–1898

Collection Origins

Julien Pierre Friez (1852–1916) was born in France. He came to the United States in 1867. A year later, he was working with Robert Henning on telegraph equipment in Ottowa, Illinois.

Friez was foreman for Ottomar Mergentheler from 1880 to 1890. Friez then moved to Baltimore where he founded Belfort Laboratories for the manufacture of scientific instruments. Later in his life, he designed meteorological recording instruments.

Physical Description

There are 40 silver gelatin photoprints. Other materials include a diploma, historical notes, five letterpress books of correspondence, and newspaper clippings.

Subjects

The photographs document the design and production of scientific instruments by Julien Pierre Friez and his colleagues at Ottomar Mergentheler and at the Belfort Laboratories. There are several photographs of unidentified colleagues of Friez, and of the World's Columbian Exposition of 1893.

Arranged: Into two series. 1) Outgoing correspondence, 1887–1894 and 1896–1898 (several of the five volumes are tab-indexed by correspondent). 2) Miscellaneous file which includes photographs.

Captioned: No.

Finding Aid: No.

Restrictions: No.

PS·5

Physical Sciences Accessioned Artifact Collection

Dates of Photographs: 1840–Present

Collection Origins

This collection was assembled by the division staff from diverse sources.

Physical Description

There are 410 photographs, including cyanotypes; daguerreotypes; silver gelatin dry plate photonegatives; and silver gelatin photonegatives, slides, and stereographs.

Subjects

The photographs document the history and practice of astronomy; astrophysics; chemistry; classical physics; geology; industrial chemistry; meteorology; and related scientific disciplines.

The photographs illustrate astronomical objects (such as the first centimeter wavelength radar echoes from the moon, the moon, the sun, and the stars); chemical apparatus (including chemical glassware); expeditions related to the physical sciences (such as the Mt. McKinley Cosmic Ray Expedition of 1932); and scientific instruments.

Arranged: By type of object and accession number.

Captioned: No.

Finding Aid: A card catalog labeled "Specimen Catalog Cards for Accessioned Items" organized by type of material and by medium. Cards for photographs filed under the "Prints and Drawings" category. A typical card includes a description of the specimen, item accession number, specimen location, the date the item was received, source, name of the photographer, photograph date, and the circumstance under which the photographs were created.

Restrictions: No.

PS·6

Physical Sciences Photograph Collection

Dates of Photographs: 1849–1978

Collection Origins

This collection was assembled by the division staff from diverse sources, including Tom Chase; the Celanese Corporation; the Dyer Company of Cleveland; Jon Eklund; Cyril Smith; the U.S. Naval Research Laboratory; the U.S. Patent Office; the University of Michigan; and other private donors.

Many of the photographs depict items within the division's collections or materials used in exhibits produced by the division. Most prints were created by OPPS.

Some of these photographs have appeared in exhibit catalogs: 1) Deborah J. Warner. *Perfect in Her Place: Women at Work in Industrial America.* Washington, D.C.: National Museum of American History, Smithsonian Institution Press, 1981. 2) Jon Eklund. *Aspects of Art and Science.* Washington, D.C.: National Museum of American History, Smithsonian Press, 1978. 3) Deborah J. Warner. *Women in Science in Nineteenth-Century America.* Washington, D.C.: National Museum of American History, Smithsonian Press, 1978.

Physical Description

This collection contains 1,500 photographs, including color dye coupler slides; daguerreotypes; silver gelatin dry plate lantern slides and photonegatives; and silver gelatin photoprints and stereographs. Many of the photographic portraits are framed, and some are signed by either the photographer or the subject.

Subjects

The photographs document the history, practice, and production of equipment for aeronautics; alchemy; astronomy; chemistry; engineering; geodesy; geomagnetics; hydraulics; mathematics; meteorology; physics; seismology; surveying; timekeeping; and weighing and measurement. Related museum exhibits are also illustrated.

Among the facilitiies documented are alchemical

laboratories; daguerrean darkrooms; Leonardo da Vinci's laboratory; Priestly's laboratory; the Pullman Car Company chemical laboratory; and the U.S. Patent Office.

Among the occupations documented are alchemists, astronomers, chemists, engineers, geologists, glazers, inventors, mathmaticians, mechanics, and surveyers.

Objects documented include compasses; daguerrean cameras; glass blowing apparatus; globes; lacquer; Leonardo da Vinci's lab apparatus and machine models; marine equipment; microscopes; military devices; minerals; mirrors; observatory instruments for triangulation; optics; pendulums; philosophical furnaces and tables; postal scale apparatus; Priestly's equipment; sextants; spectrophotometers; surveying equipment; telescopes; textiles; and wood carbonizing apparatus.

Among the inventors and scientists illustrated are William Janszoon Blaeu; Julius Bruhl; S. Chapman; Vincenzo Maria Coronelli; Marie Curie; Louis Daguerre; Sir Humphrey Davy; Johann Gabriel Doppemaier; Fritz Haber; Ko Hung; Arthur Hewith; A. Lavoisier; Edwin Libne; Justis Liebig; Albertus Magnus; William Murdock; Eugene Peligot; Alexander von Humbolt; and Alfred Werner.

Arranged: By series. 1) Curator's Slide Collection. 2) Curator's Browsing Notebook Print Collection. 3) Miscellaneous Notebook Collections. 4) Miscellaneous Photograph Files arranged topically by subject heading.

Captioned: With negative numbers. The notebooks of Leonardo da Vinci's models have photoprints captioned with sizes of the original model, construction site of the original model, and the power and use of the original item.

Finding Aid: No.

Restrictions: No.

PS·7

United States Coast and Geodetic Survey Photographs

Dates of Photographs: ND

Collection Origins

This collection was assembled by the United States Coast and Geodetic Survey as a catalog of photographic views which could be useful for illustration and study purposes. The collection was later donated to the division for research purposes.

The photographs are used to study aerial photography, cartography, currents, geodesy, geophysics, hydrography, radio, seismology, terrestrial magnetism and electricity, tides, topography, and waves.

Physical Description

There are 500 diazo photonegatives in a single photo album.

Subjects

The photographs are high contrast aerial landscape photographs of the United States. Most of the United States coastal and geodetic area is covered in this volume. There are large groups of photographs of California, Hawaii, Maine, and Massachusetts.

Arranged: Geographically by subject.

Captioned: No.

Finding Aid: A handwritten index in the album which lists geographic areas and subject classifications.

Restrictions: No.

PO

Division of Political History

Division of Political History
National Museum of American History
Smithsonian Institution
Washington, D.C. 20560
Harry Rubenstein and Larry Bird, Museum Technicians
(202) 357-2008
Hours: Monday–Friday, 10 a.m.–4 p.m.

Scope of the Collections

There are 17 photographic collections with approximately 17,100 images in the Division of Political History.

Focus of the Collections

These photographs document American political, social, and intellectual movements from the pre-Revolutionary era to the present. Division research interests focus on American reform movements; famous Americans, particularly first families; and the history of American political campaigning. The following movements are well documented: anti-Vietnam War activism; Black civil rights (with special emphasis on the Poor People's Campaign and Resurrection City); civilian patriotic endeavors during World Wars I and II; family planning; gay rights; temperance; voting rights reform; and women's rights.

Photographic Processes and Formats Represented

In addition to standard 20th century slide, photoprint, and photonegative processes and formats there are early photographic processes, such as, albumen photoprints (including cartes-de-visite and stereographs); collodion wet plate lantern slides; photo albums with mounted photoprints; platinum photoprints; salted paper photoprints; and silver gelatin dry plate photonegatives.

Other Materials Represented

This division collects business records, ephemera, and objects related to the history of political activities in the United States, such as, autograph letters; ballots; banners; broadsides; buttons; calendars; calling cards; campaign literature; cartoons; clippings; etchings; gavels; graphic prints; invitations; journals; lectures; maps; memorabilia; notes; pencil sketches; pen drawings; pins; portraits; posters; press credentials; press releases; publications; scrapbooks; sheet music; sketches; silhouettes; souvenir books; speeches; telegrams; tickets; tour itineraries; and watercolor sketches.

Access and Usage Policies

This division's collections are open to the public by appointment only. There is an accessions card catalog which serves as a finding aid to accessioned photographs. Special restrictions may apply to certain materials which prohibit the production of photographic or xerographic copies.

Publication Policies

In addition to obtaining permission from the Smithsonian Institution to reproduce a photograph, researchers may have to obtain permission from the copyright holder. The Smithsonian Institution is not necessarily the copyright holder. The preferred credit line is: "Courtesy of the Division of Political History, National Museum of American History, Smithsonian Institution."

PO·1

Charles Sumner Bird Scrapbook

Dates of Photographs: September 29–November 3, 1913

Collection Origins

This scrapbook, titled "Cruise of the Flying Squadron, September 29–November 3, 1913," was assembled by Carl H. Claudy. Claudy served as an aide to Charles Sumner Bird (1855–1927), a wealthy paper manufacturer and Progressive Party member. Claudy assembled the scrapbook to document Bird's 1913 campaign for the governorship of Massachusetts, during which Bird attempted to visit every post office and town in the state. This campaign was one of the earliest uses of the automobile in political campaigning. Bird's campaign staff was christened "The Flying Squadron."

The scrapbook was donated to the division by Claudy.

Physical Description

There are nine silver gelatin photoprints in this scrapbook. Other materials include campaign literature, clippings, and press releases.

Subjects

The photographs document Charles Sumner Bird's September 29 through November 3, 1913, political campaign for the governorship of Massachusetts. The photoprints show Bird and his staff, "The Flying Squadron," touring Massachusetts (particularly cities, post offices, and towns) by automobile.

Arranged: In chronological order.

Captioned: Some are labeled with the location and date.

Finding Aid: No.

Restrictions: No.

PO·2

Helen May Butler Collection

Dates of Photographs: 1890s–1920s

Collection Origins

Helen May Butler was the first woman band leader in the United States. For many years she was the director of the All Ladies Brass Band.

The collection was given to the Smithsonian Institution by Butler's family.

Photographers represented include William Mills and Son of Providence, Rhode Island.

Physical Description

There are 30 photographs, including albumen photoprints and silver gelatin photoprints (in two albums). Other materials include sheet music.

Subjects

The photographs are portraits of band leader Helen May Butler, her band members, and associates.

Among the groups documented are the All Ladies Brass Band; the Ladies Military Band; unidentified parades; and the Louisiana Purchase Exposition in St. Louis (1904). Individuals shown include Helen May Butler; and Tolbert R. Ingram of Denver, Colorado.

There is also a single photograph of Helen May Butler's band instruments and uniforms on display at the World Circus Museum in Baraboo, Wisconsin.

Arranged: In chronological order.

Captioned: Several of the photographs are labeled with subject, location, and date.

Finding Aid: No.

Restrictions: No.

PO·3

Cyrus West Field Collection

Dates of Photographs: Circa 1848–1892, 1958

Collection Origins

Cyrus West Field (1848–1892), a businessman and promoter, was instrumental in the laying of the first successful Atlantic Cable in 1866.

Photographers represented include Ludovico Tuminello.

Physical Description

There are eight silver gelatin photoprints. Other materials include accounts of testimonial affairs, autograph letters, business records, maps, publications, resolutions, a seal, and silver dishes.

Subjects

These photographs document the Congress Telegraphique International (photographed by Tuminello); the 1958 NMAH exhibit on Cyrus West Field; and the 1866 laying of the Atlantic Cable (photographs of an unidentified painting).

Arranged: By type of material into seven series. 1) Correspondence, 1848–1881. 2) Business records. 3) Photographs, maps, and drawings. 4) A 1958 exhibit script. 5) Miscellaneous xerographic, reprint, and original material. 6) Publications, 1867–1892. 7) Oversize materials, 1865–1866.

Captioned: Two photographs are captioned with subject information.

Finding Aid: The accession cards contain a brief description of the collection.

Restrictions: No.

PO·4

Gustavus Vasa Fox Papers

Dates of Photographs: Circa 1861–1872

Collection Origins

Gustavus Vasa Fox (1821–1883) was educated at Phillips Academy in Andover, Massachusetts, and at the United States Naval Academy in Annapolis, Maryland.

From 1861 to 1866 Fox served in the Navy, first as Chief Clerk of the Navy Department under Secretary Gideon Welles, and then as Assistant Secretary of the Navy. He was selected by President Andrew Johnson to lead an American delegation to Russia to congratulate Czar Alexander II on his escape from an assassination attempt.

The papers in this collection are a portion of the personal papers of Gustavus Vasa Fox. Fox's official papers were bequeathed by his widow to the three sons of Montgomery Blair, who published them (see the *Dictionary of American Biography*, Volume III, Part 1. New York: Charles Scribner's Sons, 1930, 1931, 1958, 1959).

This collection includes an album of cartes-de-visite photoprints of United States government officials and dignitaries from 1861 to 1866. There are also books, notes, papers, and photographs created during Fox's trip to Russia and the Grand Duke Alexis's visit to the United States.

Photographers represented include Mathew Brady and Levizski.

Physical Description

There are 170 photographs, including albumen cartes-de-visite (some sepia-toned); salted paper photoprints; and silver gelatin photoprints. Other materials include articles, clippings, correspondence, ephemera, notes, published volumes (some oversize), and speeches.

Subjects

The photographs document Gustavus Vasa Fox's visit to Russia in 1866, and include images of American, European, and Russian dignitaries and landscapes; and the visit by the Czar's son, the Grand Duke Alexis of Russia, to Massachusetts in 1871.

Many photographs illustrate the architecture, fortifications, monuments, and sculpture of St. Petersburg, Russia. Other Russian cities illustrated include Kostsoma, Malviteeno, Novgorod, Ribinsk, and Sitka (Russian America).

The photographs document Russian Orthodox religious services in Russian churches and religious objects, such as, books and reliquaries. There are also several pictures of military groups assembled in Russian town squares.

Cartes-de-visite portraits include the Grand Duke Alexis of Russia; Prince William Heinrich Adlbert of Prussia; the Blairs; Gustavus Vasa Fox; R.W. Gibbs; President Abraham Lincoln; Mary Todd Lincoln; W.S. Olcott; and William Henry Seward.

Arranged: Into five series by type of material. 1) Correspondence. 2) Banquet invitations, menus, and souvenir programs. 3) Poems, speeches, and notes of welcome to Russia. 4) Articles, notes, and clippings on Russia. 5) Oversize publications, photographs, portfolios, and portraits.

Captioned: Some with location and date, in French, German, or Russian.

Finding Aid: Immanuel M. Casanowicz. *The Gustavus Vasa Fox Collection of Russian Souvenirs in the United States National Museum.* Smithsonian Institution. Proceedings of the United States National Museum, vol. 38. Washington, D.C.: Government Printing Office, 1911. The article includes information on many of the items in the collection.

Restrictions: No.

PO·5

Adelaide Johnson Collection

Dates of Photographs: 1878–1946

Collection Origins

This collection was assembled, from several gifts, by division staff for research purposes.

The busts shown in the photographs were given to the division by Adelaide Johnson's family.

Photographic studios represented include Bachrach and Marceaux, and the Warner Photo Company of New York.

Physical Description

There are ten silver gelatin photoprints. Other materials include articles, clippings, pamphlets, portrait sculpture busts, and publications.

Subjects

These photographs document Adelaide Johnson's sculptures of American and British women's movement leaders. Among the individuals portrayed are: Susan B. Anthony; Clara Barton; Isabella Beecher Hooker; James L. Hughs; John A. Logan; Lucretia Mott; and Elizabeth Cady Stanton. There is also a portrait of Clara Barton taken outside St. Petersburg, Russia, in 1902.

Arranged: By type of material into six series. 1) Articles, clippings, and photographs of Adelaide Johnson, 1878–1940. 2) Suffrage and feminist publications, 1878–1946. 3) Pamphlets, publications, and clippings on Reform movements. 4) Obituaries. 5) Miscellaneous materials such as memorabilia. 6) Sculptures.

Captioned: With subject and dates.

Finding Aid: 1) There is a list of the miscellaneous materials in the fifth series. 2) There is a set of division accession cards arranged by catalog number and/or donor, and cross-referenced by subject.

Restrictions: No.

PO·6

League of Women Voters Collection

Dates of Photographs: 1880s–1980s

Collection Origins

This collection was assembled by the League of Women Voters from diverse sources to document the women's rights movement. Carrie Chapman Catt contributed to this collection.

Physical Description

The collection contains 75 photographs, including albumen photoprints; color dye diffusion transfer photoprints (Polaroid SX-70); one platinum photoprint; and silver gelatin photoprints (some tinted). Some of the photoprints are mounted in two albums. Other materials include calendars; clippings; correspondence (original and xerographic copies); handbills; journals; menus; pamphlets; postcards; programs; and publications.

Subjects

These photographs are primarily portraits of early members of the League of Women Voters and other feminists, as well as images of historic locations related to the women's rights movement.

Individuals shown in this collection are Susan B. Anthony, Carrie Chapman Catt, Mary Garrett Hay, Eleanor Roosevelt, and Henrietta Wald. There are also images of unidentified children.

Locations illustrated include Susan B. Anthony's birthplace and Juniper Lodge, Carrie Chapman Catt's home.

Arranged: By type of material into four series. 1) Handbills, menus, programs, and calendars. 2) Copies of journals, publications, clippings, and other literature. 3) Correspondence. 4) Postcards, photographs, and photograph albums.

Captioned: With subject and dates.

Finding Aid: No.

Restrictions: No.

PO·7

Montgomery Meigs Papers

Dates of Photographs: 1862–1890

Collection Origins

This collection was assembled by the division from two separate donations, the Montgomery C. Meigs Scrapbooks (1870–1890) and the Montgomery C. Meigs Papers (1850–1861).

Montgomery C. Meigs (1816–1892) graduated from West Point in 1836. He served as a U.S. Army engineer responsible for the construction of the Washington, D.C. Aqueduct. Later, Meigs helped construct the dome and the wings of the United States Capitol Building in Washington, D.C. This collection documents Meigs's life and work as an Army engineer.

Photographers and studios represented include Christian Koenig, and Sommer and Behles.

Some images in the sixth album were published by the U.S. Geological Survey in the *9th Annual U.S. Geological Survey.* Washington, D.C.: Government Printing Office, 1889–1890.

Physical Description

There are 825 photographs, including albumen photoprints (some stereographs) and silver gelatin photoprints (785).

Subjects

These photographs document architecture, primarily the United States Capitol Building renovations. There are several images of actual construction work on the Capitol Dome (about 1857), and the shipping of the peristyle columns in December 1857.

A separate series of cityscapes of Charleston, South Carolina, illustrate damage to buildings following a 19th century earthquake.

Other photographs document architecture of Belgium (Brussels), France (Versailles), Germany (Potsdam), Italy (Florence, Milan, and Rome), and Yugoslavia (Belgrad) about 1870.

Arranged: Into four series. 1) Sketches, 1850–1851. 2) Photographs, 1862. 3) Oversize, 1850–1861. 4) Scrapbooks, 1870–1890.

Captioned: With subject information.

Finding Aid: No.

Restrictions: No.

PO·8

National American Woman Suffrage Association Collection

Dates of Photographs: 1896–1951

Collection Origins

This collection was assembled by Mrs. Carrie Chapman Catt during her association with the National American Woman Suffrage Association.

The Association later donated the collection to the division.

The Thomas Studio of Salt Lake City created the Emmeline Wells portrait.

Physical Description

There are 20 photographs, including albumen photoprints, a salted paper photoprint, and silver gelatin photoprints. Other materials include badges, banners, broadsides, buttons, letters, medals, menus, pins, publications, and a wooden gavel.

Subjects

These photographs are primarily studio portraits of American feminists and suffragists. There are also several photographic reproductions of oil portrait paintings.

Among those portrayed are Susan B. Anthony; Carrie Chapman Catt; Lucretia Mott; Elizabeth Cady Stanton; Lucy Stone; and Emmeline Wells (a Mormon plural-wife who campaigned for women's suffrage). There is also an image of Mrs. Carrie Chapman Catt receiving the Hebrew Medal in 1951.

Arranged: By type of material.

Captioned: With subjects and dates.

Finding Aid: No.

Restrictions: No.

PO·9

National Woman's Party Collection

Dates of Photographs: 1914–1917, 1964

Collection Origins

The membership of the National Woman's Party assembled this collection from diverse sources to document civil rights workers and feminists.

The photographs of civil rights workers were created by the Black Star News Agency.

Physical Description

There are 15 photographs, including albumen photoprints (3) and silver gelatin photoprints (dating from 1964). Other materials include correspondence, newspaper clippings, and publications.

Subjects

The photographs show unidentified civil rights workers and feminists.

Arranged: By type of material into four series. 1) Correspondence, 1914–1917 and 1964. 2) Newspaper clippings, 1914. 3) Publications, 1915. 4) Photographs, 1914–1917 and 1964.

Captioned: No.

Finding Aid: No.

Restrictions: No.

PO·10

Behre Quaker Peace Collection

Dates of Photographs: November 1960–April 1962

Collection Origins

This collection was assembled from a variety of sources including *The Evening Star, The Washington Post,* and Theodore Heitzel of Haverford, Pennsylvania, to document activities of Quaker Peace activists in the 1960s. The collection was donated to the Smithsonian Institution in July 1979.

Physical Description

The collection consists of 50 silver gelatin photoprints, including several panorama prints.

Subjects

The photographs document three Quaker peace demonstrations in the early 1960s. The first protest, held on November 11, 1960, was billed as the "Quakers for Peace Witness (1660–1960)." The second protest was at the Pentagon on April 1, 1961. The third protest session, billed as the "Friends Witness for World Order," took place April 28, 1962.

The photographs show a nuclear test ban vigil which took place outside of the Pentagon on April 1, 1961; protesters with signs walking by the Jefferson Memorial on their way to the Pentagon; and protests concerning the lack of atomic shelter. There are also several photographs of protesters' briefings and prayer sessions held prior to the actual protests.

Arranged: No.

Captioned: Many are labeled with subject and date information.

Finding Aid: No.

Restrictions: No.

PO·11

Political History Glass Plate Negative Collection

Dates of Photographs: 1850s–1940s

Collection Origins

This collection was assembled by the division staff from a variety of donations.

Physical Description

There are 40 photographs, including collodion wet plate photonegatives and silver gelatin dry plate photonegatives.

Subjects

Most of these photographs document American presidents, and their families and homes (including the White House). There are photographs of a life mask of Abraham Lincoln (five views); Ida McKinley in the White House (including the Conservatory); the McKinley home; President William McKinley speaking to a crowd; President McKinley's room at his inaugural ball; Theodore Roosevelt speaking to crowds (one view taken on a railroad platform); and unidentified individuals at Grover Cleveland's inauguration.

Arranged: No.

Captioned: With subject information.

Finding Aid: No.

Restrictions: No.

PO·12

Political History Master Slide File

Dates of Photographs: 1970s–Present

Collection Origins

This collection was assembled by the division staff to document their object collections and exhibitions. It also serves as a research collection on United States political history.

Physical Description

There are 7,700 photographs, including color dye coupler slides and silver gelatin slides.

Subjects

These photographs document Division of Political History exhibitions (particularly the "Threads of History") and object collections.

Most of the images are of the United States. There are photographs of Black history, political campaigns, political conventions, protest movements, and women's history.

Artifacts shown include the Bradford Dollhouse; First Ladies' materials (including accessories, gowns, and portraits); political decorative arts materials (including ceramic and glass artifacts, furniture, metal objects, paintings, portraits, and sculpture); and White House china.

There are also images of Presidential churches, homes, and libraries.

Arranged: Into two series. 1) Slides arranged by subject heading, and occasionally further divided by subheadings. 2) Notebooks of slides arranged by subject heading.

Captioned: No.

Finding Aid: No.

Restrictions: No.

PO·13

Political History Stereograph Collection

Dates of Photographs: 1860s–1910

Collection Origins

These photographs were assembled by division staff for research purposes.

Photographers represented include B.W. Kilburn, Luke C. Killon, and Langenheim. Photographic firms represented include the American Stereoscopic Co., Bell and Bro., Loud and Co., and Underwood and Underwood.

Physical Description

There are 200 photographs, including albumen photoprints and stereographs, and silver gelatin photoprints and stereographs.

Subjects

These photographs primarily document Washington, D.C., architecture, especially the White House.

There are also images of inaugural parades, portraits of Presidents and their families, and scenes of Salem, Massachusetts.

Arranged: By assigned number of the stereograph.

Captioned: Many with subject information, date, and negative number.

Finding Aid: A card catalog, arranged numerically, which lists the card catalog number, the subject, the date, and the negative number.

Restrictions: No.

PO·14

Grace Lincoln Temple Papers

Dates of Photographs: Circa 1892–1950s

Collection Origins

Grace Lincoln Temple was an interior decorator and designer, well known for her friezes and murals, during the 1920s through the 1950s.

Temple decorated the 1904 Louisiana Purchase Exposition in St. Louis; the 1905 and 1909 Presidential inaugurations; the Smithsonian Institution Arts and Industries Building; the Smithsonian Institution Building (the Castle) Children's Room; and the Woman's Buildings at the 1895 Atlanta Exposition.

This collection of working papers documents her career, her interior design interests and projects, and her connections with prominent people of her time.

Physical Description

There are 115 photographs, including albumen photoprints and silver gelatin photoprints. Other materials include clippings, correspondence, invitations, lectures, material samples, notes, programs, scrapbooks, and sketches.

Subjects

These photographs document interior design projects and research undertaken by Grace Lincoln Temple, particularly the friezes and murals which she painted. Among the buildings shown are the 1904 Louisiana Purchase Exposition (showing Temple's work); the Smithsonian Institution Building Children's Room (circa 1900, with Grace Lincoln Temple at work); Temple's home and studio (the interior); unidentified interiors; and the Woman's Building at the 1895 Atlanta Exposition (showing Temple's work).

Many photographs (40) reproduce historic wallpaper designs. There is also a single framed portrait of Surgeon General George Sternberg in a Union Army uniform.

Arranged: By type of material into six series. 1) Correspondence, 1901 to 1937. 2) Photographs.

3) Wallpaper and other decoration material samples and interior design sketches. 4) Programs, invitations, and menus. 5) Notes and speeches. 6) Clippings and scrapbooks.

Captioned: No.

Finding Aid: The division catalog cards list accession numbers; catalog numbers; size; color; and types of items in the collection; as well as a brief biography of Temple.

Restrictions: No.

PO·15

Triest Sisters Collection

Dates of Photographs: 1858–1929

Collection Origins

This collection was assembled by the Triest sisters from records of the 1909 Alaskan Boundary Expedition (American Boundary Expedition); and from disparate photographs of Yellowstone Park and Washington, D.C.

The Triest sisters donated it to the Smithsonian Institution between 1960 and 1961.

Photographers and studios represented include Luke C. Dillonn, Harris & Ewing, Washington, D.C.; and Underwood and Underwood. Ten images of the 1909 Alaskan Boundary Expedition were published in *The World Today,* Volume XX, No. 4.

Physical Description

There are 530 photographs, including albumen cartes-de-visite and photoprints (some autographed in an album dated 1865); collodion wet plate lantern slides; cyanotypes; salted paper photoprints; and silver gelatin dry plate photonegatives. Other materials include badges, buttons, a compass, medals, pins, postcards, and a silhouette.

Subjects

These photographs consist of: 1) portraits of American generals, intelligentsia, leaders, and politicians (circa 1865); 2) images of the 1909 American Boundary Expedition to survey the Alaskan-

Canadian boundary; 3) images of Yellowstone Park (circa 1850s); and 4) miscellaneous images of the Washington, D.C., area.

Among the individuals portrayed are James Abercrombie; William Cullen Bryant; Admiral David G. Farragut; General Ulysses S. Grant; Herbert Hoover; Andrew Johnson; Andrew Mellon; Scott; Secretary of State William H. Seward; Philip Henry Sheridan; William Taft; Tom Thumb; and Union soldiers.

American Boundary Expedition images include scenes of expeditionary camps (including the main camp near Canyon City, Alaska); northern landscapes in various seasons and weather conditions (including many snow slides); staff with pack trains on the trail (including fording flooded creeks and mud slides); and survey activities (including men taking triangulations near Burwash Summit).

Arranged: No.

Captioned: With subject and location.

Finding Aid: No.

Restrictions: No.

PO·16

United States Political History Collection

Dates of Photographs: Circa 1789–Present

Collection Origins

This collection was assembled by the division staff from diverse sources to document political events in the United States.

Some of the material is original and came to the division as donations or purchases. Other material was copied from collections in the Rutherford B. Hayes Library, the Lyndon Baines Johnson Presidential Library, and the Library of Congress.

Physical Description

There are 3,300 photographs, including color dye coupler slides and silver gelatin photonegatives and photoprints. Other materials include articles, ballots, cartoons, correspondence, ephemera, photomechanical drawings, political campaign material, press releases, and prints.

Subjects

These photographs document political reform movements, presidential inaugurations, state occasions, the White House, and Washington, D.C., social life.

The political reform photographs illustrate committees and groups (including the People's Bicentennial Committee); political reformers (including Nannie Helen Burroughs); presidents enacting reform (including President Lyndon Baines Johnson handing out pens after signing the 1965 Voting Rights Act); and protestors (including anti-busing activities, civil rights protests, the Ku Klux Klan, the 1963 Labor Union March on Washington, D.C., and the Vietnam War protest movement).

The White House and Washington, D.C., social life photographs primarily document the United States First Ladies and First Families.

The United States presidential inauguration file includes photographs of conventions (including the Democratic National Convention of 1952 and an unidentified convention at the Chicago Convention Building); inaugural balls and celebrations; and portraits of United States presidents (including an informal portrait of Warren G. Harding and Woodrow Wilson in a carriage in 1921).

This file also documents each presidential inauguration from George Washington to the current president (including President Lyndon Baines Johnson's swearing-in on Air Force One on November 22, 1963, immediately following the assassination of President John F. Kennedy). Note: Prior to the late 1860s the images are photographic reproductions of graphic illustrations.

Arranged: Into seven series. 1) A signature and letters file. 2) Political campaign materials. 3) Political reform materials. 4) White House and Washington, D.C., social life. 5) Presidential inaugurations. 6) Illustrations and photographs. 7) Specimen documentation.

Captioned: No.

Finding Aid: No.

Restrictions: No.

PO·17

United States Political History Photograph Collection

Dates of Photographs: Circa 1860s–Present

Collection Origins

This collection was assembled by division staff from diverse sources. Some images were created by staff to document their research activities or to provide reference files for future research. Many of the photographs were produced by OPPS to document the division's collections and exhibitions. Other photographs are copy photoprints of materials in other collections.

The photographs have been used in two division exhibitions, "We The People" and "George Washington."

Physical Description

There are 12,000 silver gelatin photoprints. Other materials include clippings of newspaper cartoons, engravings, etchings, and other graphic materials.

Subjects

These photographs document the history of the American political process from 1789 to the present. Many images document the division's accessioned objects (including political paraphernalia, such as, campaign banners and buttons).

Other images are original portraits of members of the United States government and politicians, and photographic reproductions of portraits created in other media (including cartoons).

Also documented are ceremonies dealing with political events (such as, the Bicentennial, conventions, and inaugurations); and special events relating to the political process or to political protest and reform.

Among the individuals portrayed are notable Americans; political activists; politicians; presidents; Smithsonian Institution secretaries; unsuccessful political candidates; and vice presidents. These include Spencer Baird; General George Armstrong Custer; Cyrus W. Field; John Hay; Adelaide Johnson; Robert E. Lee; Samuel F.B. Morse; Sam Rayburn; and Grace Lincoln Temple.

Some protest movements and reform groups represented include abolition; anti-abortion rallies; antisuffrage rallies; the Child Labor Commission; the Civil Rights movement; Equal Rights Amendment rallies; the Native American Rights movement; the Alice Paul Memorial Rally; Prohibition; the Temperance Movement; the Vietnam War protest movement; the Whiskey Rebellion; and women's suffrage rallies.

Exhibitions documented include the "First Ladies Exhibit"; the "Hall of Historic Americans"; the "Political Campaign Exhibit" (1960); and "The Right to Vote–Women in Politics."

Arranged: By subject.

Captioned: Many with the negative number, date, names of the individuals shown, and the location.

Finding Aid: No.

Restrictions: No.

TX

Division of Textiles

Division of Textiles
National Museum of American History
Smithsonian Institution
Washington, D.C. 20560
Rita Adrosko, Curator
(202) 357-1889
Hours: Monday–Friday, 10 a.m.–4 p.m.

Scope of the Collections

There is one photographic collection with approximately 6,500 images in the Division of Textiles.

Focus of the Collections

These photographs document the history of textile production, technology, and use in the United States and western Europe between the 18th century and the present. Particular types of textiles documented include bands; carpets; costume fabrics; counterpanes; coverlets; dye samples; embroideries; laces; quilts; ribbons; rugs; samplers; silk pictures; and tapes. Also documented are basketry; needlework accessories; patterns; sewing machines; spinning equipment; textile machinery patent models; and weaving equipment.

Photographic Processes and Formats Represented

In addition to standard 20th century slide, print, and negative processes there are early photographic processes, such as, albumen photoprints, daguerreotypes, and tintypes. There are also some 20th century microphotographs of textile structures.

Other Materials Represented

This division collects baskets; books; fashion plates; engravings; graphic prints; machinery; textiles; tools; and weavers' pattern books.

Access and Usage Policies

This photographic collection is available to the public by appointment only. There are partial finding aids to segments of this collection. Researchers can obtain copy photoprints from OPPS at the prevailing rates. All requests should include the negative number of the requested item, which is available from the custodial division. Some photographs may not be duplicated due to copyright restrictions. Photocopying prints and duplicating of color slides is discouraged.

Publication Policies

In addition to obtaining permission from the Smithsonian Institution to reproduce a photograph, researchers may have to obtain permission from the copyright holder. The Smithsonian Institution is not necessarily the copyright holder. The approved credit line is: "Courtesy of the Smithsonian Institution, National Museum of American History, Division of Textiles." The division also reserves the right to review the information accompanying the photograph for accuracy prior to publication.

TX·1

Division of Textiles Photograph Collection

Dates of Photographs: 1912–1984

Collection Origins

This collection was assembled by division staff to document the division's exhibition activities, object collections, and research. Part of the collection was created by OPPS, and part was donated from various outside sources.

Photographic publishers represented include the Keystone View Company (stereographs of the Cheney Silk Company).

Physical Description

There are 6,500 photographs, including albumen photoprints and stereographs; color dye coupler slides; daguerreotypes; silver gelatin photomicrographs and photoprints; and tintypes.

Subjects

The photographs document fabrics, implements, and textile machinery, produced or used in the United States since the 18th century, with an emphasis on the 19th century.

The photographs document historical machines and models, such as, Elias Howe's sewing machine patent and prepatent models; a Northrup power loom with automatic bobbin changer (1895); Slater 48-spindle spinning frame and a Slater carding machine (circa 1790); an original Whitney cotton gin model; and about 4,000 patent models of inventions related to fabric designs, sewing, and textile processing.

There are also photographs of hand implements, such as, needlework tools, niddy-noddies, reels, spinning wheels, swifts, and tape looms.

The textile-related objects documented include baskets, coverlets, damask tablecloths, handkerchiefs, laces, linens, needlework pictures, quilts, samplers, sewing clamps, shawls, thimbles, and woven fabrics.

Also included are photographs of international mill workers, textile workers, and textile production procedures. The activities shown include silk production, weaving, and all phases of the cotton and wool industries, from the gathering of the natural fibers to the production of the finished piece. There are also photomicrographs of textile fibers and structure.

Arranged: Into five series by medium. 1) Silver gelatin photoprints filed by negative number. 2) Duplicate silver gelatin photoprints arranged by subject heading. 3) and 4) Original and duplicate color dye coupler slides arranged into two subseries, both series are filed by subject heading. 5) Vintage photoprints filed by accession number.

Captioned: With negative number; item catalog number; date; place of origin; and general subject information.

Finding Aid: 1) A card index which lists the negative number, accession number, patent number, and a brief description of the item. 2) A series of 123 published lists of photographs, slides, and patents on textile-related topics is available from the division.

Restrictions: No.

TR

Division of Transportation

Division of Transportation
National Museum of American History
Smithsonian Institution
Washington, D.C. 20560
William L. Withuhn, Curator
(202) 357-2025
Hours: Monday–Friday, 10 a.m.–5 p.m.

Scope of the Collections

There are 24 photographic collections with approximately 116,200 images in the Division of Transportation.

Focus of the Collections

These photographs document American maritime, railroad, and road transportation between the 18th and 20th centuries. Special holdings include images of the American Merchant Marine; automobile racing (early); buses; carriages; cars; cycles; firefighting equipment; lighthouses; locomotives; marine patents; race cars; railroad cars (e.g., Pullman); riverboats; sailing ships; trucks; and whaling.

Photographic Processes and Formats Represented

In addition to standard 20th century slide, photoprint, and photonegative processes there are early photographic processes, such as, albumen photoprints and cyanotypes.

Other Materials Represented

This division collects advertisements; albums; aperture cards; articles; automobile licenses; blueprints; builders notes; car diaries; charts; clippings; correspondence; design detail sheets; documents; drawings; gasoline credit cards; gas ration stamps; graphic prints (such as, lithographs and etchings); illustrations; journals; laboratory reports; laboratory test results; microfilm; miniature license plates; models; notes; postcards; posters; price lists; sales brochures; scrapbooks; specification sheets; statements of labor costs; technical drawings; technical repair manuals; trade catalogs; valve setting lists; and vehicles.

Access and Usage Policies

These collections are open to the public by appointment. Researchers are asked to write or call for an appointment to use the collections one week in advance of their visit. Finding aids to many photographic collections exist. The division allows limited xerographic copying by researchers. Photographic copies can be obtained from OPPS at the prevailing rate.

Publication Policies

In addition to obtaining permission from the Smithsonian Institution to reproduce a photograph, researchers may have to obtain permission from the copyright holder. The Smithsonian Institution is not necessarily the copyright holder. The preferred credit line is: "Courtesy of the National Museum of American History, Smithsonian Institution."

TR·1

A.H. Armstrong Album of Railroad Electrification Photographs

Dates of Photographs: 1890–Late 1930s

Collection Origins

A.H. Armstrong was involved in electrifying railroads and railroad stations in the United States between 1890 and the 1930s. These photographs document his work.

Physical Description

There are 75 silver gelatin photoprints mounted in a black leather album.

Subjects

The photographs document railroad electrification work, railroad factories, railroad track construction, and railroad yard work in the United States. Many photographs show men at work.

There are also a number of unidentified landscapes photographed from train windows.

Arranged: No.

Captioned: No.

Finding Aid: No.

Restrictions: No.

TR·2

Automobile Photograph Album Collection

Dates of Photographs: Circa 1905–1910

Collection Origins

The three albums in this collection appear to have been assembled by the same individual although no information is available on the circumstances of their creation. The albums document automotive history in Maryland.

Physical Description

There are 60 original photoprints in three albums including gem-sized albumen photoprints; a cyanotype; and silver gelatin photoprints (some booth pictures and postcards). Other materials include documents; handwritten notes; newspaper clippings; personal announcements; and postcards.

Subjects

The photographs document early automobiles and motorcycles in the Hagerstown, Maryland, and Washington, D.C., areas. There are images of car accidents; car racing; motorcycle riding and racing; and motor trips. Also shown are automobile showrooms; cycling; garages; ice fishing from cars; long distance car races in Maryland; and picnics from automobiles.

There are a number of photographs that document small town life and the impact of the automobile. There are photographs of women in cars; men and women courting in cars; and the use of alcohol and tobacco in cars.

There are also a small number of photographs documenting the development of a highway system in Maryland. Note: There are clippings on local divorces and car accidents mounted in the albums.

Arranged: Into three albums. 1) Car racing in the Maryland–Washington area. 2) Half of the second album deals with car racing in Maryland from 1905 to 1910; the other half with motor trips in other areas during the same time. 3) Photographs and clippings of motor trips in Maryland.

Captioned: Some with location, date, and names of individuals shown, as well as with descriptions of the vehicles.

Finding Aid: No.

Restrictions: No.

TR·3

E.B. Blakely Photographic Collection of Early American Passenger and Racing Automobiles

Dates of Photographs: 1890–1928

Collection Origins

This collection was assembled by E. B. Blakely of New York City, who also took many of the photographs.

Physical Description

There are 600 silver gelatin photographs, including 200 photoprints in two albums and 400 photonegatives (some diacetate).

Subjects

There are photographic portraits of industrialists; machinists; race car drivers; transportation inventors; and other notable persons, such as, Ned Blakely, Albert Bostwick, Gottlieb Daimler, Charles and Duryea, King Edward VII, Henry Ford, Fred Marriott, Hiram Percy Maxim, the Napier brothers, Barney Oldfield, Pliney Olds, R.E. Olds, J.W. Packard, L.B. Packard, Sidney Dillon Ripley, President Theodore Roosevelt, Jefferson Seligman, F.E. Stanley, W.K. Vanderbilt, and C.E. Woods.

There are photographs of vehicles powered by electricity, gasoline, and steam. Many of the vehicles shown were experimental. Car models and types include the Astor engine Pierce Arrow; Baby Bullet; Baker; Bent; Bird; Buick; Cadillac; Chevrolet; Christie; Cross; Cugnat; Cyclone (Fiat); Daimler; Delahaye; Duryea; Electric Carriage and Wagon Company of Philadelphia; Ford; Franklin; French-

Bertram; French-de Dion; French-Delahaye; French-Marot; French-Vinot Voiturette; Gasmobile; Haynes-Apperson; International Harvester Co.; Mechanical Horse; Mercedes; Mors; Napier; Oldsmobile; Packard; Panhard and Levassor; Pittsburgh Motor Vehicle Company; Pope-Toledo; Red Devil; Reeves Gasoline Motor carriage; Renault; REO; Riker; Sears-Roebuck; Selden; Simplex; Stanhope; Stanley; Stevens Duryea; Stutt; Triplex; Whistling Billy; White; Whitney; Winton; and Woods.

Arranged: In three series by type of material. 1) Two albums. 2) Copy photonegatives on Ilford safety film. 3) Diacetate photonegatives. The materials are not arranged within these series.

Captioned: Each page of the albums lists the builder of the automobile; type of vehicle; description of the individuals; camera setting; date; and plate number.

Finding Aid: An item-level index marked "Blakely Collection, Division of Transportation, Index," alphabetized by name of the subject or occasionally by the maker of the automobile. It is cross-referenced by the names of any other individuals in the photograph. The index also includes the negative number and page number in the original albums.

Restrictions: No.

TR·4

Charles B. Chaney, Jr., Railroad Photographs

Dates of Photographs: Circa 1850–1947

Collection Origins

This collection was assembled by Charles B. Chaney, Jr. (1875–1948), who served as a draftsman at the Brooklyn Navy Yard. The collection consists largely of photonegatives copied from old prints of locomotives, including those from eastern railroad lines, and railroad builder's pictures dating from 1850 to 1900. The location of the original prints is unknown.

There are also numerous photonegatives, taken by Chaney, of the Pennsylvania Railroad and the

Baltimore & Ohio Railroads, from about 1910 to 1947.

Physical Description

The collection includes 40,000 silver gelatin photonegatives and photoprints, including contact prints, copy negatives, and nitrate negatives. Other materials include a roll microfilm copy of the negatives.

Subjects

The photographs document early railroad equipment and parts, particularly locomotives from eastern lines, such as, the Baltimore & Ohio, and Pennsylvania lines. Many of the photographs are images of three-quarter or one-sided views of locomotives.

Among the locomotive builders whose work is documented are Baldwin, Denmead, and Rogers.

Arranged: Into four series by type of material. 1) Silver gelatin photoprints arranged by railroad. 2) Silver gelatin photonegatives on nitrate arranged by negative number (housed at OPPS). 3) Copy photonegatives arranged by negative number (housed at OPPS). 4) Roll microfilm.

Captioned: On the reverse with size, date, object title, and negative number.

Finding Aid: An index entitled "Chaney Photographs" arranged: 1) Alphabetically by railroad; 2) By name or number of the locomotive; 3) By builder; 4) By type or number of the car or locomotive; and 5) By date. It also includes descriptive remarks and the negative number.

Restrictions: No.

TR·5

Ralph E. Cropley Collection

Dates of Photographs: 1910–1960

Collection Origins

This collection was assembled by Ralph E. Cropley, a collector and amateur historian. Cropley was a

ship's purser who began documenting maritime history following World War I. The collection includes albums which were put together by Theodore Roosevelt and Franklin D. Roosevelt. These were later obtained by Cropley and added to the collection, which he donated to the Smithsonian.

Physical Description

There are 3,500 silver gelatin photoprints in 450 albums. Other materials include clippings; drawings; ephemera (including ghost stories); menus; notes; an oral history transcript; pages from books; passenger lists; reprints; and ship information, such as, sizes.

Subjects

The photographs document merchant ships; passenger ships; war ships; and other marine transportation, including sail and steam boats, from 1910 to the present.

Arranged: Into two series. 1) Sail boats. 2) Steam boats. The entries are alphabetized by the name of the ship.

Captioned: With boat name; date constructed; owner's names; date of the photograph; service area; and occasionally the ship line.

Finding Aid: No.

Restrictions: No.

TR·6

James Cunningham, Son and Company Photographs

Dates of Photographs: Circa 19th Century–1940s

Collection Origins

The James Cunningham, Son and Company of Rochester, New York, was founded in 1838 to manufacture carriages. In 1931 the company began to produce railroad crossbar switches. The company went out of business in 1931.

This collection was donated to the Automobile Section of the Free Library of Philadelphia in 1931. It was transfered to the Smithsonian Institution in 1952.

Physical Description

There are 275 photographs, including silver gelatin dry plate photonegatives and silver gelatin photoprints.

Subjects

Most of the photographs document carriages built in Rochester, New York, by the James Cunningham, Son and Company between the 1890s and the 1920s.

There are also a few photographs of commercial motorcars and horse drawn vehicles, such as, horse drawn ambulances; limousines; phaetons; touring cars; and plans of ground transportation (other than railroads).

Arranged: No.

Captioned: With assigned numbers.

Finding Aid: No.

Restrictions: No.

TR·7

John W. Griffith Papers

Dates of Photographs: 19th Century

Collection Origins

John W. Griffith (1809–1882) was an American naval architect, author, and editor. These papers reflect his interest in American naval history and architecture.

Physical Description

The collection includes four silver gelatin photoprints. Other materials include an account book, correspondence, and drawings.

Subjects

The four photographs are portraits of John W. Griffith.

Arranged: Loosely sorted by type of material.

Captioned: No.

Finding Aid: No.

Restrictions: No.

TR·8

LeRoy Halsey Photo Album

Dates of Photographs: 1897–1974

Collection Origins

This collection was assembled by LeRoy Halsey (1897–1974) of Stone Mountain, Georgia, to document the automobiles which he purchased between 1904 and 1974; and the boats which he purchased between 1897 and 1974. It was given to the Smithsonian Institution in the early 1970s.

Physical Description

There are 35 photographs, including color dye coupler photoprints and silver gelatin photoprints in one album. Other materials include driver's licenses; gas credit cards; gas ration stamps from World War II; miniature license plates; notes; and diary-type accounts of automobile and boat ownership.

Subjects

The photographs document automobiles (including Buick, Ford, and Mercury models); and boats (including power and row boats).

Arranged: In chronological order.

Captioned: On album pages with subject information, such as, the name of the automobile or boat shown; its maker; location and date bought; and type of automobile or boat.

Finding Aid: No.

Restrictions: No.

TR·9

Harrah's Automobile Collection Album

Dates of Photographs: Circa 1970s

Collection Origins

This collection documents the holdings of Harrah's Automobile Collection in Reno, Nevada. Its unknown creator may have been an employee of Harrah's.

Phycal Description

There are 200 color dye coupler photoprints which have been dry mounted onto sheets of white paper in a photo album.

Subjects

The subjects of this collection are American and European "classic" or collectible automobiles from the turn of the century to the present.

Arranged: No.

Captioned: With vehicle name; number; purchase date; cylinder; bore; top speed; manufacturer's list price; time; restoration; dates used; location used; yearly operating expense; and depreciation allowance.

Finding Aid: No.

Restrictions: No.

TR·10

Historic American Merchant Marine Survey Records

Dates of Photographs: 1880–1937

Collection Origins

This collection was produced as part of a Works Progress Administration Project (Project #6), completed under the partial sponsorship of the Smithsonian Institution. The purpose of the project was to record, principally in marine architectural drawings, information on the design and development of American watercraft. The source material was original boats, original builder's models, and original builder's plans of the sea craft. The project staff consisted of one hundred draftsmen, ship building mechanics, and researchers.

Physical Description

There are 60 original photographs, including albumen photoprints and silver gelatin photoprints. Other materials include blueprints, drawings, graphic prints, and written histories of American sea craft.

Subjects

The photographs illustrate seagoing vessels of the American Merchant Marine prior to 1937 including Bahama fishing sloops; barkentines; barks; bugeye schooners; a canal boat; cat boats; Chincoteague sailing bateaus; clam garveys; clipper ships; crab cars; diesel tugs; fishing bateaus; fishing schooners; friendship sloops; garveys; a Greek sponge dinghy; log canoes; paddle steamers; pilot boats; pot fishing skiffs; pungy schooners; schooners; schooner yachts; scow schooners; scow sloops; ships; sharpies; skipjacks; sloops; sponge fishing lateens; steam barges; steam crews; steamers; steam paddle boats; tancock whalers; towboats; tugs; whitehall boats; and yawls.

Arranged: By assigned WPA Historic American Merchant Marine Survey Record number.

Captioned: No.

Finding Aid: "Catalogue of Ship Drawings and Photographs produced by the Historic American Merchant Marine Survey Works Progress Administration, Federal Project No. 6, from the Watercraft Collection of the Smithsonian Institution United States National Museum." The "Catalogue" is an item-level index to the drawings and photographs divided by geographic regions, and then listed by survey number. Other information includes ship name; ship building date; ship type; number of drawings available; number of photographs available; and descriptions of these images.

Restrictions: No.

TR·11

Henry Hooker Carriage Photographic Collection

Dates of Photographs: 1850s–1906

Collection Origins

The images in this collection appear to be company photographs of the Henry Hooker and Company Coachmakers of New Haven, Connecticut, from around the 1830s through 1906. This collection came to the Smithsonian Institution from a private donor in Connecticut.

Physical Description

The collection includes 150 copy silver gelatin copy photoprints.

Subjects

The photographs primarily document carriages, such as, cabriolets, coaches, delivery carriages, passenger carriages, phaetons, rockaways, and sleighs.

Arranged: No.

Captioned: With the date; carriage name; descriptive information about the locale; type of view of the carriage; and the image or negative number.

Finding Aid: No.

Restrictions: No.

TR·12

Winston Langdon Collection

Dates of Photographs: Circa 1850s–1960s

Collection Origins

This collection was assembled and given to the Smithsonian Institution by Winston Langdon, a private collector.

Physical Description

There are 4,500 silver gelatin photoprints kept in 45 loose-leaf notebooks.

Subjects

Most of the photographs document U.S. sailing vessels and merchant ships, such as, brigs, Pacific sailers, and windjammers, from the 1850s to the 1960s. Some of the vessels are shown in several views.

Arranged: The photographs are first categorized as either sailing vessels or merchant vessels; next by type of ship; and then by assigned number.

Captioned: With the name and date of the ship, and the unique number assigned to each ship by Winston Langdon.

Finding Aid: Two card indexes. 1) Sailing ships. 2) Merchant ships. They are arranged alphabetically by the ship name and list the ship type; the ship number; location; name; and date of the ship.

Restrictions: No.

TR·13

Marine Transportation History Collection

Dates of Photographs: 19th–20th Century

Collection Origins

This collection was assembled by the Division of Transportation. Some of the photographs are reproductions of maps and drawings created by the William Crampf and Son Shipyard. Some of the copy materials were created for the division by OPPS from books by Howard I. Chapelle including: *American Fishing Schooners, 1825–1935.* New York: Norton, 1973; *American Sailing Craft.* New York: Crown Publishers, 1939; *American Small Sailing Craft.* New York: Norton, 1951; *The History of American Sailing Ships.* New York: W.W. Norton & Co., 1935; and *The Search for Speed Under Sail: 1700–1825.* New York: Norton, 1967. There are also photographs from Edwin T. Adney's *The Bark Canoes and Skin Boats of North America.* Washington: Smithsonian Institution, 1964; and from *Chesapeake Bay Crabbing Skiffs.*

Howard Chapelle (1900–1975) was a marine architect and historian. He served as Curator of Transportation at the United States National Museum and the National Museum of History and Technology from 1957 to 1967, and thereafter as a Senior Historian and Historian Emeritus at the National Museum of History and Technology.

Physical Description

There are 700 photographs, including silver gelatin photonegatives (copy images) and photoprints. Other materials include aperture cards (of plans); catalogs; correspondence; charts; documents (relating to marine transportation in the United States); maps; technical drawings (of lighthouses, ships, and ship equipment); and tracings.

Subjects

The photographs document United States maritime transportation history from the 19th century to the present, including boats; canoes; clippers; dredges; fishing vessels; lighthouses; light ships; men-of-war; the military sea transportation service; packets; privateers; schooners; skiffs; terrys; two-person excursion vessels; and yachts.

There are also a few images of engine and equipment building companies and ship's architects.

Arranged: Into three series. 1) Materials on lighthouses, canal boats, coast and geodetic survey vessels, the Shelburne Shipyard, and yacht watercolors are arranged by type of seagoing vessel and by subject heading. 2) Ship plan files are arranged by type of material, by type of vessel, and either by company name or by designer. 3) Negatives of ship's plan are arranged by assigned negative number.

Captioned: No.

Finding Aid: Five finding aids. 1) A punch-card index (for staff use only) which indexes the collection by craft type; type of service provided; rig; construction; number of masts; propulsion; tonnage; date; length between perpendiculars; locality; plans; plan type; reproduction condition; model; and miscellaneous construction details. 2) Researcher's aperture card file, that consists of aperture cards with black-and-white reproductions of the plans inset, filed by assigned number, the name of the ship shown, and the type of ship. 3) Printout entitled "Ship Plan List," with the source book title and plate number, vessel type, book page, and reproduction price. 4) Computer tape of information on the ship's plan list. 5) An old item-level inventory of this collection.

Restrictions: No.

TR·14

Marine Transportation Information File

Dates of Photographs: 20th Century

Collection Origins

This collection was assembled by the Division of Transportation Maritime History staff to document the history of maritime transportation. It functions as a vertical file.

Physical Description

There are 100 silver gelatin photoprints. Other materials include builder's notes, catalogs, charts, clippings, correspondence, maps, notes, photocopies, publications, reprints, and tracings.

Subjects

The photographs document United States maritime history including equipment, harbors, ports, and various types of ships used between the 17th and the 20th centuries. There are also portraits of captains, inventors (such as, Robert Fulton), and sailors (such as, Captain Nathaniel Heerreshoff). Among the activities shown are shipbuilding and whaling. Places shown include Cape May Point; ports; Savannah; and Trenton. Among the objects shown are capstans; the Douglas Fir ship: engine propeller (1861); Fulton steamboat; liberty ship; a lighthouse lens; marine patents; Mississippi river boats; motor boats; propulsion devices; specifications; and tridents.

Arranged: Alphabetically by subject heading.

Captioned: No.

Finding Aid: No.

Restrictions: No.

TR·15

Marine Transportation Photograph Collection

Dates of Photographs: 20th Century

Collection Origins

This collection was assembled by division staff from diverse sources, including copy prints made by OPPS from a variety of published and unpublished sources. There are also a few original photographs which were donated to the collection.

Physical Description

There are 6,000 silver gelatin photoprints (most are mounted copy prints).

Subjects

The photographs document the marine transportation object collections in this division and in other similar collections throughout the world. Many are photographic reproductions of drawings, photographs, and prints of American ships from the 17th century to the present. There are also photographs of ships' artifacts, ships' documents, and parts of ships, such as, sails and sail fittings.

Arranged: By OPPS negative number.

Captioned: With the ship's name; object's catalog number (if any); OPPS negative number; artist or source of the original print or drawing (if the print is a photographic copy of an original in another medium); view or setting; and with cross-references to other prints.

Finding Aid: A card index arranged alphabetically by ships' names. The index also lists caption information.

Restrictions: No.

TR·16

Maxwell-Briscoe Motor Company Notebook

Dates of Photographs: Circa 1905–1910

Collection Origins

The Maxwell-Briscoe Motor Company both produced and repaired automobiles. This collection was given to the Smithsonian Institution by a private donor from Troy, New York, in 1960.

Physical Description

There are 10 silver gelatin photoprints housed in one album. Other materials in the album include 70 pages of announcements, clippings, ephemera, reprints, and xerographic copies.

Subjects

Most of the photographs document cars, including advertisments (photographic reproductions); car transportation by dory; car production and repair shops of the Maxwell-Briscoe Motor Company; and posed portraits of people and cars. There are also photographs of farm vehicles.

Arranged: No.

Captioned: A few with subject information.

Finding Aid: No.

Restrictions: No.

TR·17

Norrell Photographic Negative Collection on Transportation

Dates of Photographs: 1850s–Present

Collection Origins

This collection was assembled by Thomas Norrell (1899–1985), an amateur historian of locomotive history in the United States. He copied photographs from other collections and purchased original historical photographs. The provenance of the materials prior to his assemblage of the collection is unclear.

Physical Description

There are 14,000 photographs, including silver gelatin dry plate photonegatives (300), and silver gelatin photonegatives (some are copies).

Subjects

Most of the photographs are of railroad locomotives in the United States. Included are a few railroad locomotives from or in Canada and Mexico.

Arranged: By type of material.

Captioned: No.

Finding Aid: 1) An item-level listing of the 300 silver gelatin dry plate photonegatives. 2) There is a plan to list the negatives by railroad and to cross-reference them by the name of the builder, name of the locomotive, location, date, construction number, and other necessary remarks.

Restrictions: No.

TR·18

Pullman Company Negative Collection

Dates of Photographs: Circa 1880–1948 (Bulk of collection from 1888–1932)

Collection Origins

This collection was created by the Pullman Company of Pullman, Illinois. The photographs provide a record of the more than 45,000 passenger railroad cars built by the Pullman car works.

The collection was given to the Smithsonian Institution in 1969 by the Pullman-Standard Company, but they retained a great majority of the post-1932 negatives for their own collections.

Physical Description

There are 42,000 photographs, including silver gelatin dry plate photonegatives; and silver gelatin photonegatives (including original nitrate and SOO15 direct duplicate copy materials) and photoprints.

Subjects

The photographs document the exteriors and interiors of Pullman Company railroad cars produced from 1880 to 1932. There are photographs of private railroad cars; street and rapid transit cars; and general railroad cars, such as, aquarium cars; auto cars; buffet-baggage cars; business cars; cafe-smoker cars; chair cars; coach-baggage coaches; coach-mail cars; coffee shop cars; combination cars; dining cars; dormitory cars; escort cars; express cars; gas-electric cars; horse cars; horse express cars; observation cars; observation-diner cars; official cars; parlor cars; parlor-lounge cars; sleepers; staff cars; and stateroom cars. Note: Most images do not contain people.

Arranged: Into three series first by type of material, then by OPPS negative number. 1) Original silver gelatin dry plate photonegatives. 2) Copy photonegatives. 3) Photoprints. The negatives are in cold storage at OPPS.

Captioned: Photoprints are labeled with the name of the railroad car depicted; the name of the railroad for whom the car was produced; the railroad car number; the date the car was produced; and the negative number of the image. Identification of all the existing negatives is not complete. Unidentified cars are simply labeled "Pullman Company Cars."

Finding Aid: Five item-level indexes. 1) "Pullman Negatives, Private Cars," organized by the name of the private patron. 2) "Pullman Negatives by Railroad, Part I (A–M)" and "Part II (N–Z)," each arranged alphabetically by the name of the railroad company. 3) "Pullman Negatives, The Pullman Company," organized by negative number. 4) "Pullman Negatives, The Pullman Street Cars and Rapid Transit," organized by the name of the client. 5) "Freight Cars."

Restrictions: No.

TR·19

Railroad and Firefighting Equipment Photograph Collection

Dates of Photographs: 20th Century

Collection Origins

This collection was assembled by the Division of Transportation staff from donations, exchanges, and purchases.

Physical Description

There are 1,300 silver gelatin photoprints.

Subjects

The photographs illustrate equipment used for firefighting and/or used on railroads, including fire buckets, fire hoses, gasoline fire trucks, hose reels, railroad cars, railroad equipment, railroad hand pumpers, railroad locomotives, railroad models, railroad offices and shops, railroad steam pumpers, railroad yard scenes, street railroads, and trolleys. There are also portraits of railroad personnel and firefighting staff.

Arranged: By subject heading, followed by subheadings and negative number.

Captioned: No.

Finding Aid: A list entitled "Firefighting Photographs in the United States National Museum" gives a brief description of the type of equipment, location where the photograph was taken, date, type of illustration, and negative number of the item.

Restrictions: No.

TR·20

Railroad and Firefighting History Collection

Dates of Photographs: 20th Century

Collection Origins

This material was assembled by the Division of Transportation from exchanges, gifts, and purchases. The collection consists mostly of original materials, with some copy prints from other collections.

Physical Description

There are 250 photographs, including color dye coupler slides and silver gelatin photoprints. Other materials include advertisements, blueprints, blueprint negatives, clippings, documents, drawings, lithographs, and posters.

Subjects

The photographs document the history of American and European railroads and firefighting activities between the late 1800s and the present.

Major railroad builders whose works are illustrated include ALCO; Baldwin; Baltimore & Ohio; General Electric; Hinkley; Lima; Mason; New Jersey Locomotive and Machine; Norris; Pennsylvania Railroad; Philadelphia and Reading Railroad; Pittsburgh Locomotive; Portland Locomotive; Rogers; Schenectady Locomotive; and Winans.

Major railroads depicted include the Baltimore & Ohio; Boston and Maine; Central of New Jersey; Erie; New York Central and Hudson River; Norfolk and Western; Pennsylvania; Philadelphia and Reading; and Southern.

There are also images of cable railways, firefighting equipment, portraits of railway employees, railroad equipment, and street railways.

Arranged: Into two series. 1) Oversized file organized by division accession numbers. 2) General or document file of photographs organized by subject heading and by negative number or division accession number.

Captioned: No.

Finding Aid: Four indexes. 1) Oversized materials for United States locomotives organized by railroad and builder. 2) British locomotives organized by railroad and builder. 3) Foreign locomotives organized by country, railroad, and builder. 4) British railroad cars organized by railroad.

Restrictions: No.

TR·21

Road Vehicles History Collection

Dates of Photographs: 20th Century

Collection Origins

This collection was assembled by division staff from copy images of original photoprints in the Edison Institute of the Henry Ford Museum in Greenfield Village near Detroit, Michigan.

Physical Description

There are 1,300 copy photographs, including silver gelatin photonegatives, photoprints, and slides. Most are copy images. Other materials include clippings, documents, notes, publications, and reprints.

Subjects

These photographs document the history of land transportation, specifically automobiles, in the United States from the 18th century to the present. Most photographs are of the products of the major manufacturers of land transportation vehicles and roads in the United States. To a lesser degree, the history of European land transportation is also covered.

There are photographs of automobiles, bicycles, buses, carriages, farming vehicles, motorcycles, recreational vehicles, and trucks. There are some photographs of pavements and roads.

Arranged: Alphabetically by name of the automobile maker or manufacturer; and then by roads and pavements.

Captioned: No.

Finding Aid: No.

Restrictions: No.

TR·22

Road Vehicles Photograph Collection

Dates of Photographs: Circa 1850–Present

Collection Origins

This collection was assembled by the Division of Transportation staff from a variety of donors and sources.

Physical Description

There are 780 silver gelatin photonegatives and photoprints.

Subjects

The photographs illustrate automobiles; carriages; cycles; horse drawn vehicles; and trucks. There are also some photographic reproductions of engravings of carriages dating from the 1850s to the 1900s.

Arranged: First by type of vehicle, then by OPPS negative number. Carriage materials are arranged by type of vehicle, original medium, and negative number.

Captioned: With the type of vehicle, date, negative number, and source of the original image.

Finding Aid: A card-index lists the subject heading of the print; OPPS negative number; object catalog number (if the object is from the Smithsonian); and date of the original photograph.

Restrictions: No.

TR·23

Dr. Walter Teskey Railroad and Locomotive Photograph Collection

Dates of Photographs: Circa 1930s

Collection Origins

Dr. Walter Teskey of Pittsburgh created these images in the Greenwood Shop of the Baltimore & Ohio Railroad in the 1930s. The original photonegatives were donated to the Smithsonian Institution. Copy photoprints and copy photonegatives were produced by OPPS.

Physical Description

There are 265 photographs, including silver gelatin photoprints and photonegatives (some are copies); and original silver gelatin photonegatives on nitrate. The original photonegatives are in cold storage at OPPS.

Subjects

The photographs document the Greenwood Shop of the Baltimore & Ohio Railroad during the 1930s. The images show locomotives, railroad yard scenes, and some railroad cars.

Arranged: No.

Captioned: With original negative numbers, and in some cases with OPPS negative numbers.

Finding Aid: No.

Restrictions: No.

TR·24

E.R. Thomas Motor Company Photograph Collection

Dates of Photographs: 1887–1910

Collection Origins

This collection was assembled by Fay Leone Faurote to document the Thomas Flyer car on behalf of the Thomas Flyer Car Company. Some of the photographs in the album were manufactured in France.

Physical Description

There are 45 photographs, including albumen photoprints, a cyanotype, and silver gelatin photoprints in two photograph albums. Other materials include newspaper clippings.

Subjects

The photographs document the Thomas Flyer automobile. The car is shown in production, in the showroom, and competing in the 1887 New York to Paris "Auto Race Around the World." The car is also seen in a variety of outdoor and indoor settings. The people in the photographs are not identified.

Arranged: The order of the photographs appears to follow the order of events in the New York to Paris "Auto Race Around the World" held in 1887.

Captioned: No.

Finding Aid: No.

Restrictions: No.

Selected Photographs
from the Collections at the
National Museum of American History
Smithsonian Institution

Anon. Picking cotton. April 1931. Silver gelatin photoprint. Consolidated Photograph Collection (AG·1). Negative #86-1507.

Anon. Storefront of Herder's Cutlery in Philadelphia, Pennsylvania. ND. Silver gelatin photoprint. Herder's Cutlery Collection (AC·27). Negative #83-7062.

Anon. "Sims in American Expeditionary Force, Vichy, France, September, 1918." George W. Sims in WWI uniform. Silver gelatin photoprint. George W. Sims Papers (AC·46). Negative #86-2692.

Anon. Portrait of Thomas A. Edison. ND. Silver gelatin photoprint. William Joseph Hammer Collection (AC·25). Negative #85-8787.

Anon. Mr. Edison (with cap, leaning against right column at top of steps) and some of his assistants in front of his laboratory at Menlo Park, New Jersey. Mr. Hammer on the steps leaning against left column. February 1880. Silver gelatin photoprint. William Joseph Hammer Collection (AC·25). Negative #85-8777.

Anon. "Vladimir Rosing, Russia's greatest tenor singing an English song, 'Lord Randall,' into the microphone, February 6, 1922." Silver gelatin photoprint. George H. Clark Radioana Collection (AC·12). Negative #76-416.

Anon. Wm. Glew Co. and workers. ND. Negative #69-401.

Anon. J.B. Simpson Co. Improved dry dock. 1889. J.B. Simpson, Inc., Records (AC·45). Negative #84-9671.

Anon. "Radio sells itself! With a portable, self-contained type of radio receiver which can be taken anywhere and operated without installation of any kind. It is easy for the small-town dealer to work up a radio interest. A demonstration can be given on the porch and, as often as not, secures permission to install a receiver in the home on a trial basis." ND. Silver gelatin photoprint. George H. Clark Radioana Collection (AC·12). Negative #76-402.

G. G. Rockwood. Mrs. Berlan-Gibbs. Photographic studio advertising piece. ND. Silver gelatin photoprint (POP chloride). Warshaw Collection of Business Americana (AC·60). Negative #88-5626.

Anon. Star Rapid Shoe Repair Shop employee picketing the shop, Washington, D.C. 1940s–1950s. Silver gelatin photoprint. American Community Life Information File (CL·1). Negative #72-11389.

Anon. Boys shooting dice. Early 1900s. Silver gelatin photoprint. American Community Life Information File (CL·1). Negative #73-2660.

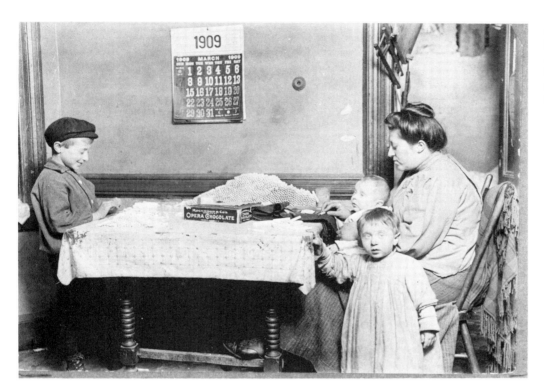

Anon. Family cigarette production. March 1909. American Community Life Information File (CL·1). Negative #73-2693.

Anon. Drug store. "Don't call us soda jerkers, instead call us fountaineers." ND. Silver gelatin photoprint. American Community Life Information File (CL·1). Negative #86-5079.

Anon. Factory girl. ND. American Community Life Information File (CL·1). Negative #73-2716.

Anon. Westinghouse Electric and Manufacturing Company dynamo. Early 1900s. Silver gelatin photoprint. Westinghouse Electric and Manufacturing Company Collection (EI·143). Negative #88-9504.

Anon. Base and condenser—Curtis Steam Turbine, Washington, D.C. Circa 1905. Silver gelatin photoprint from silver gelatin dry plate photonegative. Engineering and Industry Photograph Collection (EI·48). No negative number.

Anon. John W. Keely and some of his "etheric force" apparatus. 1886. Albumen photoprint. Engineering and Industry Oversize Collection (EI·47). Negative #81-2682.

Anon. Water or gas line in River Seine. Circa 1860s. Albumen photoprint. Engineering and Industry Photograph Collection (EI·48). Negative #86-961.

Anon. Construction on River Seine, Pont Louis Philippe. Circa 1865. Albumen photoprint. Engineering and Industry Photograph Collection (EI·48). Negative #86-11799.

Anon. "Burden's Wheel." Circa 1890s. Silver gelatin photoprint from silver gelatin dry plate photonegative. Engineering and Industry Photograph Collection (EI·48). Negative #85-7951.

Anson, N.Y. Woodworker with tools. 1850s. Ambrotype. Engineering and Industry Photograph Collection (EI·48). Negative #83-12558.

Bement Works. Fully assembled metal-cutting planer with workmen from the Bement Works of Philadelphia standing on top. 1907. Silver gelatin photoprint from silver gelatin dry plate photonegative. Engineering and Industry Negative Collection (EI·46). Negative #1628 (negative housed in division).

C. Bierstadt Stereograph Co. Roebling's Niagara Suspension Bridge. Prior to 1886. Albumen stereograph. Samuel E. Reed Covered Bridge Collection (EI·123). Negative #88-9503.

W. M. Chase Photographs. Susquehanna River near Havre de Grace Bridge, Maryland. Circa 1890. Silver gelatin photoprint from silver gelatin dry plate photonegative. Engineering and Industry Photograph Collection (EI·48). Negative #88-9501.

Frank Gilbreth. "Frank Gilbreth, motion-study pioneer, filming a subject fitted with mirrors, timing-devices, and other devices of obscure use." Circa 1916. Silver gelatin photoprint from silver gelatin dry plate photonegative. Gilbreth Collection (EI·58). Negative #83-3177.

*Frank Gilbreth.
"Woman's boots—
seeking an ideal foot-
rest at factory work
tables." ND. Silver
gelatin photoprint
from silver gelatin dry
plate photonegative.
Gilbreth Collection
(EI·58). Negative
#85-130.*

*Keystone Stereograph
View Company. Pour-
ing molten steel. ND.
Albumen photoprint.
Engineering and In-
dustry Collections
Files (EI·43). Negative
#88-9500.*

S. Morgan Smith. Part of a large turbine manufactured by S. Morgan Smith. Circa 1900. Silver gelatin photoprint. S. Morgan Smith Collection (EI·131). Negative #88-9502.

New York and Jersey Railroad Co. "Hudson River Tunnel. The first men in the history of the world to walk from New Jersey to New York under the waters of the North River. March 11, 1904." Silver gelatin photoprint. Pennsylvania Railroad, New York City Improvement Project Collection (EI·114). Negative #86-894.

*Runnels and Stateler.
Steel frame building
construction in San
Francisco, California.
June 25, 1889. Silver
gelatin photoprint. En-
gineering and Industry
Photograph Collection
(EI·48). Negative
#82-10023.*

*Anon. Ambulance and
two assistants. 1920s.
Silver gelatin photo-
print. Medical History
Photographic Refer-
ence Notebook Collec-
tion (MS·13). Negative
#72-10078.*

Anon. Surgical team in operating room. Circa 1915. Silver gelatin photoprint. Medical History Photographic Reference Notebook Collection (MS·13). Negative #77-5515.

Anon. Wounded soldiers arrive at 8225th MASH via ambulance, U.S. 8th Army, Sept. 1, 1951. [Transfer of patient from ambulance to pre-operative surgical tent during Korean War.] Silver gelatin photoprint. M*A*S*H Photograph Collection (MS·10). Negative #84-357.

Anon. Hospital interns, alumni of German Hospital [now Lennox-Hill Hospital], New York City. 1890s. Silver gelatin photoprint. American Hospital Photograph Collection (MS·1). Negative #72-9015.

Anon. Helen Keller with George Bernard Shaw and Lady Astor. ND. Silver gelatin photoprint. Medical History Photographic Reference Notebook Collection (MS·13). Negative #73-7098.

*Anon. Women work-
ers examining am-
poules at Eli Lilly and
Co. 1920s–1930s. Sil-
ver gelatin photoprint.
Eli Lilly and Company
Collection (MS·9).
Negative #73-1813.*

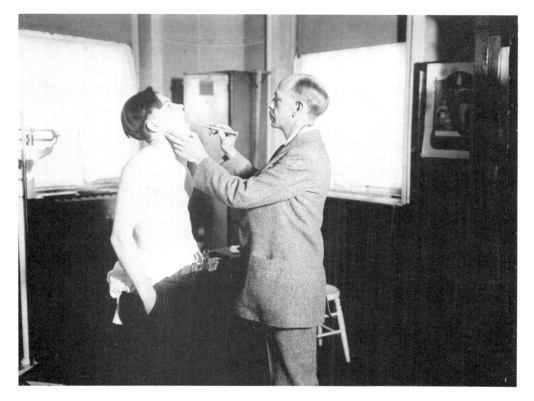

*Anon. Doctor examin-
ing boy's throat. New
York City. 1930s. Sil-
ver gelatin photoprint.
Department of Health
of the City of New
York Collection
(MS·6). Negative
#88-5407.*

Anon. Nurse weighing baby boy. 1920s. Silver gelatin photoprint. Department of Health of the City of New York Collection (MS·6). Negative #88-5406.

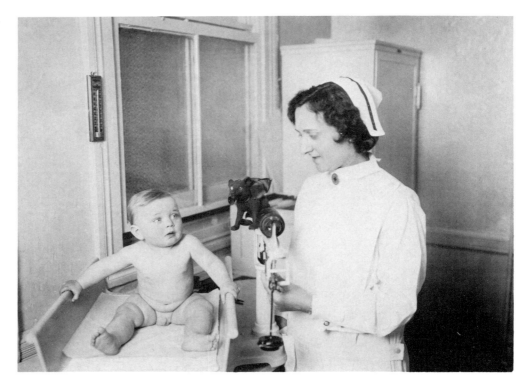

The Universal Photo Art Co. "How Bridget served the tomatoes undressed . . ." ND. Stereograph. Stereograph Collection (PH·48). Negative #81-10864.

Anon. "Spooning."
Two women with their
backs to the camera
with spoons resting on
their backs. ND. Tin-
type. Tintype Collec-
tion (PH·52). Negative
#83-226.

Anon. Bearded cobbler
at work on a bench
with hammer and
shoes. ND. Tintype.
Tintype Collection
(PH·52). Negative
#83-207.

Anon. Portrait of a man holding a photograph. ND. Tintype. Tintype Collection (PH·52). Negative #85-14829.

Anon. Postmortem portait. ND. Daguerreotype. Photographic Illustrations File (PH·41). Negative #86-11752.

Anon. Spencer F. Baird (1823–1887), Second Secretary of the Smithsonian Institution. ND. Daguerreotype. Daguerreotype Collection (PH·13). Negative #64-753.

Anon. The Tioga, a steam locomotive on a trestle bridge, with Niagara Falls in background. Norris Bros. Steam Locomotive, Philadelphia & Columbia Railroad. 1848 or later. Daguerreotype (1/2 stereograph). Daguerreotype Collection (PH·13). Negative #87-518.

Anon. Two firemen. ND. Daguerreotype. Daguerreotype Collection (PH·13). Negative #86-11588.

Anon. Portrait of a man posing with a camera and a bust of Henry Clay. ND. Daguerreotype. Dr. Walter Clark Collection (PH·11). Negative #87-2136.

Anon. Portrait of a man with a hat. ND. Ambrotype. Ambrotype Collection (PH·2). Negative #86-10616.

Anon. Portrait of two women holding hands. Each woman holds a daguerreotype. ND. Daguerreotype. Daguerreotype Collection (PH·13). Negative #86-12234.

Anon. Eastman Kodak factory. Circa 1896. Silver gelatin photoprint. Topical Photograph Collection (PH·53). Negative #81-9351.

Eugène Atget. 5 rue Arenier St. Lazare. "Pane [sic] dans le quartier pour un ancien Hôtel de Buffon." ND. Silver gelatin photoprint (POP chloride). Master Photographer Collection (PH·33). Negative #81-9467.

*Rudolf Eickemeyer, Jr.
Untitled. Girl in door-
way in Mt. Meigs, Ala-
bama. 1890. Platinum
photoprint. Rudolf
Eickemeyer Collection
(PH·17). Negative
#86-11369.*

*Rudolf Eickemeyer, Jr.
Untitled. Hog Island
boys, Virginia. 1906.
Rudolf Eickemeyer
Collection (PH·17).
Negative #87-3129.*

*Rudolf Eickemeyer, Jr.
"Forbidden Fruit."
Circa 1890. Albumen
photoprint. Rudolf
Eickemeyer Collection.
(PH·17). Negative
#86-11368.*

*Rudolf Eickemeyer, Jr.
"Squally Outlook."
1894. Carbon photo-
print. Rudolf Eicke-
meyer Collection
(PH·17). Negative
#81-9468.*

*Rudolf Eickemeyer, Jr.
Portrait of Rudolf
Eickemeyer, Sr. Circa
1884. Albumen photo-
print. Rudolf Eicke-
meyer Collection
(PH·17). Negative
#86-11359.*

*Rudolf Eickemeyer, Jr.
Portrait of Mrs. Vin-
cent Astor. 1915. Ru-
dolf Eickemeyer Col-
lection (PH·17).
Negative #86-11376.*

Frank Eugene. Portrait of Alfred Stieglitz. 1899. Gum bichromate photoprint. Master Photographer Collection (PH·33). Negative #82-7832.

Frederick H. Evans. "Le Puy: St. Michael [sic] d'Aquilla (interior)." ND. Platinum photoprint. Master Photographer Collection (PH·33). Negative #82-6135.

*Lee Friedlander.
Woman in laundro-
mat, N.Y.C. 1962. Sil-
ver gelatin photoprint.
Master Photographer
Collection (PH·33).
Negative #82-3721.*

*Francis Frith. "Pyra-
mids of El-Geezeh
[sic]." From "Egypt,
Sinai and Jerusalem: A
Series of 20 Photo-
graphic Views." 1858.
Albumen photoprint.
Master Photographer
Collection (PH·33).
Negative #82-13772.*

Attributed to Alexander Gardner. Portrait of Mathew B. Brady. Circa 1860. Silver gelatin photoprint from original collodion wet plate photonegative. Master Photographer Collection (PH·33). Negative #72-2740.

Alexander Gardner, Gardner's Photographic Art Gallery. "A rare specimen . . ." Alexander Gardner's darkroom wagon. ND. Topical Photograph Collection (PH·53). Negative #81-9305.

Gertrude Stanton Kasebier. Samuel Lone Bear. 1890s. Platinum photoprint. Gertrude Kasebier Collection (PH·29). Negative #85-7208.

Gertrude Stanton Kasebier. Unidentified Sioux man and woman. Circa 1898. Gertrude Kasebier Collection (PH·29). Negative #86-2205.

Gyorgy Kepes. Untitled abstract. 1950. Photogram. Master Photographer Collection (PH·33). Negative #10730.

André Kertész. "Mondrian's Entrance." Paris. 1926. Silver gelatin photoprint. Master Photographer Collection (PH·33). Negative #83-4634.

André Kertész. "The Kiss." Budapest. May 15, 1915. Silver gelatin photoprint. Master Photographer Collection (PH·33). Negative #83-4633.

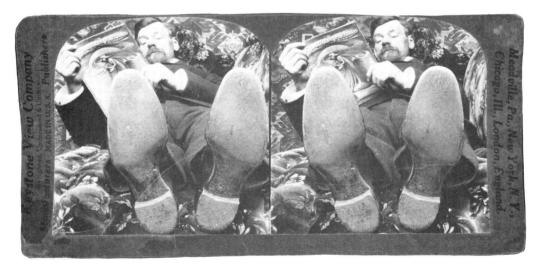

Keystone View Company (Underwood and Underwood). Reclining man reading stereoscopic photography magazine. ND. 1/2 stereograph. Stereograph Collection (PH·48). Negative #81-10878.

Heinrich Kuhn. "The Toilette." Circa 1890. Gum bichromate photoprint. Master Photographer Collection (PH·33). Negative #83-4636.

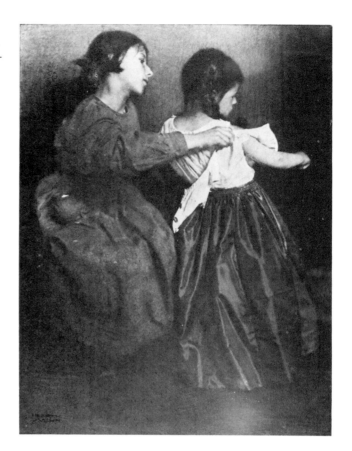

Charles R. Meade. Portrait of Louis Daguerre. 1848. Daguerreotype. Dr. Walter Clark Collection (PH·11). Negative #81-16338.

*Paul Outerbridge, Jr.
Semi-abstraction.
1923. Platinum photo-
print. Master Photog-
rapher Collection
(PH·33). Negative
#81-10427.*

*Titian Ramsay Peale.
"Great Falls of the Po-
tomac." ND. Albumen
photoprint (Whipple's
process). Titian Ram-
say Peale Collection
(PH·39). Negative
#81-7785.*

Titian Ramsay Peale. "Stereograph of Feed Store of Columbus Scriber, pm exposure, 4 October, 1863." Albumen photoprint. Titian Ramsay Peale Collection (PH·39). Negative #81-7078.

Samuel Peck & Co. or Anon. Boy wearing suit and hat. ND. Ambrotype in a union case. Note: Peck may be the maker of the case. Waterbury Collection of Union Miniature Cases (PH·56). Negative #87-8233.

B. L. Singley. "The Great Brooklyn Bridge." ND. Albumen photoprint (1/2 stereograph). Stereograph Collection (PH·48). Negative #81-9368.

Alfred Stieglitz. "The Terminal." 1893. Photogravure. Master Photographer Collection (PH·33). Negative #82-6232.

William Henry Fox Talbot or Calvert Jones. Man among ruins, House of Sallust, Pompeii. ND. Calotype photoprint. William Henry Fox Talbot Collection (PH·49). Negative #83-266.

William Henry Fox Talbot. Right half of a composite photograph of the Reading Establishment, founded by Talbot in 1843 for the production of calotype [sun] prints in Reading, England. 1843–1847. Calotype photoprint. William Henry Fox Talbot Collection (PH·49). Negative #81-10672.

*Dain Tasker. A lily.
ND. Silver gelatin ra-
diograph. Dain Tasker
Collection (PH·51).
Negative #81-10363.*

*Edward Weston.
"Nude." Circa 1936.
Silver gelatin photo-
print. Master Photog-
rapher Collection
(PH·33). Negative
#83-326.*

Edward Weston. "Pulquería, Mexico, D.F." 1926. Silver gelatin photoprint. Master Photographer Collection (PH·33). Negative #83-499.

Anon. Portrait of a young woman. ND. Tintype. Tintype Collection (PH·52). Negative #84-2022.

Anon. Couple on bike in front of White House. 1880s. Road Vehicles Photograph Collection (TR·22). Negative #79-1667.

IN THE CAB OF ENGINE 737— "HELLO, JIMMIE' LEE"!

Anon. "Conductor in the cab of engine 737—'Hello Jimmie Lee!'" ND. Railroad and Firefighters Equipment Photograph Collection (TR·19). Negative #3326.

Anon. Pie delivery wagons for the Connecticut Pie Co. ND. Road Vehicles Photograph Collection (TR·22). Negative #77-8722.

Anon. G. B. Seldon and son with early car. ND. E. B. Blakely Photographic Collection of Early American Passenger and Racing Automobiles (TR·3). Negative #41767-F.

Anon. U.S. postal "Tri-car," first used in Washington, D.C. 1908. Postal History Photograph Collection (NP·6). Negative #87-1264.

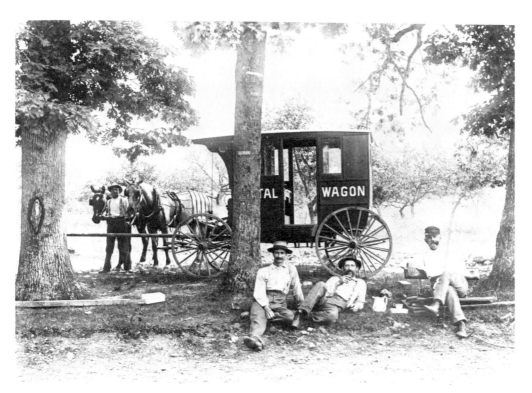

Anon. Rural postal wagon and workers on lunch break, Westminster, Maryland. ND. Postal History Photograph Collection (NP·6). Negative #46634.

Anon. Post Office and "The World Office," Indian Territory, Oklahoma. ND. Postal History Photograph Collection (NP·6). Negative #87-3450.

Anon. Eddie Gardner (right), one of America's first civilian airmail pilots, and an unidentified man in front of Gardner's single-engine airmail plane. ND. Lipsner U.S. Airmail Collection (NP·2). Negative #86-13198.

NN

National Numismatic Collections

National Numismatic Collections
National Museum of American History
Smithsonian Institution
Washington, D.C. 20560
Dr. Elvira Clain-Stefanelli, Executive Director
(202) 357-1798
Hours: Monday–Friday, 9 a.m.–4 p.m.

Scope of the Collections

There are three photographic collections with approximately 19,900 images in the National Numismatic Collections.

Focus of the Collections

The photographs are used primarily as research material dealing with the historical development of banking, finance, medals, money, and scrip worldwide. They also document bonds; checks and traveler's checks; Far Eastern currencies; monetary issues; propaganda; Russian medals and coins; and stock certificates.

Photographic Processes and Formats Represented

Photograph collections contain standard 20th century slide, photoprint, and photonegative processes, such as, silver gelatin photoprints and photonegatives.

Other Materials Represented

This division collects bills of exchange; bonds; checks (including traveler's checks); counterfeit currency; decorations; engraving plates; foreign and U.S. bank notes; medals; money; scrip; stock certificates; and tokens from the 14th century to the present.

Access and Usage Policies

Collections are open to the public by appointment. Photographic reproductions can be obtained from OPPS at the prevailing rate. The negative number of the desired item can be obtained from the National Numismatic Collections staff. In many cases interested amateur photographers may photograph original artifacts from the collections.

Publication Policies

In addition to obtaining permission from the Smithsonian Institution to reproduce a photograph, researchers may have to obtain permission from the copyright holder. The Smithsonian Institution is not necessarily the copyright holder. The preferred credit line will vary. It will always include at least the following: "Courtesy of the National Museum of American History, Smithsonian Institution, Numismatic Collections." It may also include a collection or a donor statement. Please check with the division prior to publication.

NN·1

National Numismatic Collection Photographic Files

Dates of Photographs: 1970s–Present

Collection Origins

This collection was assembled by the National Numismatic Collection staff. Many of the photographs were created by Richard Hofmeister of OPPS at the request of the staff. Over the years, each National Numismatic Collection specialist has produced photographs or slides of objects in their specialty area. Many of the negatives are housed at OPPS.

The collection was used in several publications including: 1) Vladimir Clain-Stefanelli and Elvira Clain-Stefanelli. *Chartered for Progress: Two Centuries of American Banking.* Washington, D.C.: Acropolis Books, 1975. 2) Vladimir Clain-Stefanelli and Elvira Clain-Stefanelli. *Medals Commemorating Battles of the American Revolution.* Washington, D.C.: The Museum of History and Technology, Smithsonian Institution, 1973. 3) Elvira Clain-Stefanelli. *Numismatics: An Ancient Science.* Contributions from the National Museum of History and Technology, Bulletin 229, Paper 32. Washington, D.C.: Government Printing Office, 1965. 4) Elvira Clain-Stefanelli. *Italian Coin Engravers Since 1800.* Contributions from the National Museum of History and Technology, Bulletin 229, Paper 33. Washington, D.C.: Government Printing Office, 1965.

Physical Description

There are 9,000 photographs, including color dye coupler slides and silver gelatin photonegatives and photoprints.

Subjects

The photographs document the creation and use of bonds, coins, medals, money, stocks, and tokens. Images also include exhibitions and special collections of these materials, and related occupations (including designers, engravers, and medalists).

Numismatic media illustrated include bills of exchange; checks; coins; gold certificates; legal tender notes; medals; minting (16th–18th centuries); National Bank notes; paper money (by state and era); police badges; silver certificates; and tokens.

Coins documented include coins in non-Smithsonian collections; Confederate coins; foreign coins (including Byzantine, Greek, Medieval, modern, and Roman coins); and gold coins.

Decorations illustrated include those from the Holm Collection; Indian Peace Medals; medals from the Madame Ernestine Schumann-Heink Collection; and U.D. Brenner Medals.

Bank-related images include bank exteriors and interiors; banking machinery; gold dust banking (1800–1925); portraits of international monetary policymakers and bankers; and safe deposit boxes and vaults.

Other related images show medalists, mining, NMAH exhibits, and numismatic museums. There are also photographs by the Farm Security Administration photographers (1930–1940) which depict the Great Depression.

Arranged: Partially arranged by subject heading and by medium.

Captioned: No.

Finding Aid: A list of 21 subject descriptors is being prepared.

Restrictions: No.

NN·2

Numismatics Specimen Box Photograph Collection

Dates of Photographs: 1974–1984

Collection Origins

This collection was assembled by division staff to document the division's holdings.

The photographs are interfiled with the specimens they document. The photographs serve as a duplicate file for administrative purposes and research when the original numismatics artifact is not available for viewing. Richard Hofmeister of OPPS took most of these photographs, others were taken by division staff.

Physical Description

There are 10,000 silver gelatin photoprints.

Subjects

These photographs document the holdings of the National Numismatic Collection. They are photographic facsimiles of the numismatic objects. There may be two different prints of each artifact— representing the obverse and the reverse of the coin or paper money.

The photographs reproduce coins; financial documents; international paper currency; medals; primitive media of exchange (dating from 200 B.C. to the present); rarities; and tokens.

Arranged: By subject accession number.

Captioned: Each box containing a specimen and photograph is labeled with object accession number; object inventory number; negative number; size; weight; complete attribution for the piece; name of the engraver; source of the information; name of the medium or metal; and the rim size. The photoprints are captioned on the reverse side with a negative number.

Finding Aid: No.

Restrictions: No.

Physical Description

The collection includes 900 silver gelatin photoprints and a few photonegatives.

Subjects

The photographs document the oriental artifactual holdings of the National Numismatic Collection, including oriental coins; financial documents; medals; paper currency; primitive media of exchange (dating between 200 B.C. and the present); rarities; and tokens.

Arranged: By subject headings (country or dynasty) based on Stanley Lane-Poole's *The Mohammedan Dynasties*. Paris: P. Geuthner, 1925. There are plans to reorganize the collection to better reflect the growth and development of numismatics in the Orient.

Captioned: With country or dynastic descriptors.

Finding Aid: No.

Restrictions: No.

NN·3

Oriental Numismatics Photographic Collection

Dates of Photographs: 1973–Present

Collection Origins

This collection was assembled by Raymond Hebert, Museum Specialist at the National Numismatic Collections, for research purposes. The photographs were taken by Richard Hofmeister of OPPS.

NP

National Philatelic Collections

National Philatelic Collections
National Museum of American History
Smithsonian Institution
Washington, D.C. 20560
Herbert R. Collins, Executive Director
(202) 357-1796
Hours: Wednesdays, 9 a.m.–4:30 p.m.

Scope of the Collections

There are nine photographic collections with approximately 10,500 images in the National Philatelic Collections.

Focus of the Collections

These photographs are used primarily as research material to document international postal and philatelic history. The emphasis is on internal revenue tax stamps; Panama Canal Zone stamps from 1905 through 1979; railway mail service; stamp plate proof sheets; U.S. airmail history; U.S. postal history; and U.S. stamps from 1894 through the 1980s.

Photographic Processes and Formats Represented

Collections contain standard 20th century photonegative, photoprint, and slide processes, such as, silver gelatin photoprints and photonegatives.

Other Materials Represented

This division also collects artists' designs for postage stamps; blueprints; caricatures; certified plate proof sheets for United States postage stamps; clippings; correspondence; facing slides; forms; journals; labels; ledgers; mail route schedules; mail separation schemes; memoranda; official letter-sheets; postage stamps; postal route maps; satiric sketches; shipping records; stamp models; and trip reports.

Access and Usage Policies

Collections are open to the public by appointment. Photographic reproductions may be obtained from OPPS at the prevailing rates. The negative number of the desired item may be obtained from the National Philatelic Collections staff.

Publication Policies

In addition to obtaining permission from the Smithsonian Institution to reproduce a photograph, researchers may have to obtain permission from the copyright holder. The Smithsonian Institution is not necessarily the copyright holder. The preferred credit line will vary. It will always include at least the following: "Courtesy of the National Museum of American History, Smithsonian Institution." It may also include a collection or a donor statement. Please check with the division prior to publication.

NP·1

Bureau of Engraving and Printing Certified Plate Proof Sheets

Dates of Photographs: 1894–Present

Collection Origins

The U.S. Bureau of Engraving and Printing is part of the U.S. Treasury Department. This collection documents products of the Bureau, primarily certified plate proof sheets. It was transferred to this division by the Bureau.

Physical Description

There are 1,500 silver gelatin photoprints. Other materials include about 207 cubic feet of proof sheets taken from plates prepared for the production of United States postage stamps.

Subjects

The photographs reproduce U.S. Bureau of Engraving proof sheets. The proof sheets shown were taken from the plates used to produce postage stamps from 1894 to the present.

Arranged: Chronologically by stamp issue date.

Captioned: No.

Finding Aid: No.

Restrictions: No.

NP·2

Lipsner U.S. Airmail Collection

Dates of Photographs: 1918–1928

Collection Origins

This collection was assembled by Benjamin B. Lipsner, Superintendent of the U.S. Post Office Airmail Service (1918–1925), from diverse sources.

Physical Description

There are 1,000 silver gelatin photoprints, of which 800 are mounted in 15 albums. The images are both original and news service copyrighted photographs. Other materials include clippings and scrapbooks.

Subjects

The photographs document the first decade of the U.S. Post Office Airmail Service (between 1918 and 1928), including pioneer airmail pilots, such as, Richard Byrd, and service personnel. There are many images of the May 1918 inaugural airmail flight.

Arranged: Alphabetically by subject in a self-indexing work file.

Captioned: Some photographs are labeled with date, and a subject heading.

Finding Aid: No.

Restrictions: No.

NP·3

Frederick J. Melville Collection

Dates of Photographs: 1900–1940

Collection Origins

The collection was assembled by Frederick J. Melville, British author and philatelist, to document his philatelic interests.

Physical Description

The actual number of images in the collection could not be counted due to their fragile nature and storage problems. There are 56 cubic feet of clippings and photographic materials within the collection. There appear to be both silver gelatin photonegatives and photoprints.

Subjects

This is a collection of clippings and a small number of photographs on philatelic history.

Arranged: By subject.

Captioned: No.

Finding Aid: No.

Restrictions: No access.

NP·4

Philatelic Archives of the Panama Canal Zone

Dates of Photographs: 1905–1979

Collection Origins

The Panama Canal Zone Postal Administration created this collection as a record copy of postage stamps issued within the Panama Canal Zone between 1905 and 1979.

Physical Description

There are 110 photographs, including silver gelatin photonegatives and photoprints. Other materials include documentary information on the stamps issued, photographic essays, and plate proofs.

Subjects

The photographs document stamps issued by the Panama Canal Zone Postal Administration between 1905 and 1979.

Arranged: Chronologically by stamp issue date.

Captioned: No.

Finding Aid: No.

Restrictions: No.

NP·5

Post Office Record Collection

Dates of Photographs: 19th Century

Collection Origins

The collection was assembled in parts by various local U.S. Post Offices throughout the country. It was given to the division for safekeeping.

Physical Description

There are 150 silver gelatin photoprints. Other materials include official U.S. Post Office documents.

Subjects

The photographs document the routine activities of U.S. Post Offices in a variety of locations. There are photographs of mail sorting activities; post office boxes; stamp issues; window tellers; and zip code processing.

Arranged: No.

Captioned: No.

Finding Aid: No.

Restrictions: No.

NP·6

Postal History Photograph Collection

Dates of Photographs: 19th–20th Centuries

Collection Origins

The collection was assembled by the National Philatelic Collection staff for research purposes.

Physical Description

There are 3,500 photographs, including a few color dye coupler slides, and silver gelatin photonegatives and photoprints.

Subjects

The photographs document equipment; exhibits; facilities; officials; stamp production; stamps; and transportation related to United States postal history. There are also some foreign postal history-related materials.

Objects illustrated include: boats; cartoons; chutes; city mail carts and wagons; Civil War mail; conveyor systems; equipment; furniture; letter boxes; mail locks; money orders; mail pouches; postal markings; post roads; ships (Atlantic and Pacific); and stamp cancelling machines.

People documented include: horse couriers; letter carriers; and United States postmasters. Types of mail documented include: airmail; mechanical distribution; parcel post; pigeon posts; Pony Express; private express; Railway Mail Service; star route service; United States distribution; United States Rural Free Delivery; and United States telegraph.

Among the exhibits documented are the World's Columbian Exposition Post Office Department exhibit; and exhibits held at the Smithsonian Institution, and at former installations of the National Philatelic Collection.

Arranged: Into three series by medium and by subject. 1) File prints, some organized by negative number. 2) A small number of files on United States post offices (primarily exteriors) organized by geographic area. 3) Photographs of railway postal equipment, some organized by type of equipment and by date. The staff plans to send all negatives to OPPS for storing and numbering.

Captioned: No.

Finding Aid: An item-level inventory of some of the photographs called "The National Postage Stamp Collection," gives negative numbers, dates, and descriptions.

Restrictions: No.

NP·7

Railway Mail Service Collection

Dates of Photographs: 1922–1966

Collection Origins

The Railway Mail Service was organized in 1865 as part of the U.S. Post Office Department. It operated railway post offices for the distribution and sorting of mail throughout the United States until 1969.

The bulk of this collection was created by the Railway Mail Service during the regular course of their duties from 1922 through 1966. There is also a small amount of material added later by division curators.

Physical Description

There are 1,100 photographs, including silver gelatin photonegatives and photoprints (some housed in nine albums). Other materials include blueprints (made by the Post Office Department and maintained by clerks and foremen of the Railway Mail Service); facing slides; forms; labels; mail separation schemes; memoranda books; schedules of mail routes; and trip reports.

Subjects

The photographs document the Railway Mail Service, including disasters, equipment, facilities, and staff.

The equipment photographs are of cancellation machines; delivery couches; mailboxes; mail delivery trucks; mail processing equipment; mail ships; post office mail cars and trolleys (exteriors and interiors); post office service trucks; and railway mail catcher arms.

The facilities photographs are of dead letter offices; highway post offices; and post office buildings.

Staff illustrated include letter carriers; postal clerks at work; Postmaster Generals; postriders; and window clerks. Disasters illustrated include train robberies and train wrecks.

There are also photographs of airmail service; pneumatic and streetcar mail service; railroad advertisements; railway mail; and stamp production.

Arranged: The notebooks are arranged thematically by type of railway car, car number, and railway car manufacturer.

Captioned: With narrative subject information.

Finding Aid: No.

Restrictions: No.

NP·8

Records of United States Internal Revenue Stamps

Dates of Photographs: Circa 1863–1925

Collection Origins

The Office of the Commissioner of Internal Revenue was established in the Department of the Treasury in 1862. The Office was responsible for the sale of revenue tax stamps required for commodities such as alcohol and tobacco. These records document the tax stamps issued between 1863 and 1925.

Physical Description

There are 100 silver gelatin photoprints. Other materials include journals, ledgers, and shipping records.

Subjects

The photographs document the sale of revenue tax stamps by the Internal Revenue Service between 1863 and 1925. The photographs are primarily of the proof sheets of revenue issues (stamps) attached to commodities and exports. Tax stamps represented in this collection include those for butter, flour, margarine, opium, and tobacco.

Arranged: By type of record and, then chronologically.

Captioned: No.

Finding Aid: No.

Restrictions: No.

NP·9

United States Postal Service Stamp Production Records A.K.A. U.S. Post Office Department Stamp Production Records

Dates of Photographs: 1894–Present

Collection Origins

The U.S. Post Office Department and its heir, the U.S. Postal Service, created these administrative records between 1894 and the present.

Physical Description

There are 3,000 silver gelatin photoprints. Other materials include correspondence; drawings; memoranda concerning the process of postage stamp production; stamp models (150); and original stamp designs (600).

Subjects

These photographs document every aspect of stamp production from 1894 to the present, including the actual stamp production; the artist's renditions of proposed stamps; comments on public acceptance; correspondence; and the first proposal for a stamp. Most of the images are photographic reproductions of drawings of stamps.

Arranged: By Scott numbers (chronological order by stamp production date). All material on a single stamp is kept together.

Captioned: No.

Finding Aid: No.

Restrictions: No.

PA

Public Affairs

Office of Public Affairs
National Museum of American History
Smithsonian Institution
Washington, D.C. 20560
Public Affairs Officer
(202) 357-3129
Hours: Monday–Friday, 8:45 a.m.–5:15 p.m.

Scope of the Collection

There is one photographic collection with approximately 9,700 images in the Office of Public Affairs.

Focus of the Collection

These photographs are used for public relations purposes and to document activities, such as, exhibition openings, famous visitors, new accessions, and other special events.

Photographic Processes and Formats Represented

This collection contains standard 20th century slide, photoprint, and photonegative processes, such as, color dye coupler slides and phototransparencies, and silver gelatin photonegatives and photoprints.

Other Materials Represented

This office generates and files press releases.

Access and Usage Policies

This collection is available to members of the press or scholars by appointment. Restrictions apply to some materials within the collection. These restricted materials may not be reproduced.

Publication Policies

In addition to obtaining permission from the Smithsonian Institution to reproduce a photograph, researchers may have to obtain permission from the copyright holder. The Smithsonian Institution is not necessarily the copyright holder. The preferred credit line for photographs is: "Courtesy of the National Museum of American History, Smithsonian Institution."

PA·1

Public Affairs Photograph Files

Dates of Photographs: 1964–Present

Collection Origins

This collection was assembled by the Public Affairs Office primarily from photographs created by OPPS at the request of the National Museum of American History staff. The collection documents the internal events of the museum. The images are primarily used for press releases.

Physical Description

There are 9,700 photographs, including color dye coupler phototransparencies and slides, and silver gelatin photoprints (some are contact sheets).

Subjects

The photographs document the activities, events, exhibits, and object holdings of NMAH. Among the annual and special events documented are award ceremonies, celebrity visitors, lectures, and major donations. Among the annual events illustrated are the Doubleday Lecture Series. Exhibits documented include "After the Revolution: Everyday Life in America, 1780–1800"; "A Nation of Nations"; and "Trees of Christmas." There are many photographs of exhibits about, or visits by, First Ladies. There are also photographs of exhibits on George Washington.

Arranged: Into two major series. 1) Prints and contact prints. 2) Slides. Within these series: alphabetically first by museum department, then by division, and then topically by subject heading.

Captioned: With negative number, caption, credit line, and any restrictions.

Finding Aid: Captions are filed in notebooks and in an online database.

Restrictions: Some are for reference only. No duplication allowed.

RE

The Registrar

Office of the Registrar
National Museum of American History
Smithsonian Institution
Washington, D.C. 20560
Coordinator, Security Photography Project Collection
(202) 357-1894
Manager, Objects Processing Facility
(202) 357-3296
Hours: Monday–Friday, 10 a.m.–5 p.m.

Scope of the Collections

There are two photographic collections with approximately 77,800 images in the Office of the Registrar.

Focus of the Collections

These photographs are used to document the existence and physical condition of objects which fit the following categories: 1) items being loaned to or borrowed from other institutions; 2) new accessions; 3) materials being considered for accession or loan; and 4) materials of high intrinsic value.

Photographic Processes and Formats Represented

These collections are entirely composed of 20th century color dye coupler slides and silver gelatin photoprints and photonegatives.

Other Materials Represented

Other collection materials include correspondence and registration records.

Access and Usage Policies

These collections are restricted. They are available only to Smithsonian Institution staff at the discretion of the divisional collection custodian, if the proposed use does not conflict with Smithsonian security regulations. Please write the collection custodian for more information.

Publication Policies

In addition to obtaining permission from the Smithsonian Institution to reproduce a photograph, researchers may have to obtain permission from the copyright holder. The Smithsonian Institution is not necessarily the copyright holder. High security photographs are available for publication with the permission of the division holding the collection (the division whose objects are being documented). Contact the collection custodian for details.

RE·1

High Value Security Photography Collection

Dates of Photographs: 1980–Present

Collection Origins

This security project began on April 1, 1980, under the sponsorship of the NMAH Office of the Director, in cooperation with OPPS and the Office of Protection Services. It was begun to create a photographic record of all of the silver and gold objects in the museum.

The project is now under the management of the Office of the Registrar. Other high value items, in addition to gold and silver, have been included in the project. The divisions whose high value objects have been photographed are Armed Forces History, Community Life, Costume, Domestic Life, Engineering and Industry, and Political History.

Physical Description

There are 22,800 silver gelatin photoprints. Half of the silver gelatin photonegatives and photoprints in the collection are housed at OPPS. The other half of the silver gelatin photoprints are dispersed among the following divisions: Armed Forces History, Community Life, Costume, Domestic Life, Engineering and Industry, and Political History.

Subjects

The photographs document objects belonging to six divisions of NMAH. The objects illustrated are judged to be precious either due to the materials they are made from, or because of their associational value.

Objects illustrated include canes; card cases; edged weapons; dresser sets; flatware; hand guns; holloware; icons; jewelry; Judaic Torah finials; lighting devices; match safes; medals; miniature paintings; pistols; political paraphernalia; presentation silver; silver religious artifacts; swords; Thomas Jefferson's thermometer; and watches.

Arranged: Photonegatives are filed by negative number at OPPS. The various divisions file their photoprints according to their preference. Note: Most di-

visions plan to arrange their prints by object catalog number.

Captioned: No.

Finding Aid: No.

Restrictions: No access through OPPS. Access to the collection component in a specific division is at the discretion of the division. The division should be contacted in writing.

RE·2

Objects Processing Facility Color Slide Collection

Dates of Photographs: 1979–Present

Collection Origins

The Objects Processing Facility produces record photographs to document the physical condition of an object before it is loaned to or borrowed from another institution. The Facility also documents all new accessions or material being considered for accession.

Physical Description

The collection consists of 55,000 color dye coupler slides.

Subjects

The photographs document artifacts accessioned by NMAH; artifacts borrowed by NMAH; artifacts loaned from NMAH; artifacts offered for NMAH acquisition; and NMAH artifacts which must travel.

Arranged: Slides are filed in 55 drawers by the registrar's number.

Captioned: With the name of the appropriate curatorial division and the date that the slide was made.

Finding Aid: No.

Restrictions: The collection is restricted to use by Smithsonian employees.

SE

Special Events

Office of Special Events
National Museum of American History
Smithsonian Institution
Washington, D.C. 20560
Special Events Assistant
(202) 357-3306
Hours: Monday–Friday, 9 a.m.–5 p.m.

Scope of the Collection

There is one photographic collection with approximately 1,550 images in the Office of Special Events.

Focus of the Collection

These photographs are used primarily as public relations material to document exhibition openings; lectures and speeches; object presentation ceremonies; visits by celebrities; and other special events at the National Museum of American History.

Photographic Processes and Formats Represented

This collection contains standard 20th century slide, photoprint, and photonegative processes, such as, color dye coupler slides and silver gelatin photoprints.

Other Materials Represented

This office also collects some press cutlines and press releases which occasionally accompany the photographs.

Access and Usage Policies

This collection is available to members of the press and scholars by appointment. Certain materials are restricted and photographic copies may not be made.

Publication Policies

In addition to obtaining permission from the Smithsonian Institution to reproduce a photograph, researchers may have to obtain permission from the copyright holder. The Smithsonian Institution is not necessarily the copyright holder. The preferred credit line for photographs is: "Courtesy of the National Museum of American History, Smithsonian Institution."

SE·1

Special Events Photograph Collection

Dates of Photographs: 1978, 1981–Present

Collection Origins

This collection was assembled by the Office of Special Events staff from OPPS and outside photographers' images to document NMAH special events.

Physical Descriptions

There are 1,550 silver gelatin photoprints (primarily contact prints).

Subjects

The photographs document the special events held at the NMAH since 1981. There are photographs of benefits, celebrity visits, concerts, exhibition openings, lectures, picnics, receptions, social occasions, and symposiums. Three special events are heavily documented, including the Abner Doubleday lectures; President Ronald Reagan's visit to the exhibit "The Intimate Presidency"; and a Rogers and Hammerstein concert on April 11, 1984.

Arranged: Chronologically by event.

Captioned: With negative number, name of the opening or event, date, and occasionally a description.

Finding Aid: No.

Restrictions: No.

Creators Index

The Creators Index is a list of photographers, studios, distributors, manufacturers, and collectors who produced or assembled the images in NMAH collections. Photographers are listed alphabetically by surname. Those associated with a studio may be listed under both the studio name and personal name. Corporate creators are listed in strict alphabetical order, so you will find "C.D. Fredericks and Co." under "C" rather than under "F."

Researchers unable to find a particular name in this index should first check for cross-references to pseudonyms or alternative spellings. Then, check for the names of related studios, employers, or organizations.

This index lists all creators' names appearing in this volume. Due to space requirements, it does not list all creators' names appearing in NMAH collections. The few exceptionally large collections (over 100 creators' names) were sampled to provide a representative overview of their contents.

Care was taken to list all photographers or studios who are either substantially represented in the collections, or who appear in the photographic literature and existing photographers name authority files. A fuller listing of photographers in a particular collection may be available in the original photographic survey report.

Information in parentheses following a name is generally a fuller form of the same name. Cross-references, indicated by *see,* are provided to alternate forms of the same name. Collection names or titles are also included in this index, as they may provide the only existing clues to the collection's origins.

The final authorities on names in this book were:

George Eastman House Photographers Biography File. Rochester, New York: George Eastman House, 1986–1988.

William L. Broecker, editor. *International Center of Photography Encyclopedia of Photography.* New York: A Pound Press Book, Crown Publishers, Inc., 1984.

George Walsh II, Michael Held II, and Colin Naylor. *Contemporary Photographers.* New York: St. Martins Press, 1982.

Turner Browne and Elaine Partnow. *Macmillan Biographical Encyclopedia of Photographic Artists and Innovators.* New York: Macmillan Publishers, 1983.

A. Frankfield and Co., PH48
A.H. Folsom Photo, EI117
AT&T. *See* American Telephone and Telegraph.
Abbott, Berenice, PH33
Abbott, J.H., AC60
Abrams, N., PH10
Ackerman, S.W., EI48
Actron Industries, EI20
Adams, Ansel, PH33
Adams, D.D., PH10
Adams, W.I., EI48

Adamson, Robert, PH33
Addison, Alexander, EI44
Afro-American Photographic Collection, CL7
Agrarian Accession Files, AG1
Agrarian Photograph Collection, AG1
Ahlborn, Richard, CL9
Aigner, Lucien, PH33
Alabama Mining Institute, AG2
Alaskan Railroad and Bridge Construction Collection, EI1
Albany Billiard Ball Co., AC1

Albert, J., PH10
Albert, Josef, PH33
Aldebaran, PH1
Aleo, AC37
Alinder, James, PH33
Allan Herschel Co., CL12
Alland, Alexander, AC63
Allen, Charles H., EI119
Allis Chalmers Co., EI131
Ambrotype Collection, PH2
"America on Stone" Lithography Collection, DL9

Forms and Processes Index

This index locates examples of physically distinct types of photographs. These include format (size, shape, and structure); process (material components, production process, and configuration); technique (specific manipulative procedure for obtaining a visual effect on a variety of processes); and process modifier (a group of terms which provide additional information on a process, format, or genre). Although they do not normally belong within this guide, the index stretches to include audiotape, motion picture film, videodiscs, and videotape found in Smithsonian photographic collections.

The index is heavily cross-referenced to make it more useful to researchers. For example, all 32 types of photoprints surveyed are listed under their individual names, and also under "photoprints." Major headings are off-set to the left, with subheadings placed alphabetically behind them in run-in style.

Researchers unable to find a particular process, format, or other physical description term should check for cross-references in this index. Variant terms, including broader and narrower terms and alternative spellings should be checked.

Certain ideal data elements are included for completeness of description wherever possible. These include the final image material, the binder, the base, and the format or configuration of the image. On occasion, vernacular or generic descriptive process terminology was used, such as, tintypes and ambrotypes. Such terms were used only when they adequately described a process or group of processes.

In other instances, it is also helpful to know the process variant (silver gelatin photoprint ⟨chloride⟩), or the type of process (silver gelatin photoprint ⟨DOP chloride⟩), or even the trade name (color dye coupler ⟨Kodachrome⟩). Abbreviations used are explained in the introduction.

When this information is ordered in a descriptive phrase, the order is generally: 1) final image material; 2) binder; 3) image format or configuration; 4) base (note: the base is not listed if a photoprint is on paper, or if a photonegative or phototransparency is on film); 5) developing-out or printing-out paper (DOP or POP); 6) chemical process variant; 7) trade name; and 8) other descriptive or technical detail of importance for identification. Descriptive elements (4) through (8) are enclosed within parentheses. For example, "silver gelatin photoprint (DOP chloride Velox gaslight paper)."

For consistency of treatment, a master glossary of photographic terminology has been created which standardizes the physical description of photographic formats, genres, and processes. The descriptive vocabulary also covers, to a lesser extent, certain photomechanical processes which might be confused with photographs. A limited number of copies of the draft vocabulary are available to researchers who write the Smithsonian Institution Archives.

Exceptions to the indexing rules stated above were made only when usage of a term was already consistent in the literature. Use of the phrases, "photoprints," "photonegatives," and "phototransparencies," are based on the descriptive standards set up by Elisabeth Betz Parker in her work, *Graphic Materials: Rules for Describing Original Items and Historical Collections.* Washington, D.C.: Library of Congress, 1982. Other terminology was selected from 28 publications which served as source documents for the vocabulary of photographic terminology.

Subject Index

The subject index is an alphabetical list of topics found in the collection descriptions. Included are activities (such as, factory production or eating and drinking); corporations or groups; events (such as, parades, inaugurations, or disasters); geographical areas; individuals; objects (such as, quilts, computers, or musical instruments); occupations or avocations; and photographic genre as subject (such as, landscapes or still lifes).

Broad terms used for index-building and cross-references were taken from the Library of Congress Prints and Photographs Division's publication by Elisabeth Betz Parker and Helena Zinkham, *LC Thesaurus for Graphic Materials: Topical Terms for Subject Access*. Washington, D.C.: Library of Congress, 1987. More specific terms reflect the collection descriptions in the text.

Terms preceded by the phrase *See also* are related to the initial entry, for example, "Actors *See also* Entertainers; Vaudeville shows." When a term is followed by *See* the researcher is being referred from an indexing term which is not used, to a term that is used, for example, "Biplanes. *See* Airplanes."

Researchers unable to find a particular term should check for cross-references. Variant terms, including broader and narrower terms, and alternative spellings should also be checked.

Parentheses are heavily used to provide information on ambiguous references such as exhibition sponsors or dates, names, ship or boat types, or whether a program title reference is for a motion picture, a radio show, or a television show, for example, "*Lucille Love* (Motion Picture)." Authors' names, culture groups, or musical instruments may also appear in parentheses.

For some terms, such as, names of canals, cities, ships, and parks, additional geographic information follows the term in parentheses, for example: "Pawtucket Canal (Massachusetts)." Expeditions and expositions are often followed with their dates in parentheses. Other topics which require clarification, such as, "busing (integration)," or "cables (submarine)" are followed by information in parentheses.

Publication titles, motion picture titles, and ship names are in italics. Quotes are used to distinguish television program names, radio program names, performing arts ensemble names, nicknames, demonstration titles, and exhibition names.

When photographs were created as plates for a publication or as illustrations for an exhibition, these exhibitions and publications are indexed both under their exhibition or publication title and under the names of any sponsoring museums. The name of the museum exhibition sponsor or the publication author follows the index term in parentheses.